THE COMPLETE
❖ BOOK OF ❖
INDIAN
COOKING

THE COMPLETE
❖ BOOK OF ❖
INDIAN
COOKING

The ultimate Indian cookery collection,
with over 170 delicious and authentic recipes

SHEHZAD HUSAIN AND
RAFI FERNANDEZ

LORENZ BOOKS

Paperback edition first published in 1998 by Lorenz Books

© Anness Publishing Limited 1995

Lorenz Books is an imprint of
Anness Publishing Limited
Hermes House
88-89 Blackfriars Road
London SE1 8HA

ISBN 1-85967-795-9

A CIP catalogue record for this book
is available from the British Library

Publisher: Joanna Lorenz
Project Editors: Judith Simons, Lindsay Porter
Designers: David Rowley, Ian Sandom
Jacket Designer: Nigel Partridge
Photographers: David Armstrong, Edward Allwright
Home Economists: Shehzad Husain, Stephen Wheeler
Nutritional Data: Wendy Doyle

Jacket photograph of Shehzad Husain © Tony Isbitt
Indian Fruit Salad recipe (page 230) by Stephen Wheeler

Printed and bound in China

10 9 8 7 6 5 4 3 2 1

MEASUREMENTS
Three sets of equivalent measurements have been provided
in the recipes here, in the following order: Metric, Imperial
and American. It is essential that units of measurements are
not mixed within each recipe. Where conversions result in
awkward numbers, these have been rounded for convenience,
but are accurate enough to produce successful results.

NOTE
The nutritional analyses accompanying the Low Fat Option
recipes were prepared using a computer program called
FOODBASE which is based on data from McCance &
Widdowson's The Composition of Foods, with fatty acid data
from The Institute of Brain Chemistry and Human Nutrition.
Ingredients specified as optional have not been included in
the related analysis and, where weights have not been given
in the recipes, an approximate value has been calculated.

Contents

Introduction   6

Appetizers & Snacks   13

Poultry Dishes   41

Meat Dishes   81

Fish & Seafood Dishes   123

Vegetable Dishes   155

Pulses   185

Breads & Rice Dishes   197

Side Dishes   219

Desserts & Drinks   239

Suppliers   252

Index   254

Introduction

THE vast sub-continent of India offers a range of culinary delights as rich and diverse as its people and history. Each region has its own unique cooking style: cream, yogurt, ghee and nuts feature in dishes in the north, while the south favours chillies, coconut and coconut oil. Fish and mustard oil predominate in the east while the west has incorporated the greatest number of foreign ingredients. One element unites these diverse styles – the use of spices to create the flavours and aromas distinctive of Indian cuisine.

The flavours of Indian food are appreciated all over the world and although delicious, the nutritional content of some traditional Indian dishes has been at odds with our modern view of healthy eating. Liberal use of ghee, which is clarified butter, adds an unwelcome quantity of saturated fat to Indian dishes.

In Western society, the healthy eating message is clear. Eat less fat, in particular saturated fat, less sugar and salt and more fibre. This means stepping up our intake of complex carbohydrates, fruit and vegetables and eating more fish and leaner meats. However, healthy ingredients such as fresh vegetables, lentils and pulses, and seafood are widely used in Indian cuisine. Poultry is usually cooked without the skin which is where most of the fat resides and good Indian cooks will always use lean meat or meat trimmed of excess fat. So if you want to reduce your fat intake, there is no need to forego tasty Indian food. Among the recipes in this book, you will find a selection of low-fat recipes, which have been carefully designed to give an optimum nutritional profile without sacrificing flavour.

Balti cooking is a fairly new experience in the West, but the craze has spread like wildfire, with Balti restaurants springing up overnight and becoming instantly popular. The essence of Balti cuisine is the speed of cooking – it's almost as fast as Chinese stir-frying. The equipment needed is a wok shaped pan, known as a "karahi". The type of food cooked in the karahi is eclectic, drawing its influences from many different countries such as Iran and Afghanistan, and now the West is contributing its own style.

When made at home, Balti cooking is fast, fun and simply delicious. Once you have tried the basic recipes, make up your own dishes using different combinations of ingredients.

Although the original karahi was made of cast iron, modern varieties come in a selection of metals. The essential quality is that they must be sturdy enough to withstand high cooking temperatures and sizzling oils. They are fun to use but it is not absolutely essential to use the authentic Balti pan; a fairly thick Chinese wok or deep round-based frying pan are good substitutes. Balti pans also come in small sizes for individual servings complete with wooden stands so that you can bring them to the table for serving.

Below left and below: Beef with green beans and Balti baby vegetables provide traditional flavours without sacrificing today's requirements for healthy eating.

Cooking Equipment

You should find that your own kitchen is well equipped with everything you need to produce the dishes in this book. Good-quality saucepans with heavy bases, and wooden spoons and a slotted spoon to use with them, mixing bowls, sharp knives, a chopping board, a sieve (strainer) and a rolling pin are the main essentials. A balloon whisk for beating yogurt and a pastry brush for basting kebabs (kabobs) with marinade may also be useful for some of the recipes.

A heavy-based frying pan (skillet) is a must, and you may like to try cooking some of the dishes in a traditional Indian karahi or Balti pan – a deep, round-bottomed vessel with two circular carrying handles. Karahis are very sturdy and therefore capable of withstanding high cooking temperatures and sizzling oils. Wooden stands are available, too, so the pans can be brought to the table to serve. The other specialist cooking vessel used in the Indian kitchen is a tava, a flat cast-iron frying pan used for cooking chapatis and other breads and for roasting spices, but any sturdy frying pan can be substituted.

A food processor or blender is a great labour-saving tool and will be invaluable for making pastes or puréeing ingredients. Whole spices can be freshly ground using a mortar and pestle, or, if you have one, a coffee grinder makes the job so much easier.

Cooking Equipment

1 *food processor* **2** *mortar and pestle* **3** *Balti pan, or karahi, for serving individual portions* **4** *medium mixing bowl* **5** *good quality, heavy-based saucepans in two sizes* **6** *well-seasoned traditional Balti pan, or karahi* **7** *coffee grinder* **8** *deep, round-bottomed frying pan (skillet)* **9** *large mixing bowl* **10** *sieve (strainer)* **11** *sharp knives in three sizes* **12** *slotted spoon* **13** *wooden spoons* **14** *rolling pin*

Making Ginger and Garlic Pulp

Ginger and garlic pulp is specified in many of the recipes here and it can be time-consuming to peel and process these every time. It's much easier to make the pulps in large quantities and use as needed. The method is the same for both ingredients. The pulp can be stored in an airtight container or jar in the refrigerator for four to six weeks. Alternatively, freeze in ice-cube trays kept for the purpose (the pulps will taint the trays slightly). Add 1 tsp of the pulp to each compartment, freeze, remove from the tray and store in the freezer in a plastic bag.

1 Take about 225 g/8 oz fresh ginger or garlic and soak overnight – this softens the skins and makes them easy to peel. Peel and place in a food processor or blender.

2 Process until pulped, adding a little water to get the right consistency, if necessary.

Home-Made Garam Masala

Garam masala can be purchased ready-ground in various mixtures. For an ultra-fresh, home-made variety, try this combination of spices.

4 × 2.5 cm/1 in cinnamon sticks
3 cloves
3 black peppercorns
2 black cardamom pods, with husks removed
2 tsp black cumin seeds

Grind the spices together in a coffee grinder or using a mortar and pestle until quite fine and use in any recipe calling for garam masala.

A Question of Taste

The spices used in a dish are integral to its flavour. One spice can completely alter the taste of a dish and a combination of several will also affect its colour and texture. The quantities of spices and salt specified in this book are merely a guide, so feel free to experiment.

This is particularly true of chilli powder and fresh and dried chillies; some brands and varieties are hotter than others. Experiment with quantities, adding less than specified, if wished. Much of the fiery heat of fresh chillies is contained in the seeds, and these can be removed by splitting the chillies down the middle and washing them away under cold running water. You can also remove the seeds from dried chillies. Wash your hands thoroughly with soap and water after handling cut chillies and avoid touching your face – particularly your lips and eyes – for a good while afterwards.

Cooking Tips

● The final colour and texture of a curry depend on how well you brown the onions in the first stage of cooking. Heat the oil first, add the onions, then reduce the heat slightly. Stir the onions only occasionally; excessive stirring will draw the moisture from them which will inhibit the browning process.

● Natural (plain) yogurt produces a wonderful creamy texture and is used in many of the recipes as a healthy alternative to cream. Always beat the yogurt with a fork first and then add it to the pan gradually, stirring continuously, to prevent it curdling.

● Some recipes specify whole spices, such as cinnamon sticks, cardamom pods and cloves. If wished, remove these from the dish before serving.

● There is no substitute for fresh coriander (cilantro) and the more used the better as it imparts a beautiful aroma and flavour. Happily, coriander is now readily available from most supermarkets, and more economically from Asian stores. If wished, buy a large quantity and freeze whatever you don't need. Simply cut off the roots and any thick stalks, wash the leaves in cold water and leave to drain in a sieve (strainer). When dry, chop and store in plastic bags or airtight containers in the freezer. Do not defrost before using.

Below: Spices are used both whole and ground in Indian cooking. If possible, buy whole spices and grind them at home for a more pungent aroma and intense flavour.

Choosing Ingredients

Good food, whatever the cuisine, depends on the quality of the ingredients used – as well as the skill of the cook. In India a wonderful array of fresh vegetables, fruit, herbs and spices, as well as dried spices, can be found in the numerous markets and street stalls, and a choice of the best available is often purchased on a daily basis. Nowadays, a good range of fruit, herbs and vegetables, including exotic items, can now be found in supermarkets or can be purchased from specialist Asian stores. Take advantage of the fresh produce available to produce these delicious dishes, and don't be afraid to substitute other fresh vegetables if a specified ingredient can't be found.

Meat and poultry purchased from a good butcher is best, and if you are a regular customer they will usually pre-prepare the cuts you want, trimming, skinning and boning the meat as necessary. Fresh seafood and fish is always preferable to frozen; however, frozen foods are undoubtedly a boon for the busy cook and for quick weekday meals.

The more common spices can be found in supermarkets, and the others can be purchased from Asian stores. Some spices are available ready-ground and they keep well if stored in airtight containers. In Pakistan and India we almost always buy whole spices and grind them ourselves just prior to cooking: for a special meal the flavour can't be beaten and if you have a coffee grinder it's quite quick to do.

Below: Good quality ingredients are the basis of successful cooking. Choose fruits and vegetables at their peak for best results, and ensure dry ingredients have not been stored too long for maximum flavour.

Glossary of Special Ingredients

Almonds Blanched almonds are available whole, flaked (slivered) and ground, and impart a sumptuous richness to curries. They are considered a great delicacy in India, where they are extremely expensive.

Aniseed This has a delicate liquorice flavour and sweet seeds. It is a good aid to digestion.

Asafoetida This is a resin with an acrid and bitter taste and a strong odour. Store in a jar with a strong airtight seal to prevent the smell dispersing into other ingredients.

Basmati rice If possible, try to use basmati rice for all savoury rice dishes – the delicate flavour is unbeatable.

Bay leaves The large dried leaves of the bay laurel tree are one of the oldest herbs used in cookery.

Bengal gram Bengal gram is used whole in lentil curries. The flour (besan) is used to prepare bhajias and may be used to flavour and thicken curries.

Black-eyed peas These white kidney-shaped beans with a black "eye" are available dried or canned.

Cardamom pods This spice is native to India, where it is considered to be the most prized spice after saffron. The pods can be used whole or the husks can be removed to release the seeds, and they have a slightly pungent but very aromatic taste. They come in three varieties: green, white and black. The green and white pods can be used for both sweet and savoury dishes or to flavour rice. The black pods are used only for savoury dishes.

Cashew nuts These full-flavoured nuts are a popular ingredient in many kinds of Asian cooking.

Chana dhal This is a round split yellow lentil, similar in appearance to the smaller moong dhal and the larger yellow split pea, which can be used as a substitute. It is used as a binding agent in some dishes and is widely available from Asian stores.

Chapati (ata) flour This is a type of wholemeal (whole-wheat) flour available from Asian stores and is used to make chapatis and other breads. Ordinary wholemeal flour can be used as a substitute if well sifted.

Chick-peas (garbanzos) This nutty tasting pulse is widely used in Indian vegetarian dishes.

Chillies – dried red These hot peppers are extremely fiery and should be used with caution. The heat can be toned down by removing the seeds before use. Dried chillies can be used whole or coarsely crushed.

Chillies – fresh Green chillies are not indigenous to India but have become indispensable to Indian cuisine. They are very rich in vitamins A and C.

Chilli powder Also known as cayenne pepper, this fiery ground spice should be used with caution. The heat can vary from brand to brand, so adjust quantities to suit your tastebuds.

Cinnamon One of the earliest known spices, cinnamon has an aromatic and sweet flavour. It is sold ready-ground and as sticks.

Cloves This spice is used to flavour many sweet and savoury dishes and is usually added whole.

Coconut Used to flavour both sweet and savoury dishes, fresh coconut is now frequently available from supermarkets. Desiccated (shredded) coconut and creamed coconut make acceptable substitutes for most dishes.

Coriander – fresh (cilantro) This beautifully fragrant herb is used both in cooking and sprinkled over dishes as an attractive garnish.

Coriander seeds This aromatic spice has a pungent, slightly lemony flavour. The seeds are used widely, either coarsely ground or in powdered form, in meat, fish and poultry dishes. Ground coriander, a brownish powder, is an important constituent of any mixture of curry spices.

Cumin "White" cumin seeds are oval, ridged and greenish brown in colour. They have a strong aroma and flavour and can be used whole or ground. Ready-ground cumin powder is widely available. Black cumin seeds are dark and aromatic and are used to flavour curries and rice.

Curry leaves Similar in appearance to bay leaves but with a very different flavour, these can be bought dried and occasionally fresh from Asian stores. Fresh leaves freeze well.

Fennel seeds Very similar in appearance to cumin seeds, fennel seeds have a very sweet taste and are used to flavour certain curries. They can also be chewed as a mouth-freshener after a spicy meal.

Fenugreek – fresh Sold in bunches, this herb has very small leaves and is used to flavour meat and vegetarian dishes. Always discard the stalks, which will impart a bitterness to a dish if used.

Fenugreek seeds These flat seeds are extremely pungent and slightly bitter.

Five-spice powder This is a combination of star anise, fennel, cinnamon, clove and Sichuan pepper.

Garam masala This is a mixture of spices which can be made from freshly ground spices at home or purchased ready-made. There is no set recipe, but a typical mixture might include black cumin seeds, peppercorns, cloves, cinnamon and black cardamon pods.

Garlic This is a standard ingredient, along with ginger, in most curries. It can be used pulped, crushed or chopped. Whole cloves are sometimes added to dishes.

Ghee This is clarified butter and was once the main cooking fat used in Indian cooking. Nowadays, vegetable ghee or vegetable oil – particularly corn oil – are used in its place, being lower in saturated fat.

Ginger One of the most popular spices in India and also one of the oldest, fresh ginger is an important ingredient in many curries and is now widely available. Dried powdered ginger is a useful standby.

Mace Mace is the dried covering of the nutmeg. It has a slightly bitter taste.

Mangoes Ripe fresh mangoes are used in sweet dishes, while green or unripe mangoes are sometimes used in curries and to make mango chutney.

Mango powder Made from dried unripe mangoes, this has a sour taste.

Masoor dhal These split red lentils are actually orange in colour and turn a pale yellow when cooked. Whole brown lentils are a type of red lentil with the husk intact.

Mint Indian mint has a stronger aroma than the varieties available in the West.

Moong dhal This teardrop-shaped split yellow lentil is similar to, though smaller than, chana dhal.

Mustard seeds – black Round in shape and sharp in flavour, black mustard seeds are used for flavouring curries and pickles.

Nigella Nigella is an aromatic spice with a sharp and tingling taste. It is mainly used in vegetable dishes.

Nutmeg Although not widely used in Indian cooking, nutmeg is sometimes used either freshly grated or ready-ground to add a sweet flavour.

Onion seeds Black in colour and triangular in shape, these seeds are widely used in pickles and to flavour vegetable curries.

Paneer This is a white, smooth-textured cheese, available from Asian stores. It is excellent used in combination with meat and fish or as a vegetarian replacement and it appears in several of the dishes in this book. Long-life vacuum-packed paneer is available from Indian stores and some health-food shops. (See Paneer Balti with Prawns/Shrimp for a simple recipe for home-made paneer.)

Peppercorns Black peppercorns are sometimes used whole with other whole spices, such as cloves, cardamon pods and bay leaves, to flavour curries. Otherwise, whenever possible, use freshly ground or crushed black pepper if the recipe calls for it.

Pistachios These sweet, green nuts are not indigenous to India and are therefore an expensive ingredient.

Pomegranate seeds These can be extracted from fresh pomegranates or bought in jars from Asian stores and impart a delicious tangy flavour.

Poppy seeds These seeds are usually used toasted to bring out the flavour.

Red gram Red gram is available dry or lightly oiled.

Saffron The world's most expensive spice is the dried stigmas of the saffron crocus, which is native to Asia Minor. It takes 250,000 flowers to make just 450 g/1 lb saffron. Fortunately, only a small quantity of saffron is needed to flavour and colour a dish, whether sweet or savoury. Saffron is sold as strands and in powder form, and has a beautiful flavour and aroma.

Sesame seeds These seeds have a slightly nutty taste.

Star anise Star anise is a star-shaped, liquorice-flavoured pod.

Tamarind The dried black pods of the tamarind plant are sour in taste and very sticky. Tamarind can now be bought in paste form in jars, although lemon juice can be used as a substitute.

Toor dhal A shiny split lentil, toor dhal is similar in size to chana dhal.

Turmeric This bright yellow, bitter-tasting spice is sold ground. It is used mainly for colour rather than flavour.

Urid dhal (black gram) Also known as black gram, this lentil is similar in size to moong dhal and is available either with the blackish hull retained or removed. Inside, the lentil is a creamy white. It takes a long time to cook and has a slightly drier texture than moong dhal.

Vermicelli These hair-like strands are made from wheat and are used in savoury and sweet dishes.

Walnuts Walnuts are used in sweetmeats, salads and raitas.

Below: A well-stocked store cupboard might include lentils, pulses and seeds and dried herbs and spices. Buy in quantities you know you will be able to use, as some ingredients lose their potency over time.

Appetizers & Snacks

Spicy pastries such as Vegetable Samosas and crisp Onion Bhajias are familiar starters. However, you'll find a whole host of other tempting dishes here as well. Try spicy Grilled Prawns as a first course, or go for the tasty low-fat version of Chicken Tikka. There are soups, too, some fairly fiery and others which are more subtly spiced.

Onion Bhajias

Bhajias are a classic snack of India. The same batter may be used with a variety of vegetables.

MAKES 20–25

INGREDIENTS
225 g/8 oz/2 cups gram flour (besan)
1/2 tsp chilli powder
1 tsp turmeric
1 tsp baking powder
1/4 tsp asafoetida
salt, to taste
1/2 tsp each, nigella, fennel, cumin and onion seeds, coarsely crushed
2 large onions, finely sliced
2 green chillies, finely chopped
50 g/2 oz/2 cups fresh coriander (cilantro), chopped
cold water, to mix
vegetable oil, for deep-frying

1 ▲ In a bowl, mix together the flour, chilli, turmeric, baking powder, asafoetida and salt to taste. Pass through a sieve (strainer) into a large mixing bowl.

2 Add the coarsely crushed seeds, onion, green chillies and fresh coriander (cilantro) and toss together well. Very gradually mix in enough cold water to make a thick batter surrounding all the ingredients.

3 ▲ Heat enough oil in a karahi or wok for deep-frying. Drop spoonfuls of the mixture into the hot oil and fry until they are golden brown. Leave enough space to turn the bhajias. Drain well and serve hot.

Yogurt Soup

Some communities in India add sugar to this soup. When Bhajias are added, it is served as a main dish.

SERVES 4–6

INGREDIENTS
450 ml/3/4 pint/scant 2 cups natural (plain) yogurt, beaten
4 tbsp gram flour (besan)
1/2 tsp chilli powder
1/2 tsp ground turmeric
salt, to taste
2–3 fresh green chillies, finely chopped
4 tbsp vegetable oil
4 dried red chillies
1 tsp cumin seeds
3 cloves garlic, crushed
1 piece fresh ginger, 5 cm/2 in long, crushed

3–4 curry leaves
1 tbsp chopped fresh coriander (cilantro)

1 ▲ Mix together the first 5 ingredients and pass through a strainer into a saucepan. Add the green chillies and cook gently for about 10 minutes, stirring occasionally. Be careful not to let the soup boil over.

2 ▲ Heat the oil in a frying pan (skillet) and fry the remaining spices, garlic and ginger until the dried chillies turn black. Add the curry leaves and fresh coriander (cilantro) to the pan.

3 Pour most of the oil and the spices over the yogurt soup, cover the pan and leave to rest for 5 minutes off the heat. Mix well and gently reheat for a further 5 minutes. Serve hot, garnished with the remaining oil and spices.

Onion Bhajias (top) and Yogurt Soup

Spicy Chicken and Mushroom Soup

This creamy chicken soup makes a hearty meal for a winter's night. Serve it piping hot with fresh garlic bread.

SERVES 4

INGREDIENTS

225 g/8 oz chicken, skinned and boned
75 g/3 oz/6 tbsp unsalted butter
½ tsp garlic pulp
1 tsp garam masala
1 tsp crushed black peppercorns
1 tsp salt
¼ tsp ground nutmeg
1 medium leek, sliced
75 g/3 oz/1 cup mushrooms, sliced
50 g/2 oz/⅓ cup sweetcorn (corn kernels)
300 ml/½ pint/1¼ cups water
250 ml/8 fl oz/1 cup single (light) cream
1 tbsp chopped fresh coriander (cilantro)
1 tsp crushed dried red chillies (optional)

I Cut the chicken pieces into very fine strips.

2 ▲ Melt the butter in a medium saucepan. Lower the heat slightly and add the garlic and garam masala. Lower the heat even further and add the black peppercorns, salt and nutmeg. Finally, add the chicken pieces, leek, mushrooms and sweetcorn (corn kernels), and cook for 5–7 minutes or until the chicken is cooked through, stirring constantly.

3 ▲ Remove from the heat and allow to cool slightly. Transfer three-quarters of the mixture into a food processor or blender. Add the water and process for about 1 minute.

4 Pour the resulting purée back into the saucepan with the rest of the mixture and bring to the boil over a medium heat. Lower the heat and stir in the cream.

5 ▲ Add the fresh coriander (cilantro) and taste for seasoning. Serve hot, garnished with the crushed red chillies, if wished.

Chicken and Almond Soup

This soup makes an excellent appetizer and served with Naan will also make a satisfying lunch or supper dish.

SERVES 4

INGREDIENTS

75 g/3 oz/6 tbsp unsalted butter
1 medium leek, chopped
1/2 tsp shredded ginger
75 g/3 oz/1 cup ground almonds
1 tsp salt
1/2 tsp crushed black peppercorns
1 fresh green chilli, chopped
1 medium carrot, sliced
50 g/2 oz/1/2 cup frozen peas
*115g/4 oz/3/4 cup chicken, skinned, boned
    and cubed*
1 tbsp chopped fresh coriander (cilantro)
450 ml/3/4 pint/scant 2 cups water
250 ml/8 fl oz/1 cup single (light) cream
4 coriander sprigs

1 Melt the butter in a large karahi or deep round-bottomed frying pan (skillet), and sauté the leek with the ginger until soft.

2 ▲ Lower the heat and add the ground almonds, salt, peppercorns, chilli, carrot, peas and chicken. Fry for about 10 minutes or until the chicken is completely cooked, stirring constantly. Add the chopped fresh coriander (cilantro).

3 ▲ Remove from the heat and allow to cool slightly. Transfer the mixture to a food processor or blender and process for about 1½ minutes. Pour in the water and blend for a further 30 seconds.

4 ▲ Pour back into the saucepan and bring to the boil, stirring occasionally. Once it has boiled, lower the heat and gradually stir in the cream. Cook gently for a further 2 minutes, stirring occasionally.

5 Serve garnished with the fresh coriander sprigs.

South Indian Pepper Water

This is a highly soothing broth for winter evenings, also known as Mulla-ga-tani. Serve with the whole spices or strain and reheat if you so wish. The lemon juice may be adjusted to taste, but this dish should be distinctly sour.

SERVES 4–6

INGREDIENTS
2 tbsp vegetable oil
1/2 tsp freshly ground black pepper
1 tsp cumin seeds
1/2 tsp mustard seeds
1/4 tsp asafoetida
2 dried red chillies
4–6 curry leaves
1/2 tsp turmeric
2 cloves garlic, crushed
300 ml/1/2 pint/1 1/4 cups tomato juice
juice of 2 lemons

120 ml/4 fl oz/1/2 cup water
salt, to taste
fresh coriander (cilantro), chopped, to garnish (optional)

I ▲ In a large pan, heat the oil and fry the next 8 ingredients until the chillies are nearly black and the garlic golden brown.

2 ▲ Lower the heat and add the tomato juice, lemon juice, water and salt. Bring to the boil then simmer for 10 minutes. Garnish with the chopped coriander (cilantro), if wished, and serve.

Chicken Mulligatawny

Using the original Pepper Water – Mulla-ga-tani – this dish was created by the non-vegetarian chefs during the British Raj. The recipe was imported to the West and today features on many restaurant menus where it is often called simply Mulligatawny Soup.

SERVES 4–6

INGREDIENTS
900 g/2 lb/6 1/2 cups chicken, skinned, boned and cubed
600 ml/1 pint/2 1/2 cups water
6 green cardamom pods
1 piece cinnamon stick, 5 cm/2 in long
4–6 curry leaves
1 tbsp ground coriander
1 tsp ground cumin
1/2 tsp turmeric
3 cloves garlic, crushed
12 whole peppercorns
4 cloves

1 onion, finely chopped
115 g/4 oz creamed coconut
salt, to taste
juice of 2 lemons
deep-fried onions, to garnish

I ▲ Place the chicken in a large pan with the water and cook until the chicken is tender. Skim the surface, then remove the chicken with a slotted spoon and keep warm.

2 ▲ Reheat the stock in the pan. Add all the remaining ingredients, except the chicken and deep-fried onions. Simmer for 10–15 minutes, then strain and return the chicken to the soup. Reheat the soup and serve garnished with the deep-fried onions.

South Indian Pepper Water (top) and Chicken Mulligatawny

Tomato and Coriander (Cilantro) Soup

LOW-FAT RECIPE

Although soups are not often eaten in India or Pakistan, tomato soup seems to be among the most popular ones. It is excellent on a cold winter's day.

SERVES 4

INGREDIENTS
675 g/1½ lb tomatoes
2 tbsp vegetable oil
1 bay leaf
4 spring onions (scallions), chopped
1 tsp salt
½ tsp garlic pulp
1 tsp crushed black peppercorns
2 tbsp chopped fresh coriander (cilantro)
750 ml/1¼ pints/good 3 cups water
1 tbsp cornflour (cornstarch)

Garnish
1 spring onion (scallion), chopped (optional)
2 tbsp single (light) cream (optional)

NUTRITIONAL VALUES (per portion)

Total fat	7.16 g
Saturated fat	1.37 g
Cholesterol	2.80 mg
Energy (kcals/kj)	113/474

1 ▲ To skin the tomatoes, plunge them in very hot water, then take them out more or less straight away. The skin should now peel off quickly and easily. Once this is done chop the tomatoes.

2 ▲ In a medium saucepan, heat the oil and fry the chopped tomatoes, bay leaf and chopped spring onions (scallions) for a few minutes until soft.

3 ▲ Gradually add the salt, garlic, peppercorns and fresh coriander (cilantro) to the tomato mixture, finally adding the water. Bring to the boil, lower the heat and simmer for 15–20 minutes.

4 Dissolve the cornflour (cornstarch) in a little water.

5 ▲ Remove the soup from the heat and press through a sieve (strainer).

6 ▲ Return to the pan, add the cornflour and stir over a gentle heat for about 3 minutes until thickened.

7 Pour into individual serving dishes and garnish with the chopped spring onion and cream, if using. Serve hot with bread.

COOK'S TIP

If the only fresh tomatoes available are rather pale and under-ripe, add 1 tbsp tomato purée (paste) to the pan with the chopped tomatoes to enhance the colour and flavour of the soup.

Lentil Soup

This is a simple, mildly spiced lentil soup, which is a good accompaniment to heavily spiced meat dishes.

SERVES 4–6

INGREDIENTS
1 tbsp ghee
1 large onion, finely chopped
2 cloves garlic, crushed
1 fresh green chilli, chopped
$^1/_2$ tsp turmeric
75 g/3 oz/$^1/_3$ cup split red lentils (masoor dhal)
250 ml/8 fl oz/1 cup water
salt, to taste
400 g/14 oz canned tomatoes, chopped
$^1/_2$ tsp sugar
lemon juice, to taste
200 g/7 oz/1 cup plain boiled rice or 2 potatoes, boiled (optional)
fresh coriander (cilantro), chopped, to garnish (optional)

1 ▲ Heat the ghee in a large saucepan and fry the onion, garlic, chilli and turmeric until the onion is translucent.

2 ▲ Add the lentils and water and bring to the boil. Reduce the heat, cover and cook until all the water is absorbed.

3 ▲ Mash the lentils with the back of a wooden spoon until you have a smooth paste. Add salt to taste and mix well.

4 ▲ Add the remaining ingredients and reheat the soup. To provide extra texture, fold in the plain boiled rice or potatoes cut into small cubes. Garnish with coriander (cilantro), if you like, and serve hot.

COOK'S TIP

When using lentils, first rinse in cold water and pick over to remove any small stones or loose skins.

Potato Cakes with Stuffing

*Only a few communities in India make
these unusual potato cakes known as
Petis. They can also be served as a main
meal with Tomato Salad.*

MAKES 8–10

INGREDIENTS
1 tbsp vegetable oil
1 large onion, finely chopped
2 cloves garlic, finely crushed
*1 piece fresh ginger, 5 cm/2 in long,
    finely crushed*
1 tsp ground coriander
1 tsp ground cumin
2 fresh green chillies, finely chopped
*2 tbsp each, chopped fresh coriander
    (cilantro) and mint*
*225 g/8 oz lean minced (ground) beef
    or lamb*
50 g/2 oz/¹⁄₃ cup frozen peas, thawed
salt, to taste
juice of 1 lemon
900 g/2 lb potatoes, boiled and mashed
2 eggs, beaten
breadcrumbs, for coating
vegetable oil, for shallow-frying
lemon wedges and salad leaves, to serve

1 ▲ Heat the oil and fry the next
7 ingredients until the onion is
translucent. Add the meat and peas and
fry well until the meat is cooked, then
season with salt and lemon juice. The
mixture should be very dry.

2 ▲ Divide the mashed potato into
8–10 portions, take one portion at a
time and flatten into a pancake in the
palm of your hand. Place a spoonful of
the meat in the centre and gather the
sides together to enclose the meat.
Flatten it slightly to make a round.

3 ▲ Dip the cakes in beaten egg and
then coat in breadcrumbs. Allow to chill
in the refrigerator for about 1 hour.

4 ▲ Heat the oil in a frying pan (skillet)
and shallow-fry the cakes until all the
sides are brown and crisp. Serve them
hot with lemon wedges on a bed of
salad leaves.

Chicken Naan Pockets

LOW-FAT RECIPE

This quick-and-easy dish is ideal for a quick snack lunch or supper and excellent as picnic fare. For speed, use the ready-to-bake naans available in some supermarkets and Asian stores, or try warmed pitta bread instead.

SERVES 4

INGREDIENTS
4 naan
3 tbsp natural (plain) low-fat yogurt
1½ tsp garam masala
1 tsp chilli powder
1 tsp salt
3 tbsp lemon juice
1 tbsp chopped fresh coriander (cilantro)
1 fresh green chilli, chopped
450 g/1 lb/3¼ cups chicken, skinned, boned and cubed
1 tbsp vegetable oil (optional)
8 onion rings
2 tomatoes, quartered
½ white cabbage, shredded

Garnish
lemon wedges
2 small tomatoes, halved
mixed salad leaves
fresh coriander (cilantro)

NUTRITIONAL VALUES (per portion)	
Total fat	10.85 g
Saturated fat	3.01 g
Cholesterol	65.64 mg
Energy (kcals/kj)	364/1529

1 Cut into the middle of each naan to make a pocket, then set aside.

2 Mix together the yogurt, garam marsala, chilli powder, salt, lemon juice, fresh coriander (cilantro) and chopped green chilli. Pour the marinade over the chicken pieces and leave to marinate for about 1 hour.

3 After 1 hour preheat the grill (broiler) to very hot, then lower the heat to medium. Place the chicken in a flameproof dish and grill (broil) for 15–20 minutes until tender and cooked through, turning the chicken pieces at least twice. If wished, baste with the oil while cooking.

4 ▲ Remove from the heat and fill each naan with the chicken and then with the onion rings, tomatoes and cabbage. Serve with the garnish ingredients.

Chicken Tikka

LOW-FAT RECIPE

This chicken dish is an extremely popular Indian appetizer and is quick and easy to cook. Chicken Tikka can also be served as a main course for four.

SERVES 6

INGREDIENTS
450 g/1 lb/3¼ cups chicken, skinned, boned and cubed
1 tsp ginger pulp
1 tsp garlic pulp
1 tsp chilli powder
¼ tsp turmeric
1 tsp salt
150 ml/¼ pint/⅔ cup natural (plain) low-fat yogurt
4 tbsp lemon juice
1 tbsp chopped fresh coriander (cilantro)
1 tbsp vegetable oil

Garnish
1 small onion, cut into rings
lime wedges
mixed salad
fresh coriander (cilantro)

NUTRITIONAL VALUES (per portion)	
Total fat	5.50 g
Saturated fat	1.47 g
Cholesterol	44.07 mg
Energy (kcals/kj)	131/552

1 In a medium bowl, mix together the chicken pieces, ginger, garlic, chilli powder, turmeric, salt, yogurt, lemon juice and fresh coriander (cilantro) and leave to marinate for at least 2 hours.

2 ▲ Place on a grill (broiler) tray or in a flameproof dish lined with foil and baste with the oil.

3 Preheat the grill to medium. Grill (broil) the chicken for 15–20 minutes until cooked, turning and basting 2–3 times. Serve with the garnish ingredients.

Chicken Naan Pockets (top) and Chicken Tikka

Chicken Kofta Balti with Paneer

This rather unusual appetizer looks most elegant when served in small individual karahis.

SERVES 6

INGREDIENTS
Koftas
450 g/1 lb/3¼ cups chicken, skinned, boned and cubed
1 tsp garlic pulp
1 tsp shredded ginger
1½ tsp ground coriander
1½ tsp chilli powder
½ tsp ground fenugreek
¼ tsp turmeric
1 tsp salt
2 tbsp chopped fresh coriander (cilantro)
2 fresh green chillies, chopped
600 ml/1 pint/2½ cups water
corn oil for frying

Paneer mixture
1 medium onion, sliced
1 red (bell) pepper, seeded and cut into strips
1 green (bell) pepper, seeded and cut into strips
175 g/6 oz paneer, cubed
175 g/6 oz/1 cup sweetcorn (corn kernels)

mint sprigs
1 dried red chilli, crushed (optional)

1 ▲ Put all the kofta ingredients, apart from the oil, into a medium saucepan. Bring to the boil slowly, over a medium heat, and cook until all the liquid has evaporated.

2 ▲ Remove from the heat and allow to cool slightly. Put the mixture into a food processor or blender and process for 2 minutes, stopping once or twice to loosen the mixture with a spoon.

3 ▲ Scrape the mixture into a large mixing bowl using a wooden spoon. Taking a little of the mixture at a time, shape it into small balls using your hands. You should be able to make about 12 koftas.

4 ▲ Heat the oil in a karahi or deep round-bottomed frying pan (skillet) over a high heat. Turn the heat down slightly and drop the koftas carefully into the oil. Move them around gently to ensure that they cook evenly.

5 When the koftas are lightly browned, remove them from the oil with a slotted spoon and drain on kitchen paper (paper towels). Set to one side.

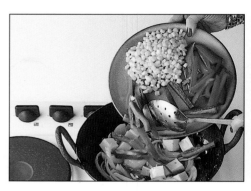

6 ▲ Heat up the oil still remaining in the karahi, and flash fry all the ingredients for the paneer mixture. This should take about 3 minutes over a high heat.

7 ▲ Divide the paneer mixture evenly between 6 individual karahis. Add 2 koftas to each serving, and garnish with mint sprigs and the crushed red chilli, if wished.

Chicken with Pineapple

This chicken has a delicate tang and is very tender. The pineapple not only tenderizes the chicken but also gives it a slight sweetness.

SERVES 6

INGREDIENTS
225 g/8 oz/1 cup canned pineapple
1 tsp ground cumin
1 tsp ground coriander
1/2 tsp garlic pulp
1 tsp chilli powder
1 tsp salt
2 tbsp natural (plain) low-fat yogurt
1 tbsp chopped fresh coriander (cilantro)
few drops orange food colouring
275 g/10 oz/2 cups chicken, skinned and boned
1/2 red (bell) pepper
1/2 yellow or green (bell) pepper
1 large onion
6 cherry tomatoes
1 tbsp vegetable oil

NUTRITIONAL VALUES (per portion)	
Total fat	6.72 g
Saturated fat	1.51 g
Cholesterol	40.63 mg
Energy (kcals/kj)	170/716

2 ▲ In a large mixing bowl, blend together the cumin, ground coriander, garlic, chilli powder, salt, yogurt, fresh coriander (cilantro) and food colouring, if using. Pour in the reserved pineapple juice and mix together.

1 ▲ Drain the pineapple juice into a bowl. Reserve 8 large chunks of pineapple and squeeze the juice from the remaining chunks into the bowl and set aside. You should have about 120 ml/4 fl oz/1/2 cup of pineapple juice.

3 ▲ Cut the chicken into bite-sized cubes, add to the yogurt and spice mixture and leave to marinate for about 1–1 1/2 hours.

4 Cut the (bell) peppers and onion into bite-sized chunks.

5 ▲ Preheat the grill (broiler) to medium. Arrange the chicken pieces, vegetables and reserved pineapple chunks alternately on 6 wooden or metal skewers.

6 ▲ Baste the kebabs (kabobs) with the oil, then place the skewers on a flameproof dish or grill tray. Grill (broil), turning and basting the chicken pieces with the marinade regularly, for about 15 minutes.

7 Once the chicken pieces are cooked, remove them from the grill and serve either with salad or plain boiled rice.

COOK'S TIP

If possible, use a mixture of chicken breast and thigh meat for this recipe.

Chicken and Pasta Balti

This is not a traditional Balti dish, as pasta is not eaten widely in India or Pakistan, however, I have included it here as it is truly delicious! The pomegranate seeds give this dish an unusual tangy flavour.

SERVES 4–6

INGREDIENTS

75 g/3 oz/³/4 cup small pasta shells (the coloured ones look most attractive)
5 tbsp corn oil
4 curry leaves
4 whole dried red chillies
1 large onion, sliced
1 tsp garlic pulp
1 tsp chilli powder
1 tsp shredded ginger
1 tsp crushed pomegranate seeds
1 tsp salt
2 medium tomatoes, chopped
175 g/6 oz/1¹/3 cups chicken, skinned, boned and cubed
225 g/8 oz/1¹/2 cups canned chick-peas (garbanzos), drained

115 g/4 oz/²/3 cup sweetcorn (corn kernels)
50 g/2 oz mange-tout (snow peas), diagonally sliced
1 tbsp chopped fresh coriander (cilantro) (optional)

1 ▲ Cook the pasta in boiling water, following the directions on the package. Add 1 tbsp of the oil to the water to prevent the pasta from sticking together. When it is cooked, drain and set to one side in a sieve (strainer).

2 ▲ Heat the remaining oil in a deep round-bottomed frying pan (skillet) or a large karahi, and add the curry leaves, whole dried chillies and the onion. Fry for about 5 minutes.

3 Add the garlic, chilli powder, ginger, pomegranate seeds, salt and tomatoes. Stir-fry for about 3 minutes.

4 ▲ Next add the chicken, chick-peas (garbanzos), sweetcorn (corn kernels) and mange-tout (snow peas) to the onion mixture. Cook over a medium heat for about 5 minutes, stirring.

5 ▲ Tip in the pasta and stir well. Cook for a further 7–10 minutes until the chicken is cooked through.

6 Serve garnished with the fresh coriander (cilantro) if wished.

Balti Lamb Chops with Potatoes

These chops are marinated before being cooked in a delicious spicy sauce. They make a good appetizer, served with a simple mixed salad.

SERVES 6–8

INGREDIENTS
8 lamb chops (about 50–75 g/2–3 oz each)
2 tbsp olive oil
150 ml/¼ pint/⅔ cup lemon juice
1 tsp salt
1 tbsp chopped fresh mint and coriander (cilantro)
150 ml/¼ pint/⅔ cup corn oil
mint sprigs
lime slices

Sauce
3 tbsp corn oil
8 medium tomatoes, roughly chopped
1 bay leaf
1 tsp garam masala
2 tbsp natural (plain) yogurt
1 tsp garlic pulp
1 tsp chilli powder
1 tsp salt
½ tsp black cumin seeds
3 black peppercorns
2 medium potatoes, peeled, roughly chopped and boiled

I ▲ Put the chops into a large bowl. Mix together the olive oil, lemon juice, salt and fresh mint and coriander (cilantro). Pour the oil mixture over the chops and rub it in well with your fingers. Leave to marinate for at least 3 hours.

2 ▲ To make the sauce, heat the corn oil in a deep round-bottomed frying pan (skillet) or a karahi. Lower the heat and add the chopped tomatoes. Stir-fry for about 2 minutes. Gradually add the bay leaf, garam masala, yogurt, garlic, chilli powder, salt, black cumin seeds and peppercorns, and stir-fry for a further 2–3 minutes.

3 Lower the heat again and add the cooked potatoes, mixing everything together well. Remove from the heat and set to one side.

4 ▲ Heat 150 ml/¼ pint/⅔ cup corn oil in a separate frying pan. Lower the heat slightly and fry the marinated chops until they are cooked through. This will take about 10–12 minutes. Remove with a slotted spoon and drain the cooked chops on kitchen paper (paper towels).

5 Heat the sauce in the karahi, bringing it to the boil. Add the chops and lower the heat. Simmer for 5–7 minutes.

6 Transfer to a warmed serving dish and garnish with the mint sprigs and lime slices.

Tandoori Masala Spring Lamb Chops

LOW-FAT RECIPE

These spicy lean and trimmed lamb chops are marinated for three hours and then cooked in the oven using very little cooking oil. They make an excellent appetizer, served with a salad, and would also serve three as a main course with a rice accompaniment.

SERVES 6

INGREDIENTS

6 spring lamb chops
2 tbsp natural (plain) low-fat yogurt
1 tbsp tomato purée (paste)
2 tsp ground coriander
1 tsp ginger pulp
1 tsp garlic pulp
1 tsp chilli powder
few drops red food colouring (optional)
1 tsp salt
1 tbsp corn oil
3 tbsp lemon juice
oil for basting

Garnish

lettuce leaves (optional)
lime wedges
1 small onion, sliced
fresh coriander (cilantro) sprigs

NUTRITIONAL VALUES (per portion)

Total fat	7.27 g
Saturated fat	2.50 g
Cholesterol	39.70 mg
Energy (kcals/kj)	116/488

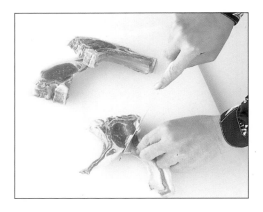

1 ▲ Rinse the chops and pat dry. Trim off any fat.

2 ▲ In a medium bowl, mix together the yogurt, tomato purée (paste), ground coriander, ginger, garlic, chilli powder, food colouring, if using, salt, oil and lemon juice.

3 ▲ Rub this mixture over the chops, using your hands, and leave to marinate for at least 3 hours.

4 ▲ Preheat the oven to 240°C/475°F/ Gas 9. Place the marinated chops in an ovenproof dish.

5 ▲ Using a brush, baste the chops with about 1 tsp of oil and cook in the preheated oven for 15 minutes. Lower the heat to 180°C/350°F/Gas 4 and cook for a further 10–15 minutes.

6 Check to see that the chops are cooked and serve immediately on a bed of lettuce leaves, if wished, and garnish with lime wedges, sliced onion and fresh coriander (cilantro) sprigs.

Vegetable Samosas

Traditional samosa pastry requires a lot of time and hard work but spring roll pastry makes an excellent substitute and is readily available. One packet will make 30 samosas. They can be frozen before or after frying.

SERVES 4–6

INGREDIENTS
1 packet spring roll pastry, thawed and wrapped in a damp dish towel
vegetable oil, for deep-frying

Filling
3 large potatoes, boiled and coarsely mashed
75 g/3 oz/³/4 cup frozen peas, cooked and drained
50 g/2 oz/¹/3 cup canned sweetcorn (corn kernels), drained
1 tsp ground coriander
1 tsp ground cumin
1 tsp mango powder

1 small onion (red if available), finely chopped
salt, to taste
2 fresh green chillies, finely chopped
2 tbsp each, chopped fresh coriander (cilantro) and mint
juice of 1 lemon

I ▲ Toss all the filling ingredients together in a large mixing bowl until well blended. Adjust seasoning of salt and lemon juice, if necessary.

2 ▲ Using one strip of pastry at a time, place 1 tbsp of the filling mixture at one end of the strip and diagonally fold the pastry to form a triangle.

3 Heat enough oil for deep-frying and fry the samosas in small batches until they are golden brown. Serve hot with Fresh Coriander (Cilantro) Relish or a chilli sauce.

Spicy Omelette

Eggs are packed with nutritional value and make wholesome and delicious dishes. This omelette, cooked with potatoes, onions and a touch of spices, can be put together quickly for an emergency meal.

SERVES 4–6

INGREDIENTS
2 tbsp vegetable oil
1 medium onion, finely chopped
¹/2 tsp ground cumin
1 clove garlic, finely crushed
1 fresh green chilli, finely chopped
few sprigs fresh coriander, chopped
1 firm tomato, chopped
1 small potato, cubed and boiled
25 g/1 oz/2 tbsp cooked peas
25g/1 oz/2 tbsp cooked sweetcorn (corn kernels)

salt and pepper, to taste
2 eggs, beaten
25 g/1 oz grated cheese
1 fresh green chilli, sliced, to garnish (optional)

I ▲ Heat the oil in a frying pan (skillet) and fry the next 9 ingredients until well blended but the tomato and potato are firm. Season to taste.

2 ▲ Increase the heat and pour in the beaten eggs. Reduce the heat, cover and cook until the bottom layer is brown. Sprinkle with the grated cheese. Place under a hot grill (broiler) and cook until the egg sets and the cheese has melted. Garnish with the fresh chilli, if wished.

Vegetable Samosas (top) and Spicy Omelette

Baked Potato with Spicy Cottage Cheese

LOW-FAT RECIPE

Always choose a variety of potato recommended for baking for this recipe, as the texture of the potato should not be too dry. This makes an excellent low-fat snack any time of the day.

SERVES 4

INGREDIENTS
4 medium baking potatoes
225 g/8 oz/1 cup low-fat cottage cheese
2 tsp tomato purée (paste)
½ tsp ground cumin
½ tsp ground coriander
½ tsp chilli powder
½ tsp salt
1 tbsp corn oil
½ tsp mixed onion and mustard seeds
3 curry leaves
2 tbsp water

Garnish
mixed salad leaves
fresh coriander (cilantro) sprigs
lemon wedges
2 tomatoes, quartered

NUTRITIONAL VALUES (per portion)	
Total fat	4.60 g
Saturated fat	0.41 g
Cholesterol	2.81 mg
Energy (kcals/kj)	335/1409

2 Transfer the cottage cheese into a heatproof dish and set aside.

3 ▲ In a separate bowl, mix together the tomato purée (paste), ground cumin, ground coriander, chilli powder and salt.

6 ▲ Cook for a further 1 minute, then pour the spicy tomato mixture onto the cottage cheese and blend everything together well.

7 ▲ Check that the potatoes are cooked right through. Unwrap the potatoes and divide the cottage cheese equally between the 4 potatoes.

8 Garnish with the mixed salad leaves, fresh coriander (cilantro) sprigs, lemon wedges and tomato quarters.

1 ▲ Preheat the oven to 180°C/350°F/Gas 4. Wash, pat dry and make a slit in the middle of each potato. Prick the potatoes a few times with a fork, then wrap them individually in foil. Bake in the preheated oven for about 1 hour until soft.

4 ▲ Heat the corn oil in a small saucepan for about 1 minute. Add the mixed onion and mustard seeds and the curry leaves and tilt the saucepan so the oil covers all the seeds and leaves.

5 When the leaves turn a shade darker and you can smell their beautiful aroma, pour the tomato purée mixture into the saucepan and lower the heat immediately to low. Add the water and mix well.

VARIATION

This recipe can also be used as the basis for a tangy vegetable accompaniment to a main meal. Instead of using baked potatoes, boil new potatoes in their skins then cut in half. Add the cooked potatoes to the spicy cottage mixture, mix together well and serve.

Prawns (Shrimp) with Pomegranate Seeds

King prawns (jumbo shrimp) are best for this dish. It makes an impressive appetizer, and is delicious served with a mixed salad.

SERVES 4

INGREDIENTS
1 tsp crushed garlic
1 tsp grated ginger
1 tsp coarsely ground pomegranate seeds
1 tsp ground coriander
1 tsp salt
1 tsp chilli powder
2 tbsp tomato purée (paste)
4 tbsp water
3 tbsp chopped fresh coriander (cilantro)
2 tbsp corn oil
12 large cooked prawns (shrimp)
1 medium onion, sliced into rings

1 Put the garlic, ginger, pomegranate seeds, ground coriander, salt, chilli powder, tomato purée (paste), water and 2 tbsp of the fresh coriander (cilantro) into a bowl. Pour in the oil and blend everything together thoroughly.

2 ▲ Peel and wash the prawns and rinse them gently under running water. Using a sharp knife, make a small slit at the back of each prawn. Open out each prawn to make a butterfly shape.

3 Add the prawns to the spice mixture, making sure they are all well coated. Leave to marinate for about 2 hours.

4 ▲ Meanwhile, cut four squares of foil, about 20 × 20 cm/8 × 8 in. Preheat the oven to 230°C/450°F/Gas 8. When the prawns are ready, place 3 prawns and a few onion rings onto each square of foil, garnishing each with a little fresh coriander, and fold up into little packages. Bake for about 12–15 minutes and open up the foil to serve.

Grilled (Broiled) Prawns (Shrimp)

Prawns (shrimp) are delicious grilled (broiled), especially when they are flavoured with spices. Buy the largest prawns you can find for this dish.

SERVES 4–6

INGREDIENTS
18 large cooked prawns (shrimp)
4 tbsp lemon juice
1 tsp salt
1 tsp chilli powder
1 tsp garlic pulp
1½ tsp soft light brown sugar
3 tbsp corn oil
2 tbsp chopped fresh coriander (cilantro)
1 fresh green chilli, sliced
1 tomato, sliced
1 small onion, cut into rings
lemon wedges

1 ▲ Peel the prawns (shrimp) and rinse them gently under cold water. Using a sharp knife, make a slit at the back of each prawn and open out into a butterfly shape. Put the remaining ingredients, with the exception of the chilli, tomato, onion and lemon wedges, in a bowl and mix together thoroughly.

2 Add the prawns to the spice mixture, making sure they are well coated, and leave to marinate for about 1 hour.

3 Place the green chilli, tomato slices and onion rings in a flameproof dish. Add the prawn mixture and cook under a very hot preheated grill (broiler) for about 10–15 minutes, basting several times with a brush. Serve immediately, garnished with the lemon wedges.

A mixed salad of cucumber, watercress, sweetcorn (corn kernels) and cherry tomatoes, garnished with lemon wedges and onion rings (top) is delicious served with Prawns (Shrimp) with Pomegranate Seeds (centre) and Grilled (Broiled) Prawns (Shrimp).

Poultry Dishes

Chicken is especially good in curries, and even the most subtle blend of spices will produce a deliciously aromatic dish. If you are in a hurry, try one of the Balti recipes; these quick stir-fried dishes are easy to cook at home. If you are entertaining, impress your friends with Khara Masala Balti Chicken — a dry-style curry with whole spices, ginger and fresh coriander.

Balti Chicken

This recipe has a beautifully delicate flavour, and is probably the most popular of all Balti dishes. Choose a young chicken as it will be more flavoursome.

SERVES 4–6

INGREDIENTS
*1–1½ kg/2½–3 lb chicken, skinned and
    cut into 8 pieces
3 tbsp corn oil
3 medium onions, sliced
3 medium tomatoes, halved and sliced
2.5 cm/1 in cinnamon stick
2 large black cardamom pods
4 black peppercorns
½ tsp black cumin seeds
1 tsp ginger pulp
1 tsp garlic pulp
1 tsp garam masala
1 tsp chilli powder
1 tsp salt
2 tbsp natural (plain) yogurt
4 tbsp lemon juice
2 tbsp chopped fresh coriander (cilantro)
2 fresh green chillies, chopped*

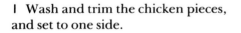

1　Wash and trim the chicken pieces, and set to one side.

2 ▲ Heat the oil in a large karahi or deep round-bottomed frying pan (skillet). Throw in the onions and fry until they are golden brown. Add the tomatoes and stir well.

3 ▲ Add the cinnamon stick, cardamoms, peppercorns, black cumin seeds, ginger, garlic, garam masala, chilli powder and salt. Lower the heat and stir-fry for 3–5 minutes.

4 ▲ Add the chicken pieces, 2 at a time, and stir-fry for at least 7 minutes or until the spice mixture has completely penetrated the chicken pieces.

5 ▲ Add the yogurt to the chicken and mix well.

6　Lower the heat and cover the pan with a piece of foil, making sure that the foil does not touch the food. Cook very gently for about 15 minutes, checking once to make sure the food is not catching on the bottom of the pan.

7 ▲ Finally, add the lemon juice, fresh coriander (cilantro) and green chillies, and serve at once.

COOK'S TIP

Chicken cooked on the bone is both tender and flavoursome. However, do substitute the whole chicken with 675 g/1½ lb boned and cubed chicken, if wished. The cooking time can be reduced at step 6, too.

Chicken in a Cashew Nut Sauce

LOW-FAT RECIPE

This chicken dish has a deliciously thick and nutty sauce, and it is best served with plain boiled rice.

SERVES 4

INGREDIENTS

2 medium onions
2 tbsp tomato purée (paste)
50 g/2 oz/¹⁄₃ cup cashew nuts
1¹⁄₂ tsp garam masala
1 tsp garlic pulp
1 tsp chilli powder
1 tbsp lemon juice
¹⁄₄ tsp turmeric
1 tsp salt
1 tbsp natural (plain) low-fat yogurt
2 tbsp corn oil
1 tbsp chopped fresh coriander (cilantro)
1 tbsp sultanas (golden raisins)
450 g/1 lb/3¹⁄₄ cups chicken, skinned, boned and cubed
175 g/6 oz/2¹⁄₂ cups button mushrooms
300 ml/¹⁄₂ pint/1¹⁄₄ cups water
1 tbsp chopped fresh coriander (cilantro)

NUTRITIONAL VALUES (per portion)

Total fat	14.64 g
Saturated fat	2.87 g
Cholesterol	64.84 mg
Energy (kcals/kj)	280/1176

2 ▲ Add the tomato purée (paste), cashew nuts, garam masala, garlic, chilli powder, lemon juice, turmeric, salt and yogurt to the processed onions.

3 Process all the ingredients in the food processor for a further 1–1¹⁄₂ minutes.

4 In a saucepan, heat the oil, lower the heat to medium and pour in the spice mixture from the food processor. Fry for about 2 minutes, lowering the heat if necessary.

5 ▲ Add the fresh coriander (cilantro), sultanas (golden raisins) and chicken and continue to stir-fry for a further 1 minute.

6 ▲ Add the mushrooms, pour in the water and bring to a simmer. Cover the saucepan and cook over a low heat for about 10 minutes.

7 ▲ After this time, check to see that the chicken is cooked through and the sauce is thick. Cook for a little longer if necessary.

8 Serve garnished with chopped fresh coriander.

1 ▲ Cut the onions into quarters and place in a food processor or blender and process for about 1 minute.

Balti Chicken with Vegetables

In this recipe the chicken and vegetables are cut into strips which makes the dish particularly attractive.

SERVES 4–6

INGREDIENTS
4 tbsp corn oil
2 medium onions, sliced
4 garlic cloves, thickly sliced
450 g/1 lb/3¼ cups chicken breast, skinned, boned and cut into strips
1 tsp salt
2 tbsp lime juice
3 fresh green chillies, chopped
2 medium carrots, cut into batons

2 medium potatoes, peeled and cut into 1 cm/½ in strips
1 medium courgette (zucchini), cut into batons
4 lime slices
1 tbsp chopped fresh coriander (cilantro)
2 fresh green chillies, cut into strips (optional)

1 Heat the oil in a large karahi or deep round-bottomed frying pan (skillet). Lower the heat slightly and add the onions. Fry until lightly browned.

2 ▲ Add half the garlic slices and fry for a few seconds before adding the chicken and salt. Cook everything together, stirring, until all the moisture has evaporated and the chicken is lightly browned.

3 ▲ Add the lime juice, green chillies and all the vegetables to the pan. Turn up the heat and add the rest of the garlic. Stir-fry for 7–10 minutes, or until the chicken is cooked through and the vegetables are just tender.

4 Transfer to a serving dish and garnish with the lime slices, fresh coriander (cilantro) and green chilli strips, if wished.

Balti Chilli Chicken

Hot and spicy would be the best way of describing this mouth-watering Balti dish. The smell of the fresh chillies cooking is indescribable!

SERVES 4–6

INGREDIENTS
5 tbsp corn oil
8 large fresh green chillies, slit
1/2 tsp mixed onion and cumin seeds
4 curry leaves
1 tsp ginger pulp
1 tsp chilli powder
1 tsp ground coriander
1 tsp garlic pulp
1 tsp salt
2 medium onions, chopped
675 g/1 1/2 lb/4 2/3 cups chicken, skinned, boned and cubed
1 tbsp lemon juice
1 tbsp roughly chopped fresh mint
1 tbsp roughly chopped fresh coriander (cilantro)
8–10 cherry tomatoes

I ▲ Heat the oil in a deep round-bottomed frying pan (skillet) or a medium karahi. Lower the heat slightly and add the slit green chillies. Fry until the skin starts to change colour.

2 ▲ Add the onion and cumin seeds, curry leaves, ginger, chilli powder, ground coriander, garlic, salt and onions, and fry for a few seconds, stirring continuously.

3 Add the chicken pieces and stir-fry for 7–10 minutes, or until the chicken is cooked right through.

4 ▼ Sprinkle on the lemon juice and add the mint and coriander (cilantro).

5 Add the cherry tomatoes and serve with Naan or Paratha.

Classic Tandoori Chicken

This is probably the most famous of Indian dishes. Marinate the chicken well and cook in an extremely hot oven for a clay oven-baked taste. If you want authentic "burnt" spots on the chicken, place the dish under a hot grill (broiler) for a few minutes after baking.

SERVES 4–6

INGREDIENTS
1.5 kg/3 lb oven-ready chicken
250 ml/8 fl oz/1 cup natural (plain) yogurt, beaten
4 tbsp tandoori masala paste
salt, to taste
6 tbsp ghee
salad leaves, to serve
lemon twist and onion slices, to garnish

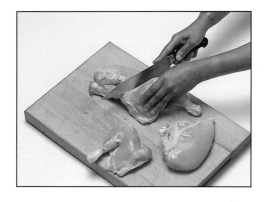

2 ▲ Cut the chicken in half down the centre and through the breast. Cut each piece in half again. Make a few deep gashes diagonally into the flesh. Mix the yogurt with the masala paste and salt. Spread the chicken evenly with the yogurt mixture, spreading some into the gashes. Leave for at least 2 hours, but preferably overnight.

4 ▲ Melt the ghee and pour over the chicken to seal the surface. This helps to keep the centre moist during the roasting period. Cook in the preheated oven for 10 minutes, then remove, leaving the oven on.

I ▲ Using a sharp knife or scissors, remove the skin from the chicken and trim off any excess fat. Using a fork, beat the flesh at random.

3 ▲ Preheat the oven to maximum heat. Place the chicken quarters on a wire rack in a deep baking tray. Spread the chicken with any excess marinade, reserve a little for basting halfway through cooking time.

5 ▲ Baste the chicken pieces with the remaining marinade. Return to the oven and switch off the heat. Leave the chicken in the oven for about 15–20 minutes without opening the door. Serve on a bed of salad leaves and garnish with the lemon twist and onion slices.

Balti Chicken in Saffron Sauce

This is a beautifully aromatic chicken dish that is partly cooked in the oven. It contains saffron, the most expensive spice in the world, and is sure to impress your guests.

SERVES 4–6

INGREDIENTS
50 g/2 oz/4 tbsp butter
2 tbsp corn oil
1–1¹/₂ kg/2¹/₂–3 lb chicken, skinned and cut into 8 pieces
1 medium onion, chopped
1 tsp garlic pulp
¹/₂ tsp crushed black peppercorns
¹/₂ tsp crushed cardamom pods
¹/₄ tsp ground cinnamon
1¹/₂ tsp chilli powder
150 ml/¹/₄ pint/²/₃ cup natural (plain) yogurt
50 g/2 oz/¹/₂ cup ground almonds
1 tbsp lemon juice
1 tsp salt
1 tsp saffron strands
150 ml/¹/₄ pint/²/₃ cup water
150 ml/¹/₄ pint/²/₃ cup single (light) cream
2 tbsp chopped fresh coriander (cilantro)

1 ▲ Preheat the oven to 180°C/350°F/ Gas 4. Melt the butter with the oil in a deep round-bottomed frying pan (skillet) or a medium karahi. Add the chicken pieces and fry until lightly browned. This will take about 5 minutes. Remove the chicken using a slotted spoon, leaving behind as much of the fat as possible.

2 ▲ Add the onion to the same pan, and fry over a medium heat. Meanwhile, mix together the garlic, black peppercorns, cardamom, cinnamon, chilli powder, yogurt, ground almonds, lemon juice, salt and saffron strands in a mixing bowl.

3 ▲ When the onions are lightly browned, pour the spice mixture into the pan and stir-fry for about 1 minute.

4 ▲ Add the chicken pieces, and continue to stir-fry for a further 2 minutes. Add the water and bring to a simmer.

5 Transfer the contents of the pan to a casserole dish and cover with a lid, or, if using a karahi, cover with foil. Transfer to the oven and cook for 30–35 minutes.

6 ▲ Once you are sure that the chicken is cooked right through, remove it from the oven. Transfer the chicken to a frying pan and stir in the cream.

7 Reheat gently on the hob for about 2 minutes. Garnish with fresh coriander (cilantro) and serve with Fruity Pullao or plain boiled rice.

COOK'S TIP

There is no substitute for saffron, so don't be tempted to use turmeric instead. It is well worth buying a small amount of saffron – either strands or in powdered form – to create this dish for a special occasion.

Spicy Masala Chicken

LOW-FAT RECIPE

These chicken pieces are grilled (broiled) and have a sweet-and-sour taste. They can be served cold with a salad and rice or hot with Masala Mashed Potatoes.

SERVES 6

INGREDIENTS
12 chicken thighs
6 tbsp lemon juice
1 tsp ginger pulp
1 tsp garlic pulp
1 tsp crushed dried red chillies
1 tsp salt
1 tsp soft brown sugar
2 tbsp clear honey
2 tbsp chopped fresh coriander (cilantro)
1 fresh green chilli, finely chopped
2 tbsp vegetable oil
fresh coriander (cilantro) sprigs

1 Prick the chicken thighs with a fork, rinse, pat dry and set aside in a bowl.

2 ▲ In a large mixing bowl, mix together the lemon juice, ginger, garlic, crushed dried red chillies, salt, sugar and honey.

3 Transfer the chicken thighs to the spice mixture and coat well. Set aside for about 45 minutes.

NUTRITIONAL VALUES (per portion)

Total fat	9.20 g
Saturated fat	2.31 g
Cholesterol	73.00 mg
Energy (kcals/kj)	189/795

4 ▲ Preheat the grill (broiler) to medium. Add the fresh coriander (cilantro) and chopped green chilli to the chicken thighs and place them on a flameproof dish.

5 ▲ Pour any remaining marinade over the chicken and baste with the oil, using a pastry brush.

6 Grill (broil) the chicken thighs under the preheated grill for 15–20 minutes, turning and basting occasionally, until cooked through and browned.

7 Transfer to a serving dish and garnish with the fresh coriander sprigs.

Tandoori Chicken

LOW-FAT RECIPE

A most popular Indian/Pakistan chicken dish which is cooked in a clay oven called a tandoor, this is extremely popular in the West and appears on the majority of the restaurant menus. Though the authentic tandoori flavour is very difficult to achieve in conventional ovens, this version still makes a very tasty dish.

SERVES 4

INGREDIENTS
4 chicken quarters
175 ml/6 fl oz/³⁄₄ cup natural (plain) low-fat yogurt
1 tsp garam marsala
1 tsp ginger pulp
1 tsp garlic pulp
1¹⁄₂ tsp chilli powder
¹⁄₄ tsp turmeric
1 tsp ground coriander
1 tbsp lemon juice
1 tsp salt
few drops red food colouring
2 tbsp corn oil

Garnish
mixed salad leaves
lime wedges
1 tomato, quartered

I ▲ Skin, rinse and pat dry the chicken quarters. Make 2 slits into the flesh of each piece, place in a dish and set aside.

NUTRITIONAL VALUES (per portion)	
Total fat	10.64 g
Saturated fat	2.74 g
Cholesterol	81.90 mg
Energy (kcals/kj)	242/1018

2 ▲ Mix together the yogurt, garam marsala, ginger, garlic, chilli powder, turmeric, ground coriander, lemon juice, salt, red colouring and oil, and beat so that all the ingredients are well mixed together.

3 Cover the chicken quarters with the spice mixture and leave to marinate for about 3 hours.

4 ▲ Preheat the oven to 240°C/475°F/ Gas 9. Transfer the chicken pieces to an ovenproof dish.

5 Bake in the preheated oven for 20– 25 minutes or until the chicken is cooked right through and browned on top.

6 Remove from the oven, transfer onto a serving dish and garnish with the salad leaves, lime and tomato.

Balti Butter Chicken

Butter Chicken is one of the most popular Balti chicken dishes, especially in the West. Cooked in butter, with aromatic spices, cream and almonds, this mild dish will be enjoyed by everyone. Serve with Colourful Pullao Rice.

SERVES 4–6

INGREDIENTS

150 ml/¼ pint/⅔ cup natural (plain) yogurt
50 g/2 oz/½ cup ground almonds
1½ tsp chilli powder
¼ tsp crushed bay leaves
¼ tsp ground cloves
¼ tsp ground cinnamon
1 tsp garam masala
4 green cardamom pods
1 tsp ginger pulp
1 tsp garlic pulp
400 g/14 oz/2 cups canned tomatoes
1¼ tsp salt
1 kg/2 lb/6½ cups chicken, skinned, boned and cubed
75 g/3 oz/6 tbsp butter
1 tbsp corn oil
2 medium onions, sliced
2 tbsp chopped fresh coriander (cilantro)
4 tbsp single (light) cream
coriander sprigs

1 ▲ Put the yogurt, ground almonds, all the dry spices, ginger, garlic, tomatoes and salt into a mixing bowl and blend together thoroughly.

2 ▲ Put the chicken into a large mixing bowl and pour over the yogurt mixture. Set aside.

3 Melt together the butter and oil in a medium karahi or deep round-bottomed frying pan (skillet). Add the onions and fry for about 3 minutes.

4 ▲ Add the chicken mixture and stir-fry for 7–10 minutes.

5 ▲ Stir in about half of the coriander (cilantro) and mix well.

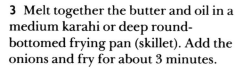

6 ▲ Pour over the cream and stir in well. Bring to the boil. Serve garnished with the remaining chopped coriander and coriander sprigs.

COOK'S TIP

Substitute natural (plain) yogurt with Greek-style yogurt for an even richer and creamier flavour.

Stuffed Roast Chicken

At one time this dish was only cooked in royal palaces and ingredients varied according to individual chefs. The saffron and the rich stuffing make it a truly royal dish.

SERVES 4–6

INGREDIENTS
1 sachet saffron powder
¹/₂ tsp ground nutmeg
1 tbsp warm milk
1.5 kg/3 lb whole chicken
6 tbsp ghee
5 tbsp hot water

Stuffing
3 medium onions, finely chopped
2 fresh green chillies, chopped
50 g/2 oz/¹/₃ cup sultanas (golden raisins)
50 g/2 oz/¹/₂ cup ground almonds
50 g/2 oz dried apricots, soaked until soft
3 hard-boiled eggs, coarsely chopped
salt, to taste

Masala
4 sprigs spring onions (scallions), chopped
2 cloves garlic, crushed
1 tsp five-spice powder
4–6 green cardamom pods
¹/₂ tsp turmeric
1 tsp freshly ground black pepper
2 tbsp natural (plain) yogurt
50 g/2 oz/1 cup desiccated (shredded) coconut, toasted

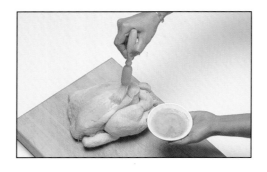

1 ▲ Mix together the saffron, nutmeg and milk. Brush the inside of the chicken with the mixture and carefully spread some over the skin. Heat 4 tbsp of the ghee in a large frying pan (skillet) and fry the chicken on all sides to seal it. Remove and keep warm.

2 ▲ To make the stuffing, in the same ghee, fry the onions, chillies, and sultanas (golden raisins) for 2–3 minutes. Remove from the heat, allow to cool and add the ground almonds, apricots, chopped eggs and salt. Toss the mixture well, then stuff the chicken.

3 ▲ Heat the remaining ghee in a large heavy pan and gently fry all the masala ingredients except the coconut for 2–3 minutes. Add the water. Place the chicken on the bed of masala, cover the pan and cook until the chicken is tender. Remove the chicken from the pan and set aside, keeping warm.

4 ▲ Return the pan to the heat and cook to reduce excess fluids in the masala. When the mixture thickens, pour over the chicken. Sprinkle with toasted coconut and serve hot.

Chicken Curry

Chicken curry is always popular whether served at a family dinner or a banquet. This version is cooked covered, giving a thin consistency. If you would prefer it thick, cook uncovered for the last 15 minutes.

SERVES 4–6

INGREDIENTS

4 tbsp vegetable oil
4 cloves
4–6 green cardamom pods
1 piece cinnamon stick, 5 cm/2 in long
3 whole star anise
6–8 curry leaves
1 large onion, finely chopped
1 piece fresh ginger, 5 cm/2 in long, crushed
4 cloves garlic, crushed
4 tbsp mild curry paste
1 tsp turmeric
1 tsp five-spice powder
1.5 kg/3 lb chicken, skinned and jointed
400 g/14 oz canned tomatoes, chopped
115 g/4 oz creamed coconut
1/2 tsp sugar
salt, to taste
50 g/2 oz/2 cups fresh coriander (cilantro), chopped

I ▲ Heat the oil in a pan and fry the cloves, cardamoms, cinnamon stick, star anise and curry leaves until the cloves swell and the curry leaves are slightly burnt.

2 ▲ Add the onion, ginger and garlic and fry until the onion turns brown. Add the curry paste, turmeric and five-spice powder and fry until the oil separates.

3 ▲ Add the chicken pieces and mix well. When all the pieces are evenly sealed, cover and cook until the meat is nearly done.

4 ▲ Add the chopped tomatoes and the creamed coconut. Simmer gently until the coconut dissolves. Mix well and add the sugar and salt. Fold in the chopped fresh coriander (cilantro), then reheat and serve hot.

Balti Chicken with Lentils

This is rather an unusual combination of flavours, but I do recommend you try it. The mango powder gives a delicious tangy flavour to this spicy dish.

SERVES 4–6

INGREDIENTS
75 g/3 oz/½ cup chana dhal (split yellow
    lentils)
4 tbsp corn oil
2 medium leeks, chopped
6 large dried red chillies
4 curry leaves
1 tsp mustard seeds
2 tsp mango powder
2 medium tomatoes, chopped
½ tsp chilli powder
1 tsp ground coriander
1 tsp salt
450 g/1 lb/3¼ cups chicken, skinned,
    boned and cubed
1 tbsp chopped fresh coriander (cilantro)

I Wash the lentils carefully and remove any stones.

2 ▲ Put the lentils into a saucepan with enough water to cover, and boil for about 10 minutes until they are soft but not mushy. Drain and set to one side in a bowl.

3 ▲ Heat the oil in a medium karahi or deep round-bottomed frying pan (skillet). Lower the heat slightly and throw in the leeks, dried red chillies, curry leaves and mustard seeds. Stir-fry gently for a few minutes.

4 ▲ Add the mango powder, tomatoes, chilli powder, ground coriander, salt and chicken, and stir-fry for 7–10 minutes.

5 ▲ Mix in the cooked lentils and fry for a further 2 minutes, or until you are sure that the chicken is cooked right through.

6 Garnish with fresh coriander (cilantro) and serve with Paratha.

COOK'S TIP

Chana dhal, a split yellow lentil, is available from Asian stores. However, split yellow peas are a good substitute.

Hot Chicken Curry

LOW-FAT RECIPE

This curry has a nice thick sauce, and I make it using red and green (bell) peppers for extra colour. It can be served with either Wholemeal (Whole-Wheat) Chapatis or plain boiled rice.

SERVES 4

INGREDIENTS
2 tbsp corn oil
1/4 tsp fenugreek seeds
1/4 tsp onion seeds
2 medium onions, chopped
1/2 tsp garlic pulp
1/2 tsp ginger pulp
1 tsp ground coriander
1 tsp chilli powder
1 tsp salt
400 g/14 oz/1 3/4 cups canned tomatoes
2 tbsp lemon juice
350 g/12 oz/2 1/2 cups chicken, skinned, boned and cubed
2 tbsp chopped fresh coriander (cilantro)
3 fresh green chillies, chopped
1/2 red (bell) pepper, cut into chunks
1/2 green (bell) pepper, cut into chunks
fresh coriander (cilantro) sprigs

NUTRITIONAL VALUES (per portion)	
Total fat	9.83 g
Saturated fat	2.03 g
Cholesterol	48.45 mg
Energy (kcals/kj)	205/861

1 ▲ In a medium saucepan, heat the oil and fry the fenugreek and onion seeds until they turn a shade darker. Add the chopped onions, garlic and ginger and fry for about 5 minutes until the onions turn golden brown. Lower the heat to very low.

2 ▲ Meanwhile, in a separate bowl, mix together the ground coriander, chilli powder, salt, tomatoes and lemon juice.

3 ▲ Pour this mixture into the saucepan and turn up the heat to medium. Stir-fry for about 3 minutes.

4 ▲ Add the chicken pieces and stir-fry for 5–7 minutes.

5 ▲ Add the fresh coriander (cilantro), green chillies and the sliced (bell) peppers. Lower the heat, cover the saucepan and let this simmer for about 10 minutes until the chicken is cooked.

6 Serve hot, garnished with fresh coriander sprigs.

COOK'S TIP

For a milder version of this delicious curry, simply omit some or all of the fresh green chillies.

Moghul-Style Chicken

This delicate curry, Moghlai Murgh, can be served as an appetizer followed by spicier curries and rice. Saffron is crucial to the flavour, but as it is very expensive save this dish for special occasions.

SERVES 4–6

INGREDIENTS

2 eggs, beaten with salt and pepper
4 chicken breasts, rubbed with a little garam masala
6 tbsp ghee
1 large onion, finely chopped
1 piece fresh ginger, 5 cm/2 in long, finely crushed
4 cloves garlic, finely crushed
4 cloves
4 green cardamom pods
1 piece cinnamon stick, 5 cm/2 in long
2 bay leaves
15–20 strands of saffron
150 ml/¼ pint/⅔ cup natural (plain) yogurt, beaten with 1 tsp cornflour (cornstarch)
salt, to taste
5 tbsp double (heavy) cream
50 g/2 oz/½ cup ground almonds

1 ▲ Brush the chicken breasts with the beaten eggs. In a frying pan (skillet), heat the ghee and fry the chicken. Remove and keep warm.

2 ▲ In the same ghee, fry the onion, ginger, garlic, cloves, cardamoms, cinnamon and bay leaves. When the onion turns golden, remove the pan from the heat, allow to cool a little and add the saffron and yogurt. Mix well to prevent the yogurt from curdling.

3 ▲ Return the chicken mixture to the pan with any juices and gently cook until the chicken is tender. Adjust the seasoning if necessary.

4 ▲ Just before serving, fold in the cream and ground almonds. Serve hot.

Chicken in a Hot Red Sauce

In India, small chickens are used for this dish and served as an individual appetizer with chapatis. If you wish to serve it as a starter, use 4 poussins instead of chicken joints. Skin them first and make small gashes with a sharp knife to allow the spices to seep in.

SERVES 4–6

INGREDIENTS

4 tsp kashmiri masala paste
4 tbsp tomato ketchup
1 tsp Worcestershire sauce
1 tsp five-spice powder
salt, to taste
1 tsp sugar
8 chicken joints, skinned but not boned
3 tbsp vegetable oil
1 piece fresh ginger, 5 cm/2 in long, finely shredded
4 cloves garlic, finely crushed
juice of 1 lemon
few fresh coriander (cilantro) leaves, finely chopped

1 ▲ To make the marinade, mix together the kashmiri masala, tomato ketchup, Worcestershire sauce, five-spice powder, salt and sugar. Allow to rest in a warm place until the sugar has dissolved.

2 ▲ Rub the chicken pieces with the marinade and allow to rest for a further 2 hours, or overnight if possible.

3 ▲ Heat the oil in a frying pan (skillet) and fry half the ginger and all the garlic until golden brown. Add the chicken pieces, and fry without overlapping until both sides are sealed. Cover and cook until the chicken is nearly tender and the sauce clings with the oil separating.

4 ▲ Sprinkle the chicken with the lemon juice, remaining ginger and fresh coriander (cilantro). Mix well, reheat and serve hot.

Balti Baby Chicken in Tamarind Sauce

The tamarind in this recipe gives the dish a sweet-and-sour flavour; this is also quite a hot Balti.

SERVES 4–6

INGREDIENTS
4 tbsp tomato ketchup
1 tbsp tamarind paste
4 tbsp water
1½ tsp chilli powder
1½ tsp salt
1 tbsp sugar
1½ tsp ginger pulp
1½ tsp garlic pulp
2 tbsp desiccated (shredded) coconut
2 tbsp sesame seeds
1 tsp poppy seeds
1 tsp ground cumin
1½ tsp ground coriander
2 × 450 g/1 lb baby chickens, skinned and cut into 6–8 pieces each
5 tbsp corn oil
8 tbsp curry leaves
½ tsp onion seeds
3 large dried red chillies
½ tsp fenugreek seeds
10–12 cherry tomatoes
3 tbsp chopped fresh coriander (cilantro)
2 fresh green chillies, chopped

2 ▲ Add the chilli powder, salt, sugar, ginger, garlic, coconut, sesame and poppy seeds, ground cumin and ground coriander to the mixture.

3 ▲ Add the chicken pieces and stir until they are well coated with the spice mixture. Set to one side.

1 ▲ Put the tomato ketchup, tamarind paste and water into a large mixing bowl and use a fork to blend everything together.

4 ▲ Heat the oil in a deep round-bottomed frying pan (skillet) or a large karahi. Add the curry leaves, onion seeds, dried red chillies and fenugreek seeds and fry for about 1 minute.

5 ▲ Lower the heat to medium and add the chicken pieces, along with their sauce, 2 or 3 pieces at a time, mixing as you go. When all the pieces are in the pan, stir them around well using a slotted spoon.

6 Simmer gently for about 12–15 minutes, or until the chicken is thoroughly cooked.

7 ▲ Finally, add the tomatoes, fresh coriander (cilantro) and green chillies, and serve with Fried Rice with Cashew Nuts, if wished.

Chicken with Green Mango

Green, unripe mango is used for making various dishes on the Indian sub-continent, including pickles, chutneys and some meat, chicken and vegetable dishes. This is a fairly simple chicken dish to prepare and is served with rice and dhal.

SERVES 4

INGREDIENTS

1 medium green (unripe) mango
450 g/1 lb/3¼ cups chicken, skinned, boned and cubed
¼ tsp onion seeds
1 tsp ginger pulp
½ tsp garlic pulp
1 tsp chilli powder
¼ tsp turmeric
1 tsp salt
1 tsp ground coriander
2 tbsp corn oil
2 medium onions, sliced
4 curry leaves
300 ml/½ pint/1¼ cups water
2 medium tomatoes, quartered
2 fresh green chillies, chopped
2 tbsp chopped fresh coriander (cilantro)

NUTRITIONAL VALUES (per portion)

Total fat	11.03 g
Saturated fat	2.43 g
Cholesterol	64.12 mg
Energy (kcals/kj)	269/1131

VARIATION

A good, firm cooking apple can be used instead of green mango, if wished. Prepare and cook in exactly the same way.

1 ▲ To prepare the mango, peel the skin and slice the flesh thickly. Discard the stone (seed) from the middle. Place the mango slices in a small bowl, cover and set aside.

2 ▲ Place the chicken cubes in a bowl and add the onion seeds, ginger, garlic, chilli powder, turmeric, salt and ground coriander. Mix the spices into the chicken and add half the mango slices to this mixture as well.

3 ▲ In a medium saucepan, heat the oil and fry the sliced onions until golden brown. Add the curry leaves.

4 ▲ Gradually add the chicken pieces, stirring all the time.

5 ▲ Pour in the water, lower the heat and cook for about 12–15 minutes, stirring occasionally, until the chicken is cooked through and the water has been absorbed.

6 ▲ Add the remaining mango slices, the tomatoes, green chillies and fresh coriander (cilantro) and serve hot.

Chicken and Tomato Balti

If you like tomatoes, you will love this chicken recipe. It makes a semi-dry Balti and is good served with a lentil dish and plain boiled rice.

SERVES 4

INGREDIENTS
4 tbsp corn oil
6 curry leaves
½ tsp mixed onion and mustard seeds
8 medium tomatoes, sliced
1 tsp ground coriander
1 tsp chilli powder
1 tsp salt
1 tsp ground cumin
1 tsp garlic pulp
675 g/1½ lb/4⅔ cups chicken, skinned, boned and cubed
150 ml/¼ pint/⅔ cup water
1 tbsp sesame seeds, roasted
1 tbsp chopped fresh coriander (cilantro)

1 ▲ Heat the oil in a deep round-bottomed frying pan (skillet) or a medium karahi. Add the curry leaves and mixed onion and mustard seeds and stir well.

2 ▲ Lower the heat slightly and add the tomatoes.

3 ▲ While the tomatoes are gently cooking, mix together the ground coriander, chilli powder, salt, ground cumin and garlic in a bowl. Tip the spices onto the tomatoes.

4 ▲ Add the chicken pieces and stir together well. Stir-fry for about 5 minutes.

5 Pour on the water and continue cooking, stirring occasionally, until the sauce thickens and the chicken is cooked through.

6 ▲ Sprinkle the sesame seeds and fresh coriander (cilantro) over the top of the dish and serve.

COOK'S TIP

Sesame seeds are available from Asian and health food stores. There are two types – unroasted seeds, which are white, and roasted ones, which are lightly browned. To roast sesame seeds at home, simply tip a quantity into a frying pan (skillet) over a high heat for about 1 minute. Shake the pan constantly to prevent the seeds burning. Use immediately or store in a screw-topped jar.

Chicken in Spicy Onions

Murgh Do Piyaza is one of the few dishes of India in which onions appear prominently. Chunky onion slices infused with toasted cumin seeds and shredded ginger add a delicious contrast to the flavour of the chicken.

SERVES 4–6

INGREDIENTS

1.5 kg/3 lb chicken, jointed and skinned
1/2 tsp turmeric
1/2 tsp chilli powder
salt, to taste
4 tbsp oil
4 small onions, finely chopped
175 g/6 oz/6 cups fresh coriander (cilantro), coarsely chopped
1 piece fresh ginger, 5 cm/2 in long, finely shredded
2 fresh green chillies, finely chopped
2 tsp cumin seeds, dry-roasted
5 tbsp natural (plain) yogurt
5 tbsp double (heavy) cream
1/2 tsp cornflour (cornstarch)

2 ▲ Reheat the oil and add 3 of the chopped onions, most of the fresh coriander (cilantro), half the ginger, the green chillies and the cumin seeds and fry until the onions are translucent. Return the chicken to the pan with any juices and mix well. Cover and cook gently for 15 minutes.

3 ▲ Remove the pan from the heat and allow to cool a little. Mix together the yogurt, cream and cornflour (cornstarch) and gradually fold into the chicken, mixing well.

4 ▲ Return the pan to the heat and gently cook until the chicken is tender. Just before serving, stir in the reserved onion, coriander and ginger. Serve hot.

I ▲ Rub the chicken joints with the turmeric, chilli powder and salt. Heat the oil in a frying pan (skillet) and fry the chicken pieces in batches until both sides are sealed. Remove and keep warm.

Hot Sweet-and-Sour Duck Casserole

This recipe can be made with any game bird, or even rabbit. It is a distinctively sweet, sour and hot dish best eaten with rice as an accompaniment.

SERVES 4–6

INGREDIENTS

1.5 kg/3 lb duck, jointed and skinned
4 bay leaves
3 tbsp salt
5 tbsp vegetable oil
juice of 5 lemons
8 medium-sized onions, finely chopped
50 g/2 oz garlic, crushed
50 g/2 oz chilli powder
300 ml/¹/₂ pint/1¹/₄ cups pickling vinegar
115 g/4 oz fresh ginger, finely sliced or shredded
115 g/4 oz/¹/₂ cup sugar
50 g/2 oz garam masala

I ▲ Place the duck, bay leaves and salt in a large pan and cover with cold water. Bring to the boil then simmer for 30–45 minutes, or until the duck is fully cooked. Remove the pieces of duck and keep warm. Reserve the liquid as a base for stock or soups.

2 ▲ In a large pan, heat the oil and lemon juice until it reaches smoking point. Add the onions, garlic and chilli powder and fry the onions until they are golden brown.

3 ▲ Add the vinegar, ginger and sugar and simmer until the sugar dissolves and the oil has separated from the masala.

4 ▲ Return the duck to the pan and add the garam masala. Mix well, then reheat until the masala clings to the pieces of duck and the sauce is thick. Adjust the seasoning if necessary. If you prefer a thinner sauce, add a little of the reserved stock.

Khara Masala Balti Chicken

Whole spices (khara) are used in this recipe, giving it a wonderfully rich flavour. This is a dry dish so it is best served with Raita and Paratha.

SERVES 4

INGREDIENTS
3 curry leaves
¹/4 tsp mustard seeds
¹/4 tsp fennel seeds
¹/4 tsp onion seeds
¹/2 tsp crushed dried red chillies
¹/2 tsp white cumin seeds
¹/4 tsp fenugreek seeds
¹/2 tsp crushed pomegranate seeds
1 tsp salt
1 tsp shredded ginger
3 garlic cloves, sliced
4 tbsp corn oil
4 fresh green chillies, slit
1 large onion, sliced
1 medium tomato, sliced
675 g/1¹/2 lb/4²/3 cups chicken, skinned, boned and cubed
1 tbsp chopped fresh coriander (cilantro)

I ▲ Mix together the curry leaves, mustard seeds, fennel seeds, onion seeds, crushed red chillies, cumin seeds, fenugreek seeds, crushed pomegranate seeds and salt in a large bowl.

2 ▲ Add the shredded ginger and garlic cloves.

3 ▲ Heat the oil in a medium karahi or deep round-bottomed frying pan (skillet). Add the spice mixture and throw in the green chillies.

4 ▲ Tip in the onion and stir-fry over a medium heat for 5–7 minutes.

5 ▲ Finally add the tomato and chicken pieces, and cook over a medium heat for about 7 minutes. The chicken should be cooked through and the sauce reduced.

6 ▲ Stir everything together over the heat for a further 3–5 minutes, and **serve garnished with chopped fresh coriander (cilantro).**

Karahi Chicken with Mint

LOW-FAT RECIPE

For this tasty dish, the chicken is first boiled before being quickly stir-fried in a little oil, to ensure that it is cooked through despite the short cooking time.

SERVES 4

INGREDIENTS

275 g/10 oz/2 cups chicken breast fillet, skinned and cut into strips
300 ml/1/2 pint/11/4 cups water
2 tbsp soya oil
2 small bunches spring onions (scallions), roughly chopped
1 tsp shredded fresh ginger
1 tsp crushed dried red chilli
2 tbsp lemon juice
1 tbsp chopped fresh coriander (cilantro)
1 tbsp chopped fresh mint
3 tomatoes, seeded and roughly chopped
1 tsp salt
mint and coriander (cilantro) sprigs

NUTRITIONAL VALUES (per portion)	
Total fat	8.20 g
Saturated fat	1.57 g
Cholesterol	30.42 mg
Energy (kcals/kj)	155/649

1 ▲ Put the chicken and water into a saucepan, bring to the boil and lower the heat to medium. Cook for about 10 minutes or until the water has evaporated and the chicken is cooked. Remove from the heat and set aside.

2 Heat the oil in a frying pan (skillet) or saucepan and stir-fry the spring onions (scallions) for about 2 minutes until soft.

3 ▲ Add the boiled chicken strips and stir-fry for about 3 minutes over a medium heat.

4 ▲ Gradually add the ginger, dried chilli, lemon juice, fresh coriander (cilantro), fresh mint, tomatoes and salt and gently stir to blend all the flavours together.

5 Transfer to a serving dish and garnish with the fresh mint and coriander sprigs.

Karahi Chicken with Fresh Fenugreek

LOW-FAT RECIPE

Fresh fenugreek is a flavour that not many people are familiar with and this recipe is a good introduction to this delicious herb.

SERVES 4

INGREDIENTS

115 g/4 oz/³/4 cup chicken thigh meat, skinned and cut into strips
115 g/4 oz/³/4 cup chicken breast fillet, cut into strips
1/2 tsp garlic pulp
1 tsp chilli powder
1/2 tsp salt
2 tsp tomato purée (paste)
2 tbsp soya oil
1 bunch fenugreek leaves
1 tbsp fresh chopped coriander (cilantro)
300 ml/1/2 pint/1 1/4 cups water

1 ▲ Bring a saucepan of water to the boil, add the chicken strips and cook for about 5–7 minutes. Drain and set aside.

2 ▲ In a mixing bowl, combine the garlic, chilli powder and salt with the tomato purée (paste).

NUTRITIONAL VALUES (per portion)

Total fat	8.15 g
Saturated fat	1.64 g
Cholesterol	32.48 mg
Energy (kcals/kj)	128/536

3 Heat the oil in a large saucepan. Lower the heat and add the tomato purée and spice mixture.

4 ▲ Add the chicken pieces and stir-fry for 5–7 minutes. Lower the heat further.

5 ▲ Add the fenugreek leaves and fresh coriander (cilantro). Continue to stir-fry for 5–7 minutes.

6 Pour in the water, cover and cook for about 5 minutes and serve hot with rice or Wholemeal (Whole-Wheat) Chapatis.

COOK'S TIP

When preparing fresh fenugreek, use only the leaves and discard the stems which are very bitter in flavour.

Sweet-and-Sour Balti Chicken

This dish combines a sweet-and-sour flavour with a creamy texture. It is delicious served with Colourful Pullao Rice or Naan.

SERVES 4

INGREDIENTS
3 tbsp tomato purée (paste)
2 tbsp Greek-style yogurt
1½ tsp garam masala
1 tsp chilli powder
1 tsp garlic pulp
2 tbsp mango chutney
1 tsp salt
½ tsp sugar (optional)
4 tbsp corn oil
675 g/1½ lb/4⅔ cups chicken, skinned, boned and cubed
150 ml/¼ pint/⅔ cup water
2 fresh green chillies, chopped
2 tbsp chopped fresh coriander (cilantro)
2 tbsp single (light) cream

1 ▲ Blend together the tomato purée (paste), yogurt, garam masala, chilli powder, garlic, mango chutney, salt and sugar (if using) in a medium mixing bowl.

2 ▲ Heat the oil in a deep round-bottomed frying pan (skillet) or a large karahi. Lower the heat slightly and pour in the spice mixture. Bring to the boil and cook for about 2 minutes, stirring occasionally.

3 ▲ Add the chicken pieces and stir until they are well coated.

4 Add the water to thin the sauce slightly. Continue cooking for 5–7 minutes, or until the chicken is tender.

5 ▲ Finally add the fresh chillies, coriander (cilantro) and cream, and cook for a further 2 minutes until the chicken is cooked through.

Balti Chicken Pasanda

*P*asanda dishes are firm favourites in Pakistan, but they are also becoming well known in the West.

SERVES 4

INGREDIENTS

4 tbsp Greek-style yogurt
½ tsp black cumin seeds
4 cardamom pods
6 whole black peppercorns
2 tsp garam masala
2.5 cm/1 in cinnamon stick
1 tbsp ground almonds
1 tsp garlic pulp
1 tsp ginger pulp
1 tsp chilli powder
1 tsp salt
675 g/1½ lb/4⅔ cups chicken, skinned, boned and cubed
5 tbsp corn oil
2 medium onions, diced
3 fresh green chillies, chopped
2 tbsp chopped fresh coriander (cilantro)
120 ml/4 fl oz/½ cup single (light) cream

3 ▲ Pour in the chicken mixture and stir until it is well blended with the onions.

4 ▲ Cook over a medium heat for 12–15 minutes or until the sauce thickens and the chicken is cooked through.

5 ▲ Add the green chillies and fresh coriander (cilantro), and pour in the cream. Bring to the boil and serve garnished with more coriander, if wished.

COOK'S TIP

This Balti dish has a lovely thick sauce and is especially good served with one of the rice dishes from this book.

1 ▲ Mix the yogurt, cumin seeds, cardamoms, peppercorns, garam masala, cinnamon stick, ground almonds, garlic, ginger, chilli powder and salt in a medium mixing bowl. Add the chicken pieces and leave to marinate for about 2 hours.

2 Heat the oil in a large karahi or deep round-bottomed frying pan (skillet). Throw in the onions and fry for 2–3 minutes.

Boiled Egg Curry

This dish is usually served with a biryani or pullao but it is equally good with Fried Whole Fish.

SERVES 3–6

INGREDIENTS
2 tsp white poppy seeds
2 tsp white sesame seeds
2 tsp whole coriander seeds
2 tbsp desiccated (shredded) coconut
350 ml/12 fl oz/1½ cups tomato juice
2 tsp gram flour (besan)
1 tsp ginger pulp
1 tsp chilli powder
¼ tsp asafoetida
salt, to taste
1 tsp sugar
6 hard-boiled eggs, halved
2 tbsp sesame oil

1 tsp cumin seeds
4 dried red chillies
6–8 curry leaves
4 cloves garlic, finely sliced

1 ▲ Heat a frying pan (skillet) and dry-fry the poppy, sesame and coriander seeds for 3–4 minutes. Add the desiccated (shredded) coconut and dry-fry until it browns. Cool and grind the ingredients together using a pestle and mortar or a food processor.

2 Take a little of the tomato juice and mix with the gram flour (besan) to a smooth paste. Add the ginger, chilli powder, asafoetida, salt and sugar and the ground spices. Add the remaining tomato juice, place in a saucepan and simmer gently for 10 minutes.

3 ▲ Add the hard-boiled eggs and cover with the sauce. Heat the oil in a frying pan and fry the remaining ingredients until the chillies turn dark brown. Pour the spices and oil over the egg curry, fold the ingredients together and reheat. Serve hot.

Eggs Baked on Chipsticks

Parsis love eggs, and have developed a variety of unique egg-based dishes such as this one.

SERVES 3–6

INGREDIENTS
225 g/8 oz ready-salted chipsticks
2 fresh green chillies, finely chopped
few fresh coriander (cilantro) leaves, finely chopped
¼ tsp turmeric
4 tbsp vegetable oil
5 tbsp water
6 eggs
salt and freshly ground black pepper, to taste
spring onion (scallion) tassles, to garnish

1 In a bowl, mix the chipsticks, chillies, coriander and turmeric. Heat 2 tbsp of the oil in a small non-stick frying pan (skillet). Add the chipstick mixture and water. Cook until the chipsticks have softened, then fry without stirring until crisp.

2 ▲ Place a plate over the frying pan, holding them tightly together turn the pan over. Remove the pan from the plate. Heat the remaining oil in the pan and slide the pancake back in and brown the other side.

3 ▲ Gently break the eggs on to the pancake, cover the frying pan and allow the eggs to set over a low heat. Season and cook until the base is crisp. Serve hot, garnished with spring onion (scallion) tassles.

Boiled Egg Curry (top) and Eggs Baked on Chipsticks

Meat Dishes

Lamb is the favourite Indian meat and there are lots of recipes to choose from here. Try Balti-style lamb kebabs or lamb koftas, or go for the more traditional Lamb with Spinach. For devotees of really fiery hot curries, Kashmiri-Style Lamb has the perfect hot chilli taste, while Moghul-style Roast Lamb will make a spectacular — and spicy — Sunday lunch.

Balti Lamb Tikka

This is a traditional tikka recipe, in which the lamb is marinated in yogurt and spices. The lamb is usually cut into cubes, but the cooking time can be halved by cutting it into strips instead, as I have done in this recipe.

SERVES 4

INGREDIENTS
450 g/1 lb lamb, cut into strips
175 ml/6 fl oz/3/4 cup natural (plain) yogurt
1 tsp ground cumin
1 tsp ground coriander
1 tsp chilli powder
1 tsp garlic pulp
1 tsp salt
1 tsp garam masala
2 tbsp chopped fresh coriander (cilantro)
2 tbsp lemon juice
2 tbsp corn oil
1 tbsp tomato purée (tomato paste)

1 large green (bell) pepper, seeded and sliced
3 large fresh red chillies

1 ▲ Put the lamb strips, yogurt, ground cumin, ground coriander, chilli powder, garlic, salt, garam masala, fresh coriander (cilantro) and lemon juice into a large mixing bowl and stir thoroughly. Set to one side for at least 1 hour to marinate.

2 ▲ Heat the oil in a deep round-bottomed frying pan (skillet) or a medium karahi. Lower the heat slightly and add the tomato purée (paste).

3 ▲ Add the lamb strips to the pan, a few at a time, leaving any excess marinade behind in the bowl.

4 Cook the lamb, stirring frequently, for 7–10 minutes or until it is well browned.

5 ▲ Finally, add the green (bell) pepper slices and the whole red chillies. Heat through, checking that the lamb is cooked through, and serve.

Balti Minced (Ground) Lamb with Potatoes and Fenugreek

The combination of lamb with fresh fenugreek works very well in this dish, which is delicious accompanied by plain boiled rice and mango pickle. Only use the fenugreek leaves, as the stalks can be rather bitter. This dish is traditionally served with rice.

SERVES 4

INGREDIENTS

450 g/1 lb lean minced (ground) lamb
1 tsp ginger pulp
1 tsp garlic pulp
1¹/₂ tsp chilli powder
1 tsp salt
¹/₄ tsp turmeric
3 tbsp corn oil
2 medium onions, sliced
2 medium potatoes, peeled, par-boiled and
  roughly diced
1 bunch fresh fenugreek, chopped
2 tomatoes, chopped
50 g/2 oz/¹/₂ cup frozen peas
2 tbsp chopped fresh coriander (cilantro)
3 fresh red chillies, seeded and sliced

3 ▲ Add the minced lamb and stir-fry over a medium heat for 5–7 minutes.

4 ▲ Stir in the potatoes, chopped fenugreek, tomatoes and peas and cook for a further 5–7 minutes, stirring continuously.

5 Just before serving, stir in the fresh coriander (cilantro) and garnish with fresh red chillies.

1 ▲ Put the minced (ground) lamb, ginger, garlic, chilli powder, salt and turmeric into a large bowl, and mix together thoroughly. Set to one side.

2 Heat the oil in a deep round-bottomed frying pan (skillet) or a medium karahi. Throw in the onion and fry for about 5 minutes until golden brown.

Moghul-Style Roast Lamb

This superb dish is just one of many fine examples of the fabulous rich food once enjoyed by Moghul emperors. Try it as a variation to the roast beef.

SERVES 4–6

INGREDIENTS

4 large onions, chopped
4 cloves garlic
1 piece fresh ginger, 5 cm/2 in long, chopped
3 tbsp ground almonds
2 tsp ground cumin
2 tsp ground coriander
2 tsp turmeric
2 tsp garam masala
4–6 fresh green chillies
juice of 1 lemon
salt, to taste
300 ml/½ pint/1¼ cups natural (plain) yogurt, beaten
1.8 kg/4 lb leg of lamb
8–10 cloves
4 firm tomatoes, halved and grilled, to serve
watercress, to garnish
1 tbsp flaked (slivered) almonds, to garnish

1 ▲ Place the first 11 ingredients in a food processor and blend to a smooth paste. Gradually add the yogurt and blend until smooth. Grease a large, deep baking tray and preheat the oven to 190°C/375°F/Gas 5.

2 ▲ Remove most of the fat and skin from the lamb. Using a sharp knife, make deep pockets above the bone at each side of the thick end. Make deep diagonal gashes on both sides.

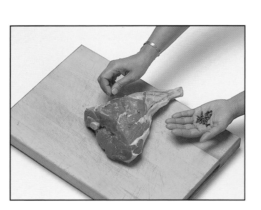

3 ▲ Push the cloves into the leg of lamb at random.

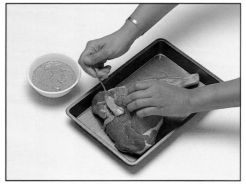

4 ▲ Place the lamb on the baking tray and push some of the spice mixture into the pockets and gashes.

5 ▲ Spread the remaining spice mixture evenly all over the lamb. Loosely cover the whole tray with foil. Roast in the preheated oven for 2–2½ hours or until the lamb is cooked, removing the foil for the last 10 minutes of cooking time.

6 ▲ Remove from the oven and allow to rest for 10 minutes before carving. Serve with grilled tomatoes, garnished with watercress and garnish the joint with the flaked (slivered) almonds.

Lamb with Spinach

*Lamb with Spinach, or Saag Goshth, is
a well-known recipe from the Punjab,
and a great favourite of mine. It is
important to use red (bell) peppers as
they add such a distinctive flavour to the
dish. Serve with plain boiled rice, Naan
or Paratha.*

SERVES 4–6

INGREDIENTS
1 tsp ginger pulp
1 tsp garlic pulp
1½ tsp chilli powder
1 tsp salt
1 tsp garam masala
6 tbsp corn oil
2 medium onions, sliced
675 g/1½ lb lean lamb, cut into 5 cm/2 in
*   cubes*
600–900 ml/1–1½ pints/2½–3¾ cups
*   water*
400 g/14 oz fresh spinach
1 large red (bell) pepper, seeded and
*   chopped*
3 fresh green chillies, chopped
3 tbsp chopped fresh coriander (cilantro)
1 tbsp lemon juice (optional)

1 Mix together the ginger, garlic, chilli
powder, salt and garam masala in a
bowl. Set to one side.

2 Heat the oil in a medium saucepan.
Add the onions and fry for 10–12
minutes or until well browned.

3 Add the cubed lamb to the sizzling
onions and stir-fry for about 2 minutes.

4 ▲ Tip in the spice mixture and stir
thoroughly until the meat pieces are
well coated.

5 Pour in the water and bring to the
boil. As soon as it is boiling, cover the
pan and lower the heat. Cook gently for
25–35 minutes without letting the
contents of the pan burn.

6 ▲ If there is still a lot of water in the
pan when the meat has become tender,
remove the lid and boil briskly to
evaporate any excess.

7 ▲ Meanwhile, wash and chop the
spinach roughly before blanching it for
about 1 minute in a pan of boiling
water. Drain well.

8 ▲ Add the spinach to the lamb as
soon as the water has evaporated. Fry
over a medium heat for 7–10 minutes,
using a wooden spoon in a semi-
circular motion, scraping the bottom of
the pan as you stir.

9 ▲ Add the red (bell) pepper, green
chillies and fresh coriander (cilantro) to
the pan and stir over a medium heat for
2 minutes. Sprinkle on the lemon juice
(if using) and serve immediately.

COOK'S TIP

*Frozen spinach can also be used for the
dish, but try to find whole leaf spinach
rather than the chopped kind. Allow the
frozen spinach to thaw, then drain well;
there is no need to blanch it.*

Kashmiri-Style Lamb

This curry originated in Kashmir, and derives its name – Rogan Josh – from the chillies originally used in the dish. The chilli powder may be reduced for a milder flavour, just add the paprika and 2 tsp tomato purée (paste) to retain the colour.

SERVES 4–6

INGREDIENTS
4 tbsp vegetable oil
¼ tsp asafoetida
900 g/2 lb lean lamb, cubed
1 piece fresh ginger, 5 cm/2 in long, crushed
2 cloves garlic, crushed
4 tbsp rogan josh masala paste
1 tsp chilli powder or 2 tsp sweet paprika

8–10 strands saffron (optional), plus more for garnishing
salt, to taste
about 150 ml/¼ pint/⅔ cup natural (plain) yogurt, beaten

1 ▲ Heat the oil in a pan and fry the asafoetida and lamb, stirring well to seal the meat. Reduce the heat, cover and cook for about 10 minutes.

2 Add all the remaining ingredients except the yogurt and almonds and mix well. If the meat is too dry, add a very small quantity of boiling water. Cover the pan and cook on a low heat for a further 10 minutes.

3 ▲ Remove the pan from the heat and leave to cool a little. Add the yogurt, 1 tbsp at a time, stirring constantly to avoid curdling. Return to a low heat and cook uncovered until thick. Garnish with a spoonful of yogurt and a few saffron strands.

Hot Dry Meat Curry

This dish is nearly as hot as Phaal (India's hottest curry) but the spices can still be distinguished above the chilli.

SERVES 4–6

INGREDIENTS
2 tbsp vegetable oil
1 large onion, finely sliced
1 piece fresh ginger, 5 cm/2 in long, crushed
4 cloves garlic, crushed
6–8 curry leaves
3 tbsp extra hot curry paste
3 tsp chilli powder
1 tsp five-spice powder
1 tsp turmeric
salt, to taste
900 g/2 lb lean lamb, beef or pork, cubed
175 ml/6 fl oz/¾ cup thick coconut milk
chopped tomato and coriander (cilantro) leaves, to garnish

1 Heat the oil in a large saucepan and fry the sliced onion, ginger, garlic and curry leaves until the onion is soft, stirring occasionally. Stir in the curry paste, chilli, five-spice powder, turmeric and salt and cook for a few moments, stirring frequently.

2 ▲ Add the meat and stir well over a medium heat to seal and evenly brown the meat pieces. Keep stirring until the oil separates. Cover and cook for about 20 minutes.

3 ▲ Add the coconut milk, mix well and simmer until the meat is cooked. Towards the end of cooking, uncover the pan to reduce the excess liquid. Garnish and serve hot.

Kashmiri-Style Lamb (top) and Hot Dry Meat Curry

Spicy Lamb Tikka

One of the best ways of tenderizing meat is to marinate it in papaya, which must be unripe or it will lend its sweetness to what should be a savory dish. Papaya, or paw-paw, is readily available from most large supermarkets.

SERVES 4

INGREDIENTS
675 g/1½ lb lean lamb, cubed
1 unripe papaya
3 tbsp natural (plain) yogurt
1 tsp ginger pulp
1 tsp chilli powder
1 tsp garlic pulp
¼ tsp turmeric
2 tsp ground coriander
1 tsp ground cumin
1 tsp salt
2 tbsp lemon juice
1 tbsp chopped fresh coriander (cilantro), plus extra to garnish
¼ tsp red food colouring
300 ml/½ pint/1¼ cups corn oil
lemon wedges
onion rings

1 ▲ Place the lamb in a large mixing bowl. Peel the papaya, cut in half and scoop out the seeds. Cut the flesh into cubes and blend in a food processor or blender until it is pulped, adding about 1 tbsp water if necessary.

2 ▲ Pour 2 tbsp of the papaya pulp over the lamb cubes and rub it in well with your fingers. Set to one side for at least 3 hours.

3 ▲ Meanwhile, mix together the yogurt, ginger, chilli powder, garlic, turmeric, ground coriander, ground cumin, salt, lemon juice, fresh coriander (cilantro), red food colouring and 2 tbsp of the oil, and set to one side.

4 ▲ Pour the spicy yogurt mixture over the lamb and mix together well.

5 ▲ Heat the remaining oil in a deep round-bottomed frying pan (skillet) or a karahi. Lower the heat slightly and add the lamb cubes, a few at a time.

6 Deep-fry each batch for 5–7 minutes or until the lamb is thoroughly cooked and tender. Keep the cooked pieces warm while the remainder is fried.

7 Transfer to a serving dish and garnish with lemon wedges, onion rings and fresh coriander. Serve with Raita and freshly baked Naan.

COOK'S TIP

A good-quality meat tenderizer, available from supermarkets, can be used in place of the papaya. However, the meat will need a longer marinating time and should ideally be left to tenderize overnight.

Lamb with Peas and Mint

LOW-FAT RECIPE

A simple minced (ground) lamb dish, this is easy to prepare and very versatile. It is equally delicious whether served with plain boiled rice or Wholemeal (Whole-Wheat) Chapatis.

SERVES 4

INGREDIENTS
2 tbsp corn oil
1 medium onion, chopped
1/2 tsp garlic pulp
1/2 tsp ginger pulp
1/2 tsp chilli powder
1/4 tsp turmeric
1 tsp ground coriander
1 tsp salt
2 medium tomatoes, sliced
275 g/10 oz lean leg of lamb, minced (ground)
1 large carrot, sliced or cut into batons
75 g/3 oz/1/2 cup petit pois
1 tbsp chopped fresh mint
1 tbsp chopped fresh coriander (cilantro)
1 fresh green chilli, chopped
coriander (cilantro) sprigs

NUTRITIONAL VALUES (per portion)	
Total fat	12.37 g
Saturated fat	3.83 g
Cholesterol	55.89 mg
Energy (kcals/kj)	210/882

1 ▲ In a medium saucepan or a deep frying pan (skillet), heat the oil and fry the chopped onions over a medium heat for 5 minutes until golden.

2 ▲ Meanwhile, in a small mixing bowl, blend together the garlic, ginger, chilli powder, turmeric, ground coriander and salt.

3 ▲ When the onions are ready, add the sliced tomatoes and the spice mixture and stir-fry for about 2 minutes.

4 ▲ Add the minced (ground) lamb to the mixture and stir-fry for about 7–10 minutes.

5 ▲ Break up any lumps of meat which may form, using a potato masher if necessary.

6 Finally add the carrot, petit pois, fresh mint, coriander (cilantro) and the fresh green chilli and mix all these together well.

7 Stir-fry for another 2–3 minutes and serve hot, garnished with the coriander sprigs.

Khara Masala Lamb

Whole spices (khara) are used in this curry so you should warn the diners of their presence! Delicious served with freshly baked Naan or a rice accompaniment, this dish is best made with good-quality spring lamb.

SERVES 4

INGREDIENTS
5 tbsp corn oil
2 medium onions, chopped
1 tsp shredded ginger
1 tsp sliced garlic
6 whole dried red chillies
3 cardamom pods
2 cinnamon sticks
6 black peppercorns
3 cloves
½ tsp salt
450 g/1 lb boned leg of lamb, cubed
600 ml/1 pint/2½ cups water
2 fresh green chillies, sliced
2 tbsp chopped fresh coriander (cilantro)

1 Heat the oil in a large saucepan. Lower the heat slightly and fry the onions until they are lightly browned.

2 ▲ Add half the ginger and half the garlic and stir well.

3 ▲ Throw in half the red chillies, the cardamoms, cinnamon, peppercorns, cloves and salt.

4 ▲ Add the lamb and fry over a medium heat. Stir continuously with a semi-circular movement, using a wooden spoon to scrape the bottom of the pan. Continue in this way for about 5 minutes.

5 Pour in the water, cover with a lid and cook over a medium-low heat for 35–40 minutes, or until the water has evaporated and the meat is tender.

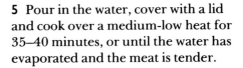

6 ▲ Add the rest of the ginger, garlic and dried red chillies, along with the fresh green chillies and fresh coriander (cilantro).

7 ▲ Continue to stir over the heat until you see some free oil on the sides of the pan. Transfer to a serving dish and serve immediately.

COOK'S TIP

The action of stirring the meat and spices together using a semi-circular motion, as described in step 4, is called bhoono-ing. It ensures that the meat becomes well-coated and combined with the spice mixture before the cooking liquid is added.

Spicy Meat Loaf

This mixture is baked in the oven and provides a hearty meal on cold winter days.

SERVES 4–6

INGREDIENTS
5 eggs
450 g/1 lb lean minced (ground) beef
2 tbsp ginger pulp
2 tbsp garlic pulp
6 fresh green chillies, chopped
2 small onions, finely chopped
1/2 tsp turmeric
50 g/2 oz/2 cups fresh coriander, chopped
175 g/6 oz potato, grated
salt, to taste
salad leaves, to serve
lemon twist, to garnish

1 ▲ Preheat the oven to 180°C/350°F/ Gas 4. Beat 2 eggs until fluffy and pour into a greased baking tray.

2 Knead together the meat, ginger and garlic, 4 green chillies, 1 chopped onion, 1 beaten egg, the turmeric, fresh coriander, potato and salt. Pack into the baking tray and smooth the surface. Cook in the preheated oven for 45 minutes.

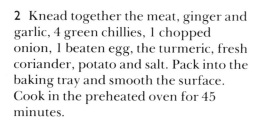

3 ▲ Beat the remaining eggs and fold in the remaining green chillies and onion. Remove the baking tray from the oven and pour the mixture all over the meat. Return to the oven and cook until the eggs have set. Serve hot on on a bed of salad leaves, garnished with a twist of lemon.

Koftas

Serve these tasty kebabs piping hot with Naan, Raita and Tomato Salad. Leftover kebabs can be coarsely chopped and packed into pitta bread spread with Fresh Coriander (Cilantro) Relish to serve as a quick snack.

MAKES 20–25

INGREDIENTS
450 g/1 lb lean minced (ground) beef or lamb
2 tbsp ginger pulp
2 tbsp garlic pulp
4 fresh green chillies, finely chopped
1 small onion, finely chopped
1 egg
1/2 tsp turmeric
1 tsp garam masala
50 g/2 oz/2 cups fresh coriander (cilantro), chopped
4–6 fresh mint leaves, chopped, or 1/2 tsp mint sauce

175 g/6 oz raw potato
salt, to taste
vegetable oil, for deep-frying

1 ▲ Place the first 10 ingredients in a large bowl. Grate the potato into the bowl, and season with salt. Knead together to blend well and form a soft dough.

2 Shape the mixture into portions the size of golf balls. Set aside on a plate and leave the koftas to rest for about 25 minutes.

3 ▲ In a karahi or frying pan (skillet), heat the oil to medium-hot and fry the koftas in small batches until they are golden brown in colour. Drain well and serve hot.

Spicy Meat Loaf (top) and Koftas

Balti Minced (Ground) Lamb Koftas with Vegetables

These koftas look most attractive served on their bed of vegetables, especially if you make them quite small.

SERVES 4

INGREDIENTS
Koftas
450 g/1 lb lean minced (ground) lamb
1 tsp garam masala
1 tsp ground cumin
1 tsp ground coriander
1 tsp garlic pulp
1 tsp chilli powder
1 tsp salt
1 tbsp chopped fresh coriander (cilantro)
1 small onion, finely diced
150 ml/¼ pint/²⁄₃ cup corn oil

Vegetables
3 tbsp corn oil
1 bunch spring onions (scallions), roughly chopped
½ large red (bell) pepper, seeded and chopped
½ large green (bell) pepper, seeded and chopped
175 g/6 oz/1 cup sweetcorn (corn kernels)
225 g/8 oz/1½ cups canned butter beans, drained
½ small cauliflower, cut into florets (flowerets)
4 fresh green chillies, chopped

1 tsp chopped fresh mint
1 tbsp chopped fresh coriander (cilantro)
1 tbsp shredded ginger
lime slices
1 tbsp lemon juice

1 Put the minced (ground) lamb into a food processor or blender and process for about 1 minute.

2 ▲ Transfer the lamb into a medium bowl. Add the garam masala, ground cumin, ground coriander, garlic, chilli powder, salt, fresh coriander (cilantro) and onion, and use your fingers to blend everything thoroughly.

3 Cover the bowl and set aside in the refrigerator.

4 ▲ Heat the oil for the vegetables in a deep round-bottomed frying pan (skillet) or a medium karahi. Add the spring onions (scallions) and stir-fry for about 2 minutes.

5 ▲ Add the (bell) peppers, sweetcorn (corn kernels), butter beans, cauliflower and green chillies, and stir-fry over a high heat for about 2 minutes. Set to one side.

6 ▲ Using your hands, roll small pieces of the kofta mixture into golf-ball sized portions. It should make between 12 and 16 koftas.

7 ▲ Heat the oil for the koftas in a frying pan. Lower the heat slightly and add the koftas, a few at a time. Shallow-fry each batch, turning the koftas, until they are evenly browned.

8 Remove from the oil with a slotted spoon, and drain on kitchen paper (paper towels).

9 ▲ Put the vegetable mixture back over a medium heat, and add the cooked koftas. Stir the mixture gently for about 5 minutes, or until everything is heated through.

10 Garnish with the mint, coriander, shredded ginger and lime slices. Just before serving, sprinkle over the lemon juice.

Spicy Spring Lamb Roast

LOW-FAT RECIPE

There are a number of ways of roasting lamb and several different spice mixtures which people use. This is one of my favourite variations.

SERVES 6

INGREDIENTS
1.5 kg/3 lb leg spring lamb
1 tsp chilli powder
1 tsp garlic pulp
1 tsp ground coriander
1 tsp ground cumin
1 tsp salt
2 tsp desiccated (shredded) coconut
2 tsp ground almonds
3 tbsp natural (plain) low-fat yogurt
2 tbsp lemon juice
2 tbsp sultanas (golden raisins)
2 tbsp corn oil

Garnish
mixed salad leaves
fresh coriander (cilantro) sprigs
2 tomatoes, quartered
1 large carrot, cut into julienne strips
lemon wedges

NUTRITIONAL VALUES (per portion)	
Total fat	11.96 g
Saturated fat	4.70 g
Cholesterol	67.38 mg
Energy (kcals/kj)	197/825

1 ▲ Preheat the oven to 180°C/350°F/ Gas 4. Trim off the fat, rinse and pat dry the leg of lamb and set aside on a sheet of foil large enough to enclose the whole joint.

2 ▲ In a medium bowl, mix together the chilli powder, garlic, ground coriander, ground cumin and salt.

3 ▲ Grind together in a food processor the desiccated (shredded) coconut, ground almonds, yogurt, lemon juice and sultanas (golden raisins).

4 ▲ Add the contents of the food processor to the spice mixture together with the corn oil and mix together. Pour this onto the leg of lamb and rub over the meat.

5 Enclose the meat in the foil and place in an ovenproof dish. Cook in the preheated oven for about 1½ hours.

6 ▲ Remove the lamb from the oven, open the foil and using the back of a spoon spread the mixture evenly over the meat. Return the lamb, uncovered, to the oven for another 45 minutes or until it is cooked right through and is tender.

7 Slice the meat and serve with the garnish ingredients.

COOK'S TIP

If you don't have any ready-ground almonds to hand, simply process flaked (slivered) or whole blanched almonds in a food processor or coffee grinder.

Lamb Chops Kashmiri-Style

These chops are cooked in a unique way, being first boiled in milk, and then fried. Despite the large number of spices used in this recipe, the actual dish has a mild flavour, and is delicious served with fried rice and a lentil dish.

SERVES 4

INGREDIENTS

8–12 lamb chops, about 50–75 g/2–3 oz each
1 piece cinnamon bark
1 bay leaf
½ tsp fennel seeds
½ tsp black peppercorns
3 green cardamom pods
1 tsp salt
600 ml/1 pint/2½ cups milk
150 ml/¼ pint/⅔ cup evaporated milk
150 ml/¼ pint/⅔ cup natural (plain) yogurt
2 tbsp plain (all-purpose) flour
1 tsp chilli powder
1 tsp ginger pulp
½ tsp garam masala
½ tsp garlic pulp
pinch of salt
300 ml/½ pint/1¼ cups corn oil
mint sprigs
lime quarters

1 ▲ Trim the lamb chops and place them in a large saucepan with the cinnamon bark, bay leaf, fennel seeds, peppercorns, cardamoms, salt and milk. Bring to the boil over a high heat.

2 ▲ Lower the heat and cook for 12–15 minutes, or until the milk has reduced to about half its original volume. At this stage, add the evaporated milk and lower the heat further. Simmer until the chops are cooked through and the milk has evaporated.

3 ▲ While the chops are cooking, blend together the yogurt, flour, chilli powder, ginger, garam masala, garlic and a pinch of salt in a mixing bowl.

4 ▲ Remove the chops from the saucepan and discard the whole spices. Add the chops to the spicy yogurt mixture.

5 ▲ Heat the oil in a deep round-bottomed frying pan (skillet) or medium karahi. Lower the heat slightly and add the chops. Fry until they are golden brown, turning them once or twice as they cook.

6 Transfer to a serving dish, and garnish with mint sprigs and lime quarters.

COOK'S TIP

These delicious lamb chops, with their crunchy yogurt coating, make ideal finger food to serve at a buffet or drinks party.

Mince Kebabs

Serve this Indian hamburger in a bun with chilli sauce and salad or unaccompanied as an appetizer.

SERVES 4–6

INGREDIENTS
2 onions, finely chopped
250 g/9 oz lean lamb, cut into small cubes
50 g/2 oz bengal gram
1 tsp cumin seeds
1 tsp garam masala
4–6 fresh green chillies
1 piece fresh ginger, 5 cm/2 in long, crushed
salt, to taste
175 ml/6 fl oz/¾ cup water

few fresh coriander (cilantro) and mint leaves, chopped
juice of 1 lemon
1 tbsp gram flour (besan)
2 eggs, beaten
vegetable oil, for shallow-frying
½ lime

1 Put the first 8 ingredients and the water into a pan and bring to the boil. Simmer, covered, until the meat and dhal are cooked.

2 Remove the lid and cook uncovered to reduce the excess liquid. Cool, and grind to a paste.

3 ▲ Place the mixture in a mixing bowl and add the fresh coriander (cilantro) and mint, lemon juice and flour. Knead well. Divide into 10–12 portions and roll each into a ball, then flatten slightly. Chill for 1 hour. Dip the kebabs in the beaten egg and shallow-fry each side until golden brown. Serve hot with the lime.

Portuguese Pork

This dish displays the influence of Portuguese cooking on Indian cuisine.

SERVES 4–6

INGREDIENTS

115 g/4 oz deep-fried onions, crushed
4 red chillies, or 1 tsp chilli powder
4 tbsp vindaloo masala paste
6 tbsp white wine vinegar
6 tbsp tomato purée (paste)
¹/₂ tsp fenugreek seeds
1 tsp turmeric
1 tsp crushed mustard seeds, or ¹/₂ tsp
*   mustard powder*
salt, to taste
1¹/₂ tsp sugar
900 g/2 lb boneless pork spareribs, cubed
250 ml/8 fl oz/1 cup water
plain boiled rice, to serve

1 ▲ Place all the ingredients except the water and rice in a heavy steel pan and mix well. Marinate for about 2 hours.

2 ▲ Transfer to a frying pan (skillet), add the water and mix well. Bring to the boil and simmer gently for about 2 hours. Adjust the seasoning. Serve hot with the plain boiled rice.

Balti Mini Lamb Kebabs (Kabobs) with Baby Onions

This is rather an unusual Balti dish as the kebabs (kabobs) are first grilled (broiled) before being added to the karahi for the final stage of cooking.

SERVES 6

INGREDIENTS
450 g/1 lb lean minced (ground) lamb
1 medium onion, finely chopped
1 tsp garam masala
1 tsp garlic pulp
2 medium fresh green chillies, finely chopped
2 tbsp chopped fresh coriander (cilantro)
1 tsp salt
1 tbsp plain (all-purpose) flour
4 tbsp corn oil
12 baby onions
4 fresh green chillies, sliced
12 cherry tomatoes
2 tbsp chopped fresh coriander

1 ▲ Blend together the minced (ground) lamb, onion, garam masala, garlic, green chillies, fresh coriander (cilantro), salt and flour in a medium bowl. Use your hands to make sure that all the ingredients are thoroughly mixed together.

2 Transfer the mixture to a food processor and process for about 1 minute, to make the mixture even finer in texture.

3 ▲ Put the mixture back into the bowl. Break off small pieces, about the size of a lime, and wrap them around skewers to form small sausage shapes. Put about 2 kebabs (kabobs) on each skewer.

4 ▲ Once you have used up all the mixture, baste the kebabs with 1 tbsp of the oil and place under a preheated hot grill (broiler) for 12–15 minutes, turning and basting occasionally, until they are evenly browned.

5 ▲ Heat the remaining 3 tbsp of the oil in a deep round-bottomed frying pan (skillet) or a medium karahi. Lower the heat slightly and add the whole baby onions. As soon as they start to darken, add the fresh chillies and tomatoes.

6 ▲ Remove the mini kebabs from their skewers and add them to the onion and tomato mixture. Stir gently for about 3 minutes to heat them through.

7 Transfer to a serving dish and garnish with fresh coriander. Serve with Spicy Balti Potatoes and Paratha.

Stuffed Aubergines (Eggplants) with Lamb

LOW-FAT RECIPE

Minced (ground) lamb and aubergines (eggplants) go really well together. This is an attractive dish, using different coloured (bell) peppers in the lightly spiced stuffing mixture.

SERVES 4

INGREDIENTS
2 medium aubergines (eggplants)
2 tbsp vegetable oil
1 medium onion, sliced
1 tsp ginger pulp
1 tsp chilli powder
1 tsp garlic pulp
$1/4$ tsp turmeric
1 tsp salt
1 tsp ground coriander
1 medium tomato, chopped
350 g/12 oz lean leg of lamb, minced (ground)
1 medium green (bell) pepper, roughly chopped
1 medium orange (bell) pepper, roughly chopped
2 tbsp chopped fresh coriander (cilantro)

Garnish
$1/2$ onion, sliced
2 cherry tomatoes, quartered
fresh coriander (cilantro) sprigs

I Preheat the oven to 180°C/350°F/Gas 4. Cut the aubergines (eggplants) in half lengthways and scoop out most of the flesh and discard. Place the aubergine shells in a lightly greased ovenproof dish.

NUTRITIONAL VALUES (per portion)	
Total fat	13.92 g
Saturated fat	4.36 g
Cholesterol	67.15 mg
Energy (kcals/kj)	239/1003

2 In a medium saucepan, heat 1 tbsp oil and fry the sliced onion until golden brown.

3 ▲ Gradually stir in the ginger, chilli powder, garlic, turmeric, salt and ground coriander. Add the chopped tomato, lower the heat and stir-fry for about 5 minutes.

4 ▲ Add the minced (ground) lamb and continue to stir-fry over a medium heat for 7–10 minutes.

5 ▲ Add the chopped (bell) peppers and fresh coriander (cilantro) to the lamb mixture and stir well.

6 ▲ Spoon the lamb mixture into the aubergine shells and brush the edge of the shells with the remaining oil. Bake in the preheated oven for 20–25 minutes until cooked through and browned on top.

7 Serve with the garnish ingredients and either a green salad or plain boiled rice.

VARIATION

For a special occasion, stuffed baby aubergines (eggplants) look particularly attractive. Use 4 small aubergines, leaving the stalks intact, and prepare and cook as described above. Reduce the baking time slightly, if necessary. Large tomatoes or courgettes also make an excellent alternative to aubergines.

Beef Madras

This popular South Indian curry is mainly prepared by Muslims and is traditionally made with beef.

SERVES 4–6

INGREDIENTS
4 tbsp vegetable oil
1 large onion, finely sliced
3–4 cloves
4 green cardamom pods
2 whole star anise
4 fresh green chillies, chopped
2 red chillies, chopped (fresh or dried)
3 tbsp Madras masala paste
1 tsp turmeric
450 g/1 lb lean beef, cubed
4 tbsp tamarind juice
salt, to taste

sugar, to taste
fresh coriander (cilantro) sprigs, to garnish

I ▲ Heat the oil in a pan and fry the onion until it is golden brown. Lower the heat and add all the spice ingredients and fry for a further 2–3 minutes.

2 Add the beef to the pan and mix well. Cover and cook on a low heat until the beef is tender. Remove the lid from the pan and cook uncovered on a higher heat for the last few minutes to reduce any excess liquid.

3 ▲ Fold in the tamarind juice, salt and sugar. Reheat the dish and serve hot, garnished with the fresh coriander (cilantro) sprigs.

Lamb Korma

This is a creamy, aromatic dish with no 'hot' taste. It comes from the kitchens of the Nizam of Hyderabad.

SERVES 4–6

INGREDIENTS
1 tbsp white sesame seeds
1 tbsp white poppy seeds
50 g/2 oz blanched almonds
2 fresh green chillies, seeded
6 cloves garlic, sliced
1 piece fresh ginger, 5 cm/2 in long, sliced
1 onion, finely chopped
3 tbsp ghee or vegetable oil
6 green cardamom pods
1 piece cinnamon stick, 5 cm/2 in long
4 cloves
900 g/2 lb lean lamb, cubed
1 tsp ground cumin
1 tsp ground coriander
salt, to taste

300 ml/¹/₂ pint/1 ¹/₄ cups double (heavy) cream mixed with ¹/₂ tsp cornflour (cornstarch)
roasted sesame seeds, to garnish

I ▲ Heat a frying pan (skillet) without any liquid and dry-roast the first 7 ingredients. Cool the mixture and grind to a fine paste using a pestle and mortar or food processor. Heat the ghee or oil in a frying pan.

2 Fry the cardamom pods, cinnamon and cloves over a medium heat until the cloves swell. Add the lamb, ground cumin and coriander and the prepared paste, and season. Cover the pan and cook until the lamb is almost done, stirring occasionally.

3 ▲ Remove from the heat, cool a little and gradually fold in the cream, reserving 1 tsp to garnish. To serve, gently reheat the lamb uncovered and serve hot, garnished with the sesame seeds and the remaining cream.

Balti Stuffed Vegetables

Aubergines (eggplants) and (bell) peppers make an excellent combination. Here they are stuffed with an aromatic lamb filling and served on a bed of sautéed onions.

SERVES 6

INGREDIENTS
3 small aubergines (eggplants)
1 each red, green and yellow (bell) peppers

Stuffing
3 tbsp corn oil
3 medium onions, sliced
1 tsp chilli powder
¼ tsp turmeric
1 tsp ground coriander
1 tsp ground cumin
1 tsp ginger pulp
1 tsp garlic pulp
1 tsp salt
450 g/1 lb lean minced (ground) lamb
3 fresh green chillies, chopped
2 tbsp chopped fresh coriander (cilantro)

Sautéed onions
3 tbsp corn oil
1 tsp mixed onion, mustard, fenugreek and white cumin seeds
4 dried red chillies
3 medium onions, roughly chopped
1 tsp salt
1 tsp chilli powder
2 medium tomatoes, sliced
2 fresh green chillies, chopped
2 tbsp chopped fresh coriander

I Prepare the vegetables. Slit the aubergines (eggplants) lengthways up to the stalks; keep the stalks intact. Cut the tops off the (bell) peppers and remove the seeds. You can retain the pepper tops and use them as 'lids' once the vegetables have been stuffed, if wished.

2 Make the stuffing. Heat the oil in a medium saucepan. Add the onions and fry for about 3 minutes. Lower the heat and add the chilli powder, turmeric, ground coriander, ground cumin, ginger, garlic and salt, and stir-fry for about 1 minute. Add the minced (ground) lamb to the pan and turn up the heat.

3 ▲ Stir-fry for 7–10 minutes or until the mince is cooked, using a wooden spoon to scrape the bottom of the pan. Throw in the green chillies and fresh coriander (cilantro) towards the end. Remove from the heat, cover and set to one side.

4 Make the sautéed onions. Heat the oil in a deep round-bottomed frying pan (skillet) or a karahi and throw in the mixed onion, mustard, fenugreek and white cumin seeds together with the dried red chillies, and fry for about 1 minute. Add the onions and fry for about 2 minutes or until soft.

5 Add the salt, chilli powder, tomatoes, green chillies and fresh coriander. Cook for a further minute. Remove from the heat and set to one side.

6 ▲ The minced lamb should by now be cool enough to stuff the prepared aubergines and peppers. Fill the vegetables quite loosely with the meat mixture.

7 ▲ As you stuff the vegetables, place them on top of the sautéed onions in the karahi. Cover with foil, making sure the foil doesn't touch the food, and cook over a low heat for about 15 minutes.

8 The dish is ready as soon as the aubergines and peppers are tender. Serve with a dish of plain boiled rice or Colourful Pullao Rice.

VARIATION

Large beef tomatoes are also delicious stuffed with the lightly spiced lamb mixture. Simply cut off the tops and scoop out the cores, seeds and some of the pulp and cook as described above.

Beef with Green Beans

LOW-FAT RECIPE

Green beans cooked with beef is a variation on the traditional recipe using lamb. The sliced red (bell) pepper used here makes this dish colourful as well as delicious.

SERVES 4

INGREDIENTS
275 g/10 oz fine green beans, cut into 2.5 cm/1 in pieces
2 tbsp vegetable oil
1 medium onion, sliced
1 tsp ginger pulp
1 tsp garlic pulp
1 tsp chilli powder
1¼ tsp salt
¼ tsp turmeric
2 tomatoes, chopped
450 g/1 lb beef, cubed
1.2 litres/2 pints/5 cups water
1 tbsp chopped fresh coriander (cilantro)
1 red (bell) pepper, sliced
2 fresh green chillies, chopped

NUTRITIONAL VALUES (per portion)

Total fat	11.60 g
Saturated fat	2.89 g
Cholesterol	66.96 mg
Energy (kcals/kj)	241/1011

1 ▲ Boil the green beans in salted water for about 5 minutes, then drain and set aside.

2 ▲ Heat the oil in a large saucepan and fry the sliced onion until it turns golden brown.

3 ▲ Mix together the ginger, garlic, chilli powder, salt, turmeric and chopped tomatoes. Spoon this mixture into the onions and stir-fry for 5–7 minutes.

4 Add the beef and stir-fry for a further 3 minutes. Pour in the water, bring to a boil and lower the heat. Cover and cook for 45 minutes to 1 hour until most of the water has evaporated and the meat is tender.

5 ▲ Add the green beans and mix everything together well.

6 ▲ Finally, add the red (bell) pepper, fresh coriander (cilantro) and chopped green chillies and cook, stirring, for a further 7–10 minutes.

7 Serve hot with Wholemeal (Whole-Wheat) Chapatis.

COOK'S TIP

Frying onions in very little oil requires some patience. They will take a little longer to brown and should be stirred only occasionally. Excessive stirring will draw the moisture out of the onions and make them even more difficult to fry.

Steak and Kidney with Spinach

When this dish is cooked in India, the spinach is often pulverized. Here, it is coarsely chopped and added in the last stages of cooking, which retains the nutritional value of the spinach and gives the dish a lovely appearance.

SERVES 4–6

INGREDIENTS

2 tbsp vegetable oil
1 large onion, finely chopped
1 piece fresh ginger, 5 cm/2 in long, crushed
4 cloves garlic, crushed
4 tbsp mild curry paste, or 4 tbsp mild curry powder
¹/₄ tsp turmeric
salt, to taste
900 g/2 lb steak and kidney, cubed
450 g/1 lb fresh spinach, trimmed, washed and chopped or 450 g/1 lb frozen spinach, thawed and drained
4 tbsp tomato purée (paste)
2 large tomatoes, finely chopped

1 ▲ Heat the oil in a frying pan (skillet) and fry the onion, ginger and garlic until the onion is soft and the ginger and garlic turn golden brown.

3 ▲ Add the spinach and tomato purée (paste) and mix well. Cook uncovered until the spinach is softened and most of the liquid evaporated.

2 ▲ Lower the heat and add the curry paste or powder, turmeric, salt and meat and mix well. Cover and cook until the meat is just tender.

4 ▲ Fold in the chopped tomatoes. Increase the heat and cook for about 5 minutes.

Lentils with Lamb and Tomatoes

This dish is full of protein and has a deliciously light texture. Serve with Colourful Pullao Rice.

SERVES 4

INGREDIENTS
4 tbsp corn oil
1 bay leaf
2 cloves
4 black peppercorns
1 medium onion, sliced
450 g/1 lb lean lamb, boned and cubed
¼ tsp turmeric
1½ tsp chilli powder
1 tsp crushed coriander seeds
2.5 cm/1 in cinnamon stick
1 tsp garlic pulp
1½ tsp salt
1.5 litres/2½ pints/6¼ cups water
50 g/2 oz/⅓ cup round yellow lentils (chana dhal), or yellow split peas
2 medium tomatoes, quartered
2 fresh green chillies, chopped
1 tbsp chopped fresh coriander (cilantro)

1 ▲ Heat the oil in a deep round-bottomed frying pan (skillet) or a karahi. Lower the heat slightly and add the bay leaf, cloves, peppercorns and onion. Fry for about 5 minutes, or until the onions are golden brown.

2 ▲ Add the cubed lamb, turmeric, chilli powder, coriander seeds, cinnamon stick, garlic and most of the salt, and stir-fry for about 5 minutes over a medium heat.

3 Pour in 900 ml/1½ pints/3¾ cups of the water and cover the pan with a lid or foil, making sure the foil does not come into contact with the food. Simmer over a low heat for about 35–40 minutes, or until the water has evaporated and the lamb is tender.

4 Put the lentils into a saucepan with 600 ml/1 pint/2½ cups water and boil for about 12–15 minutes, or until the water has almost evaporated and the lentils are soft enough to be easily mashed. If the lentils are too thick, add up to 150 ml/¼ pint/⅔ cup water to loosen them.

5 ▲ When the lamb is tender, stir-fry the mixture using a wooden spoon, until some free oil begins to appear on the sides of the pan.

6 ▲ Add the cooked lentils to the lamb and mix together well.

7 ▲ Add the tomatoes, chillies and fresh coriander (cilantro) and serve.

COOK'S TIP

Boned and cubed chicken can be used in place of the lamb. At step 3, reduce the amount of water to 300 ml/½ pint/1¼ cups and cook uncovered, stirring occasionally, for 10–15 minutes or until the water has evaporated and the chicken is cooked through.

Hot-and-Sour Meat and Lentil Curry

Dhansak is one of the best-known Parsi dishes and is a favourite for Sunday lunch. This dish has a hot, sweet-and-sour flavour, through which should rise the slightly bitter flavour of fenugreek.

SERVES 4–6

INGREDIENTS

6 tbsp vegetable oil
5 fresh green chillies, chopped
1 piece fresh ginger, 2.5 cm/1 in long, crushed
3 cloves garlic crushed
2 bay leaves
1 piece cinnamon stick, 5 cm/2 in long
900 g/2 lb lean lamb, cubed
600 ml/1 pint/2¹/₂ cups water
175 g/6 oz/²/₃ cup red gram
50 g/2 oz/¹/₄ cup each bengal gram, small split yellow lentils (moong dhal) and split red lentils (masoor dhal)
2 potatoes, cubed and soaked in water
1 aubergine (eggplant), cubed and soaked in water
4 onions, finely sliced, deep-fried and drained
50 g/2 oz fresh spinach, trimmed, washed and chopped or 50 g/2 oz frozen spinach, thawed and drained
25 g/1 oz fenugreek leaves, fresh or dried
115 g/4 oz carrots or pumpkin, cubed
115 g/4 oz/4 cups fresh coriander (cilantro), chopped
50 g/2 oz fresh mint, chopped, or 1 tbsp mint sauce
2 tbsp dhansak masala
2 tbsp sambhar masala
salt, to taste
2 tsp brown sugar
4 tbsp tamarind juice
1 clove garlic, sliced

COOK'S TIP

Chicken or prawns (shrimp) can be used instead of the lamb. If using chicken, reduce the cooking time so that the meat does not become shredded or stringy; if you are using prawns, cook only until the tails turn bright orange/pink in colour.

1 ▲ Heat 3 tbsp of the oil in a saucepan or deep frying pan (skillet) and fry the green chillies, ginger and crushed garlic cloves for 2 minutes. Add the bay leaves, cinnamon, lamb and water. Bring to the boil then simmer until the lamb is half cooked.

2 ▲ Drain the water into another pan and put the lamb aside. Add the lentils to the water and cook until they are tender. Mash the lentils with the back of a spoon.

3 ▲ Drain the potatoes and aubergine (eggplant) and add to the lentils with 3 of the deep-fried onions, the spinach, fenugreek and carrot or pumpkin. Add some hot water if the mixture is too thick. Cook until the vegetables are tender, then mash again with a spoon, keeping the vegetables a little coarse.

4 ▲ Heat 1 tbsp of the oil in a frying pan (skillet) and gently fry the fresh coriander (cilantro) and mint (saving a little to garnish) with the dhansak and sambhar masala, salt and sugar. Add the lamb and fry gently for about 5 minutes.

5 ▲ Return the lamb and spices to the lentil and vegetable mixture and stir well. As lentils absorb fluids, adjust the consistency if necessary. Heat gently until the lamb is fully cooked.

6 ▲ Add the tamarind juice and mix well. Heat the remaining oil and fry the sliced clove of garlic until golden brown. Pour over the dhansak. Garnish with the remaining deep-fried onion and the reserved coriander and mint. Serve hot.

Fish & Seafood Dishes

Fish and shellfish have a surprising affinity with spices, either fairly fiery mixtures as in Balti Prawns in Hot Sauce, or as part of a blend of other aromatic ingredients, such as lime, coriander, coconut and chillies. These are used to great effect in Balti Fish Fillets in Spicy Coconut Sauce. Even just a light spicing works, too — Fish and Vegetable Kebabs make a tasty lunch dish.

Balti Fried Fish

As a child in Pakistan, I used to hear fishmongers calling out the contents of their day's catch from stalls on wheels. Nowadays, seafood is readily available in the many fish markets.

SERVES 4–6

INGREDIENTS

675 g/1½ lb cod, or any other firm, white fish
1 medium onion, sliced
1 tbsp lemon juice
1 tsp salt
1 tsp garlic pulp
1 tsp crushed dried red chillies
1½ tsp garam masala
2 tbsp chopped fresh coriander (cilantro)
2 medium tomatoes
2 tbsp cornflour (cornstarch)
150 ml/¼ pint/⅔ cup corn oil

1 Skin the fish and cut into small cubes. Put into the refrigerator to chill.

2 ▲ Put the onion into a bowl and add the lemon juice, salt, garlic, crushed red chillies, garam masala and fresh coriander (cilantro). Mix together well and set to one side.

3 ▲ Skin the tomatoes by dropping them into boiling water for a few seconds. Remove with a slotted spoon and gently peel off the skins. Chop the tomatoes roughly and add to the onion mixture in the bowl.

4 ▲ Place the contents of the bowl into a food processor or blender and process for about 30 seconds.

5 Remove the fish from the refrigerator. Pour the contents of the food processor or blender over the fish and mix together well.

6 ▲ Add the cornflour (cornstarch) and mix again until the fish pieces are well coated.

7 ▲ Heat the oil in a deep round-bottomed frying pan (skillet) or a karahi. Lower the heat slightly and add the fish pieces, a few at a time. Turn them gently with a slotted spoon as they will break easily. Cook for about 5 minutes until the fish is lightly browned.

8 Remove the fish pieces from the pan and drain on kitchen paper (paper towels) to absorb any excess oil. Keep warm and continue frying the remaining fish. This dish is delicious served with Apricot Chutney and Paratha.

COOK'S TIP

For busy cooks, canned tomatoes can be used instead of fresh ones – there are no skins to remove!

Prawns (Shrimp) and Fish in Herb Sauce

Bengalis are famous for their seafood dishes and always use mustard oil in recipes because it imparts a unique taste, flavour and aroma. No feast in Bengal is complete without one of these celebrated fish dishes.

SERVES 4–6

INGREDIENTS

3 cloves garlic
1 piece fresh ginger, 5 cm/2 in long
1 large leek, roughly chopped
4 fresh green chillies
1 tsp vegetable oil (optional)
4 tbsp mustard oil, or vegetable oil
1 tbsp ground coriander
¹/₂ tsp fennel seeds
1 tbsp crushed yellow mustard seeds, or 1 tsp mustard powder
175 ml/6 fl oz/³/₄ cup thick coconut milk
225 g/8 oz huss or monkfish fillets, cut into thick chunks
225 g/8 oz fresh king prawns (jumbo shrimp), peeled and deveined with tails intact
salt, to taste
115 g/4 oz/4 cups fresh coriander (cilantro), chopped
2 fresh green chillies, to garnish

1 ▲ In a food processor, grind the garlic, ginger, leek and chillies to a coarse paste. Add a little vegetable oil if the mixture is too dry and process the mixture again.

2 ▲ In a frying pan (skillet), heat the mustard or vegetable oil with the paste until it is well blended. Keep the window open and take care not to overheat the mixture as any smoke from the mustard oil will sting the eyes.

3 ▲ Add the ground coriander, fennel seeds, mustard and coconut milk to the pan. Gently bring to the boil and then simmer, uncovered, for about 5 minutes.

4 ▲ Add the fish and simmer for 2 minutes, then fold in the prawns (shrimp) and cook until the prawns turn a bright orange/pink colour. Season with salt, fold in the fresh coriander (cilantro) and serve hot. Garnish with the fresh green chillies, if wished.

Pickled Fish Steaks

This dish is served cold, often as an appetizer. It also makes an ideal main course on a hot summer's day served with a crisp salad. Make a day or two in advance to allow the flavours to blend.

SERVES 4–6

INGREDIENTS
juice of 4 lemons
1 piece fresh ginger, 2.5 cm/1 in long, finely sliced
2 cloves garlic, finely minced
2 fresh red chillies, finely chopped
3 fresh green chillies, finely chopped
4 thick fish steaks (any firm fish)
4 tbsp vegetable oil
4–6 curry leaves
1 onion, finely chopped
1/2 tsp turmeric
1 tbsp ground coriander
150 ml/1/4 pint/2/3 cup pickling vinegar
3 tsp sugar
salt, to taste
salad leaves, to garnish
1/2 tomato, to garnish

1 ▲ In a bowl, mix the lemon juice with the ginger, garlic and chillies. Pat the fish dry and rub the mixture on all sides of the fish. Allow to marinate for 3–4 hours in the refrigerator.

2 ▲ Heat the oil in a frying pan (skillet) and fry the curry leaves, onion, turmeric and coriander until the onion is translucent.

3 ▲ Place the fish steaks in the frying pan with the marinade and cover with the onion mixture. After 5 minutes, turn the fish over gently to prevent damaging the steaks.

4 ▲ Pour in the vinegar and add the sugar and salt. Bring to the boil, then lower the heat and simmer until the fish is cooked. Carefully transfer the steaks to a large platter or individual serving dishes and pour over the vinegar mixture. Chill for 24 hours before garnishing and serving.

Fish and Vegetable Kebabs (Kabobs)

LOW-FAT RECIPE

This is a very attractive dish and served on its own will also make an excellent appetizer for eight people.

SERVES 4

INGREDIENTS

275 g/10 oz cod fillets, or any other firm, white fish fillets
3 tbsp lemon juice
1 tsp ginger pulp
2 fresh green chillies, very finely chopped
1 tbsp very finely chopped fresh coriander (cilantro)
1 tbsp very finely chopped fresh mint
1 tsp ground coriander
1 tsp salt
1 red (bell) pepper
1 green (bell) pepper
1/2 medium cauliflower
8–10 button mushrooms
8 cherry tomatoes
1 tbsp soya oil
1 lime, quartered

NUTRITIONAL VALUES (per portion)

Total fat	4.34 g
Saturated fat	0.51 g
Cholesterol	32.54 mg
Energy (kcals/kj)	130/546

1 ▲ Cut the fish fillets into large chunks.

2 ▲ In a large mixing bowl, blend together the lemon juice, ginger, chopped green chillies, fresh coriander (cilantro), mint, ground coriander and salt. Add the fish chunks and leave to marinate for about 30 minutes.

3 ▲ Cut the red and green (bell) peppers into large squares and divide the cauliflower into individual florets (flowerets).

4 ▲ Preheat the grill (broiler) to hot. Arrange the peppers, cauliflower florets, mushrooms and cherry tomatoes alternately with the fish pieces on 4 skewers.

5 ▲ Baste the kebabs (kabobs) with the oil and any remaining marinade. Transfer to a flameproof dish and grill (broil) under the hot grill for 7–10 minutes or until the fish is cooked right through.

6 Garnish with the lime quarters, if wished, and serve the kebabs either on their own or with Saffron and Cardamom Flavoured Rice.

VARIATION

Do use different vegetables to the ones suggested, if wished. For example, try baby corn cobs instead of mushrooms and broccoli or one of the new cultivated brassicas in place of the cauliflower.

Chunky Fish Balti with Peppers

Try to find as many different colours of (bell) peppers as possible to make this very attractive dish.

SERVES 2–4

INGREDIENTS

450 g/1 lb cod, or any other firm, white
   fish
1½ tsp ground cumin
2 tsp mango powder
1 tsp ground coriander
½ tsp chilli powder
1 tsp salt
1 tsp ginger pulp
3 tbsp cornflour (cornstarch)
150 ml/¼ pint/⅔ cup corn oil
1 each green, orange and red (bell)
   peppers, seeded and chopped
8–10 cherry tomatoes

1 ▲ Skin the fish and cut into small cubes. Put the cubes into a large mixing bowl and add the ground cumin, mango powder, ground coriander, chilli powder, salt, ginger and cornflour (cornstarch). Mix together thoroughly until the fish is well coated.

2 ▲ Heat the oil in a deep round-bottomed frying pan (skillet) or a medium karahi. Lower the heat slightly and add the fish pieces, 3 or 4 at a time. Fry for about 3 minutes, turning constantly.

3 Drain the fish pieces on kitchen paper (paper towels) and transfer to a serving dish. Keep warm and fry the remaining fish pieces.

4 ▲ Fry the (bell) peppers in the remaining oil for about 2 minutes. They should still be slightly crisp. Drain on kitchen paper.

5 Add the cooked peppers to the fish on the serving dish and garnish with the cherry tomatoes. Serve immediately with Raita and Paratha, if wished.

Balti Fish Fillets in Spicy Coconut Sauce

*U*se fresh fish fillets to make this dish if
you can, as they have much more flavour
than frozen ones. However, if you are
using frozen fillets, ensure that they are
completely thawed before using.

SERVES 4

INGREDIENTS
2 tbsp corn oil
1 tsp onion seeds
4 dried red chillies
3 garlic cloves, sliced
1 medium onion, sliced
2 medium tomatoes, sliced
2 tbsp desiccated (shredded) coconut
1 tsp salt
1 tsp ground coriander
4 flatfish fillets, such as plaice, sole or
  flounder, each about 75 g/3 oz
150 ml/¼ pint/⅔ cup water
1 tbsp lime juice
1 tbsp chopped fresh coriander (cilantro)

2 ▲ Add the tomatoes, coconut, salt
and coriander and stir thoroughly.

3 ▲ Cut each fish fillet into 3 pieces.
Drop the fish pieces into the mixture
and turn them over gently until they
are well coated.

4 Cook for 5–7 minutes, lowering the
heat if necessary. Add the water, lime
juice and fresh coriander (cilantro) and
cook for a further 3–5 minutes until the
water has mostly evaporated. Serve
immediately with rice.

I ▲ Heat the oil in a deep round-
bottomed frying pan (skillet) or a
karahi. Lower the heat slightly and add
the onion seeds, dried red chillies,
garlic slices and onion. Cook for 3–4
minutes, stirring once or twice.

Fish Fillets with a Chilli Sauce

LOW-FAT RECIPE

For this recipe, the fish fillets are first marinated with fresh coriander (cilantro) and lemon juice, then cooked under a hot grill (broiler) and served with a chilli sauce. It is delicious accompanied with Saffron and Cardamom Flavoured Rice.

SERVES 4

INGREDIENTS

4 flatfish fillets, such as plaice, sole or
   flounder, about 115 g/4 oz each
2 tbsp lemon juice
1 tbsp finely chopped fresh coriander
   (cilantro)
1 tbsp vegetable oil
lime wedges
coriander (cilantro) sprig

Sauce

1 tsp ginger pulp
2 tbsp tomato purée (paste)
1 tsp sugar
1 tsp salt
1 tbsp chilli sauce
1 tbsp malt vinegar
300 ml/¹/₂ pint/ 1¹/₄ cups water

NUTRITIONAL VALUES (per portion)

Total fat	5.28 g
Saturated fat	0.78 g
Cholesterol	47.25 mg
Energy (kcals/kj)	140/586

1 ▲ Rinse, pat dry and place the fish fillets in a medium bowl. Add the lemon juice, fresh coriander (cilantro) and oil and rub into the fish. Leave to marinate for at least 1 hour.

2 ▲ Mix together all the sauce ingredients, pour into a small saucepan and simmer over a low heat for about 6 minutes, stirring occasionally.

3 Preheat the grill (broiler) to medium. Place the fillets under the grill for about 5–7 minutes.

4 ▲ When the fillets are cooked, remove and arrange them on a warmed serving dish.

5 The chilli sauce should now be fairly thick – about the consistency of a thick chicken soup.

6 ▲ Pour the sauce over the fillets, garnish with the lime wedges and coriander sprig and serve with rice.

VARIATION

For a subtle change in flavour, substitute the lemon juice in the marinade with an equal quantity of lime juice.

Balti Prawns (Shrimp) in Hot Sauce

This sizzling prawn (shrimp) dish is cooked in a fiery hot and spicy sauce. Not only does this sauce contain chilli powder, it is enhanced further by the addition of ground green chillies mixed with other spices. If the heat gets too much for anyone with a delicate palate, the addition of Raita will help to soften the piquant flavour.

SERVES 4

INGREDIENTS

2 medium onions, roughly chopped
2 tbsp tomato purée (paste)
1 tsp ground coriander
¼ tsp turmeric
1 tsp chilli powder
2 medium fresh green chillies
3 tbsp chopped fresh coriander (cilantro)
2 tbsp lemon juice
1 tsp salt
3 tbsp corn oil
16 cooked king prawns (jumbo shrimp)
1 fresh green chilli, chopped (optional)

1 ▲ Put the onions, tomato purée (paste), ground coriander, turmeric, chilli powder, 2 whole green chillies, 2 tbsp of the fresh coriander (cilantro), the lemon juice and salt into the bowl of a food processor. Process for about 1 minute. If the mixture seems too thick, add a little water to loosen it.

2 ▲ Heat the oil in a deep round-bottomed frying pan (skillet) or a karahi. Lower the heat slightly and add the spice mixture. Fry the mixture for 3–5 minutes or until the sauce has thickened slightly.

3 ▲ Add the prawns (shrimp) and stir-fry quickly over a medium heat.

4 As soon as the prawns are heated through, transfer them to a serving dish and garnish with the rest of the fresh coriander and the chopped green chilli, if using. Serve immediately.

COOK'S TIP

Cooked prawns (shrimp) have been used in all the seafood recipes. However, raw prawns – if you can find them – are especially delicious. Remove the black vein along the back of each prawn and extend the cooking time if necessary. The prawns will turn pink when they are cooked through.

Karahi Prawns (Shrimp) and Fenugreek

The black-eyed peas, prawns (shrimp) and paneer in this recipe mean that it is rich in protein. The combination of both ground and fresh fenugreek makes this a very fragrant and delicious dish. When preparing fresh fenugreek, use the leaves whole, but discard the stalks which would add a bitter flavour to the dish.

SERVES 4–6

INGREDIENTS

4 tbsp corn oil
2 medium onions, sliced
2 medium tomatoes, sliced
1½ tsp garlic pulp
1 tsp chilli powder
1 tsp ginger pulp
1 tsp ground cumin
1 tsp ground coriander
1 tsp salt
150 g/5 oz paneer, cubed
1 tsp ground fenugreek
1 bunch fresh fenugreek leaves
115 g/4 oz cooked prawns (shrimp)
2 fresh red chillies, sliced
2 tbsp chopped fresh coriander (cilantro)
50 g/2 oz/⅓ cup canned black-eye peas, drained
1 tbsp lemon juice

I ▲ Heat the oil in a deep round-bottomed frying pan (skillet) or a karahi. Lower the heat slightly and add the onions and tomatoes. Fry for about 3 minutes.

2 ▲ Add the garlic, chilli powder, ginger, ground cumin, ground coriander, salt, paneer and the ground and fresh fenugreek. Lower the heat and stir-fry for about 2 minutes.

3 ▲ Add the prawns (shrimp), red chillies, fresh coriander (cilantro) and the black-eyed peas and mix well. Cook for a further 3–5 minutes, stirring occasionally, or until the prawns are heated through.

4 Finally sprinkle on the lemon juice and serve.

Prawns (Shrimp) with Okra

This dish has a sweet taste with a strong chilli flavour. It should be cooked fast to prevent the okra from breaking up and releasing its distinctive, sticky interior.

SERVES 4–6

INGREDIENTS

4–6 tbsp oil
*225 g/8 oz okra, washed, dried and left
    whole*
4 cloves garlic, crushed
*1 piece fresh ginger, 5 cm/2 in long,
    crushed*
4–6 fresh green chillies, cut diagonally
½ tsp turmeric
4–6 curry leaves
1 tsp cumin seeds
*450 g/1 lb fresh king prawns (jumbo
    shrimp), peeled and deveined*
salt, to taste
2 tsp brown sugar
juice of 2 lemons

1 ▲ Heat the oil in a frying pan (skillet) and fry the okra over a fairly high heat until they are slightly crisp and browned on all sides. Remove from the oil and put to one side on a piece of kitchen paper (paper towel).

2　In the same oil, gently fry the garlic, ginger, chillies, turmeric, curry leaves and cumin seeds for 2–3 minutes. Add the prawns (shrimp) and mix well. Cook until the prawns are tender.

3 ▲ Add the salt, sugar, lemon juice and fried okra. Increase the heat and quickly fry for a further 5 minutes, stirring gently to prevent the okra from breaking. Adjust the seasoning, if necessary. Serve hot.

Fried Whole Fish

In southern India, fish is prepared daily in some form or other but most often it is just fried and served with a lentil curry and a nice hot pickle.

SERVES 4–6

INGREDIENTS

1 small onion, coarsely chopped
4 cloves garlic
*1 piece fresh ginger, 5 cm/2 in long,
    chopped*
1 tsp turmeric
2 tsp chilli powder
salt, to taste
4 red mullet
vegetable oil, for shallow-frying
1 tsp cumin seeds
3 fresh green chillies, finely sliced
lime slices, to serve

1 ▲ Using a food processor, grind the first 6 ingredients to a smooth paste. Make gashes on both sides of the fish and rub them with the paste. Leave to rest for 1 hour in a cool place. Lightly pat the fish dry with kitchen paper (paper towel) without removing the paste. Excess fluid will be released as the salt dissolves.

2 ▲ Heat the oil in a large frying pan (skillet) and fry the cumin seeds and chillies for about 1 minute. Fry the fish in batches. When the first side is sealed, turn the fish over very gently to ensure they do not break. Fry until they are golden brown on both sides, drain well and serve hot with lime slices.

*Prawns (Shrimp) with Okra (top) and
Fried Whole Fish*

Paneer Balti with Prawns (Shrimp)

Although paneer is not widely eaten in Pakistan, it makes an excellent substitute for red meat. Here it is combined with king prawns (jumbo shrimp) to make one of my favourite dishes.

SERVES 4

INGREDIENTS
12 cooked king prawns (jumbo shrimp)
175 g/6 oz paneer
2 tbsp tomato purée (paste)
4 tbsp Greek-style yogurt
1½ tsp garam masala
1 tsp chilli powder
1 tsp garlic pulp
1 tsp salt
2 tsp mango powder
1 tsp ground coriander
115 g/4 oz/8 tbsp butter
1 tbsp corn oil
3 fresh green chillies, chopped
3 tbsp chopped fresh coriander (cilantro)
150 ml/¼ pint/⅔ cup single (light) cream

1 ▲ Peel the king prawns (jumbo shrimp) and cube the paneer.

2 Blend the tomato purée (paste), yogurt, garam masala, chilli powder, garlic, salt, mango powder and ground coriander in a mixing bowl and set to one side.

3 ▲ Melt the butter with the oil in a deep round-bottomed frying pan (skillet) or a medium karahi. Lower the heat slightly and quickly fry the paneer and prawns for about 2 minutes. Remove with a slotted spoon and drain on kitchen paper (paper towels).

4 ▲ Pour the spice mixture into the fat left in the pan and stir-fry for about 1 minute.

5 ▲ Add the paneer and prawns, and cook for 7–10 minutes, stirring occasionally, until the prawns are heated through.

6 ▲ Add the fresh chillies and most of the coriander (cilantro), and pour in the cream. Heat through for about 2 minutes, garnish with the remaining coriander and serve.

HOME-MADE PANEER

To make paneer at home, bring 1 litre/1¾ pints/4 cups milk to the boil over a low heat. Add 2 tbsp lemon juice, stirring continuously and gently until the milk thickens and begins to curdle. Strain the curdled milk through a sieve (strainer) lined with muslin (cheesecloth). Set aside under a heavy weight for about 1½–2 hours to press to a flat shape about 1 cm/½ in thick.

Make the paneer a day before you plan to use it in a recipe; it will then be firmer and easier to handle. Cut and use as required; it will keep for about one week in the refrigerator.

Grilled (Broiled) Fish Fillets

LOW-FAT RECIPE

The nice thing about fish is that it can be grilled (broiled) beautifully without sacrificing any flavour. For this recipe I have used a minimum amount of oil to baste the fish.

SERVES 4

INGREDIENTS
4 medium flatfish fillets, such as plaice, sole or flounder, about 115 g/ 4 oz each
1 tsp garlic pulp
1 tsp garam masala
1 tsp chilli powder
1/4 tsp turmeric
1/2 tsp salt
1 tbsp finely chopped fresh coriander (cilantro)
1 tbsp vegetable oil
2 tbsp lemon juice

NUTRITIONAL VALUES (per portion)	
Total fat	5.63 g
Saturated fat	0.84 g
Cholesterol	47.25 mg
Energy (kcals/kj)	143/599

I ▲ Line a flameproof dish or grill (broiler) tray with foil. Rinse and pat dry the fish fillets and put them on the foil-lined dish or tray.

2 ▲ In a small bowl, mix together the garlic, garam masala, chilli powder, turmeric, salt, fresh coriander (cilantro), oil and lemon juice.

3 ▲ Using a pastry brush, baste the fish fillets evenly all over with the spice and lemon juice mixture.

4 Preheat the grill to very hot, then lower the heat to medium. Grill (broil) the fillets for about 10 minutes, basting occasionally, until they are cooked right through.

5 Serve immediately with an attractive garnish, such as grated carrot, tomato quarters and lime slices, if wished.

Glazed Garlic Prawns (Shrimp)

LOW-FAT RECIPE

A fairly simple and quick dish to prepare, it is best to peel the prawns (shrimp) as this helps them to absorb maximum flavour. Serve as a main course with accompaniments, or with a salad as an appetizer.

SERVES 4

INGREDIENTS

1 tbsp vegetable oil
3 garlic cloves, roughly chopped
3 tomatoes, chopped
1/2 tsp salt
1 tsp crushed dried red chillies
1 tsp lemon juice
1 tbsp mango chutney
1 fresh green chilli, chopped
15–20 cooked king prawns (jumbo shrimp), peeled
fresh coriander (cilantro) sprigs
2 spring onions (scallions), chopped (optional)

NUTRITIONAL VALUES (per portion)	
Total fat	3.83 g
Saturated fat	0.54 g
Cholesterol	30.37 mg
Energy (kcals/kj)	90/380

1 ▲ In a medium saucepan, heat the oil and add the chopped garlic.

2 ▲ Lower the heat and add the chopped tomatoes along with the salt, crushed chillies, lemon juice, mango chutney and chopped fresh chilli.

3 ▲ Finally add the prawns (shrimp), turn up the heat and stir-fry these quickly, until heated through.

4 Transfer to a serving dish. Serve garnished with fresh coriander (cilantro) sprigs and chopped spring onions (scallions), if wished.

Balti Prawns (Shrimp) and Vegetables in Thick Sauce

Here, tender prawns (shrimp), crunchy vegetables and a thick curry sauce combine to produce a dish rich in flavour and texture. Fruity Pullao is a perfect accompaniment, although plain rice is a good alternative.

SERVES 4

INGREDIENTS

3 tbsp corn oil
1 tsp mixed fenugreek, mustard and onion seeds
2 curry leaves
1/2 medium cauliflower, cut into small florets (flowerets)
8 baby carrots, halved lengthways
6 new potatoes, thickly sliced
50 g/2 oz/1/2 cup frozen peas
2 medium onions, sliced
2 tbsp tomato purée (paste)
1 1/2 tsp chilli powder
1 tsp ground coriander
1 tsp ginger pulp
1 tsp garlic pulp
1 tsp salt
2 tbsp lemon juice
450 g/1 lb cooked prawns (shrimp)
2 tbsp chopped fresh coriander (cilantro)
1 fresh red chilli, seeded and sliced
120 ml/4 fl oz/1/2 cup single (light) cream

I ▲ Heat the oil in a deep round-bottomed frying pan (skillet) or a large karahi. Lower the heat slightly and add the fenugreek, mustard and onion seeds and the curry leaves.

2 ▲ Turn up the heat and add the cauliflower, carrots, potatoes and peas. Stir-fry quickly until browned, then remove from the pan with a slotted spoon and drain on kitchen paper (paper towels).

3 Add the onions to the oil left in the karahi and fry over a medium heat until golden brown.

4 ▲ While the onions are cooking, mix together the tomato purée (paste), chilli powder, ground coriander, ginger, garlic, salt and lemon juice and pour the paste onto the onions.

5 Add the prawns (shrimp) and stir-fry over a low heat for about 5 minutes or until they are heated through.

6 ▲ Add the fried vegetables to the pan and mix together well.

7 ▲ Add the fresh coriander (cilantro) and red chilli and pour over the cream. Bring to the boil and serve immediately.

VARIATION

Monkfish is an excellent alternative to the prawns (shrimp) used in this recipe, as it is a firm-fleshed fish that will not break up when fried. Cut the monkfish into chunks, add to the onion and spice mixture at step 5 and stir-fry over a low heat for 5–7 minutes or until the fish is cooked through.

Stuffed Fish

Every community in India prepares stuffed fish but the Parsi version must rank top of the list. The most popular fish in India is the pomfret. These are available from Indian and Chinese grocers or large supermarkets.

SERVES 4

INGREDIENTS
2 large pomfrets, or Dover or lemon sole
2 tsp salt
juice of 1 lemon

Masala
8 tbsp desiccated (shredded) coconut
*115 g/4 oz/4 cups fresh coriander
    (cilantro), including the tender stalks*
8 fresh green chillies (or to taste)
1 tsp cumin seeds
6 cloves garlic
2 tsp sugar
2 tsp lemon juice

I ▲ Scale the fish and cut off the fins. Gut the fish and remove the heads, if desired. Using a sharp knife, make 2 diagonal gashes on each side, then pat dry with kitchen paper (paper towel).

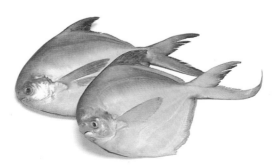

2 ▲ Rub the fish inside and out with salt and lemon juice and allow to stand in a cool place for about 1 hour. Pat dry thoroughly.

3 ▲ For the masala, grind all the ingredients together using a pestle and mortar or food processor. Stuff the fish with the masala mixture and rub any remaining into the gashes and all over the fish on both sides.

4 ▲ Place each fish on a separate piece of greased foil. Tightly wrap the foil over each fish. Place in a steamer and steam for 20 minutes, or bake for 30 minutes at 200°C/400°F/Gas 6 or until cooked. Remove the fish from the foil and serve hot.

COOK'S TIP

In India, this fish dish is always steamed wrapped in banana leaves. Banana leaves are generally available from Indian or Chinese grocers but vine leaves from Greek food shops could be used instead.

Parsi Prawn (Shrimp) Curry

This dish comes from the west coast of India, where fresh seafood is eaten in abundance. Fresh king prawns (jumbo shrimp) or 'tiger' prawns are ideal.

SERVES 4–6

INGREDIENTS

4 tbsp vegetable oil
1 medium onion, finely sliced
6 cloves garlic, finely crushed
1 tsp chilli powder
1½ tsp turmeric
2 medium onions, finely chopped
4 tbsp tamarind juice
1 tsp mint sauce
1 tbsp demerara sugar
salt, to taste
450 g/1 lb fresh king prawns (jumbo shrimp), peeled and deveined
75 g/3 oz/3 cups fresh coriander (cilantro), chopped

I ▲ Heat the oil in a frying pan (skillet) and fry the sliced onion until golden brown. In a bowl, mix the garlic, chilli powder and turmeric with a little water to form a paste. Add to the browned onion and simmer for 3 minutes.

2 ▲ Add the chopped onions to the pan and fry until they become translucent, stirring frequently. Stir in the tamarind juice, mint sauce, sugar and salt and gently simmer for a further 3 minutes.

3 ▲ Pat the prawns (shrimp) dry with kitchen paper (paper towel). Add to the spice mixture with a small amount of water and stir-fry until the prawns turn a bright orange/pink colour.

4 ▲ When the prawns are cooked, add the fresh coriander (cilantro) and stir-fry over a high heat for a few minutes to thicken the sauce. Serve hot.

Prawn (Shrimp) and Spinach Pancakes (Crêpes)

LOW-FAT RECIPE

Serve these delicious filled pancakes (crêpes) hot with the Spicy Baby Vegetable Salad. Try to use red onions for this recipe, although they are not essential.

MAKES 4–6 PANCAKES (CRÊPES)

INGREDIENTS
Pancakes (Crêpes)
175 g/6 oz/1½ cups plain (all-purpose) flour
½ tsp salt
3 eggs
1½ cups semi-skimmed (2%) milk
15 g/½ oz/1 tbsp low-fat margarine

Filling
2 tbsp vegetable oil
2 medium red onions, sliced
½ tsp garlic pulp
2.5 cm/1 in piece ginger, shredded
1 tsp chilli powder
1 tsp garam masala
1 tsp salt
2 tomatoes, sliced
225 g/8 oz frozen leaf spinach, thawed and drained
115 g/4 oz cooked prawns (shrimp)
2 tbsp chopped fresh coriander (cilantro)

Garnish
1 tomato, quartered
fresh coriander (cilantro) sprigs
lemon wedges

NUTRITIONAL VALUES (per portion)	
Total fat	14.04 g
Saturated fat	3.19 g
Cholesterol	173.33 mg
Energy (kcals/kj)	373/1568

1 ▲ To make the pancakes (crêpes), sift the flour and salt together. Beat the eggs and add to the flour, beating continuously. Gradually stir in the milk. Leave to stand for 1 hour.

2 Heat the oil in a deep frying pan (skillet) and fry the sliced onions over a medium heat until golden.

3 ▲ Gradually add the garlic, ginger, chilli powder, garam masala and salt, followed by the tomatoes and spinach, stir-frying constantly.

4 ▲ Add the prawns (shrimp) and fresh coriander (cilantro). Cook for a further 5–7 minutes or until any excess water has been absorbed. Keep warm.

5 ▲ Heat about ½ tsp of the low-fat margarine in a 25 cm/10 in non-stick frying pan (skillet) or pancake pan. Pour in about one-quarter of the pancake batter, tilting the pan so the batter spreads well, coats the bottom of the pan and is evenly distributed.

6 ▲ When fine bubbles begin to appear on top, flip it over using a spatula and cook for a further minute or so. Transfer to a plate and keep warm. Cook the remaining pancakes in the same way.

7 Fill the pancakes with the spinach and prawns and garnish with the tomato and fresh coriander sprigs. Serve warm with lemon wedges.

Seafood Balti with Vegetables

In this dish, the spicy seafood is cooked separately and combined with the vegetables at the last minute to give a truly delicious combination of flavours.

SERVES 4

INGREDIENTS
Seafood
225 g/½ lb cod, or any other firm, white
  fish
225 g/½ lb cooked prawns (shrimp)
6 crab sticks, halved lengthways
1 tbsp lemon juice
1 tsp ground coriander
1 tsp chilli powder
1 tsp salt
1 tsp ground cumin
4 tbsp cornflour (cornstarch)
150 ml/¼ pint/⅔ cup corn oil

Vegetables
150 ml/¼ pint/⅔ cup corn oil
2 medium onions, chopped
1 tsp onion seeds
½ medium cauliflower, cut into florets
  (flowerets)
115 g/4 oz French (green) beans, cut into
  2.5 cm/1 in lengths
175 g/6 oz/1 cup sweetcorn (corn kernels)
1 tsp shredded ginger
1 tsp chilli powder
1 tsp salt
4 fresh green chillies, sliced
2 tbsp chopped fresh coriander (cilantro)
lime slices

1 Skin the fish and cut into small cubes. Put into a medium mixing bowl with the prawns (shrimps) and crab sticks, and put to one side.

2 ▲ In a separate bowl, mix together the lemon juice, ground coriander, chilli powder, salt and ground cumin. Pour this over the seafood and mix together thoroughly using your hands.

3 Sprinkle on the cornflour (cornstarch) and mix again until the seafood is well coated. Set to one side in the refrigerator for about 1 hour to allow the flavours to develop.

4 ▲ To make the vegetable mixture, heat the oil in a deep round-bottomed frying pan (skillet) or a karahi. Throw in the onions and the onion seeds, and stir-fry until lightly browned.

5 Add the cauliflower, French (green) beans, sweetcorn (corn kernels), ginger, chilli powder, salt, green chillies and fresh coriander (cilantro). Stir-fry for about 7–10 minutes over a medium heat, making sure that the cauliflower florets (flowerets) retain their shape.

6 ▲ Spoon the fried vegetables around the edge of a shallow dish, leaving a space in the middle for the seafood, and keep warm.

7 ▲ Wash and dry the pan, then heat the oil to fry the seafood pieces. Fry the seafood pieces in 2–3 batches, until they turn a golden brown. Remove with a slotted spoon and drain on kitchen paper (paper towels).

8 Arrange the seafood in the middle of the dish of vegetables and keep warm while you fry the remaining seafood. Garnish with lime slices and serve. Plain boiled rice and Raita make ideal accompaniments.

Prawns (Shrimp) with Vegetables

This is a light and nutritious dish, excellent served either on a bed of lettuce leaves, with plain boiled rice or Wholemeal (Whole-Wheat) Chapatis.

SERVES 4

INGREDIENTS

2 tbsp chopped fresh coriander (cilantro)
1 tsp salt
2 fresh green chillies, seeded if wished
3 tbsp lemon juice
2 tbsp vegetable oil
20 cooked king prawns (jumbo shrimp), peeled
1 medium courgette (zucchini), thickly sliced
1 medium onion, cut into 8 chunks
8 cherry tomatoes
8 baby corn cobs
mixed salad leaves

NUTRITIONAL VALUES (per portion)

Total fat	6.47 g
Saturated fat	0.85 g
Cholesterol	29.16 mg
Energy (kcals/kj)	109/458

1 ▲ Place the chopped coriander (cilantro), salt, green chillies, lemon juice and oil in a food processor and grind these together for a few seconds.

2 ▲ Remove the contents from the processor and transfer to a medium mixing bowl.

3 ▲ Add the peeled prawns (shrimp) to this mixture and stir to make sure that all the prawns are well coated. Set aside to marinate for about 30 minutes.

4 Preheat the grill (broiler) to very hot, then turn the heat down to medium.

5 ▲ Arrange the vegetables and prawns alternately on 4 skewers. When all the skewers are ready place them under the preheated grill for 5–7 minutes until cooked and browned.

6 Serve immediately on a bed of mixed salad leaves.

COOK'S TIP

King prawns (jumbo shrimp) are a luxury, but worth choosing for a special dinner. For a more economical variation, substitute the king prawns with 450 g/1 lb ordinary prawns.

Bombay Duck Pickle

Bomil is an unusual fish found off the west coast of India during the monsoon season. It is salted and dried in the sun and is characterized by a strong smell and distinctive piquancy. How this fish acquired the name Bombay duck in the Western world still remains a mystery!

SERVES 4–6

INGREDIENTS
6–8 pieces bomil (Bombay duck), soaked in water for 5 minutes
4 tbsp vegetable oil
2 fresh red chillies, chopped
1 tbsp sugar
450 g/1 lb cherry tomatoes, halved
115 g/4 oz deep-fried onions

1 ▲ Pat the soaked fish dry with kitchen paper (paper towel). Heat the oil in a frying pan (skillet) and fry the Bombay duck pieces for about 30–45 seconds on both sides until crisp. Be careful not to burn them or they will taste bitter. Drain well on kitchen paper. When cool, break the fish into small pieces.

2 ▲ In the same oil, cook the remaining ingredients until the tomatoes become pulpy and the onions are blended into a sauce. Fold in the Bombay duck pieces and serve hot or cold.

Fish Cakes

These tasty fish cakes can be made slightly larger and served as fish burgers, or made into small balls to serve as cocktail snacks.

MAKES 20

INGREDIENTS
450 g/1 lb firm, white fish, skinned
2 medium potatoes, peeled, boiled and mashed
4 spring onions (scallions), finely chopped
4 fresh green chillies, finely chopped
1 piece fresh ginger, 5 cm/2 in long, finely crushed
few fresh coriander (cilantro) and mint leaves, chopped
salt and freshly ground black pepper, to taste
2 eggs
breadcrumbs, for coating
vegetable oil, for shallow-frying
chilli sauce or sweet chutney, to serve
lemon wedges, to serve

1 ▲ Place the fish in a lightly greased steamer and steam until cooked. Remove the pan from the heat.

2 ▲ Place the potatoes, spring onions (scallions), spices, fresh coriander and mint, seasonings and 1 egg in a large bowl. When the fish is cool, crumble it coarsely into the bowl and mix well.

3 ▲ Shape the mixture into cakes. Beat the remaining egg and dip the cakes in it, then coat with the breadcrumbs. Heat the oil and fry the cakes until brown on all sides.

Bombay Duck Pickle (top) and Fish Cakes

Vegetable Dishes

The range of vegetables available today lends inspiration for side dishes, and both subtle and hot spicing will enhance their fresh flavour. Choose from everyday accompaniments like Curried Cauliflower or Bombay Potatoes, one of the delicious main meal vegetable curries, or try a more unusual side dish such as Okra in Yogurt or Karahi Shredded Cabbage.

Okra in Yogurt

This tangy vegetable dish can be served as an accompaniment, but also makes an excellent vegetarian meal served with Tarka Dhal and Wholemeal (Whole-Wheat) Chapatis.

SERVES 4

INGREDIENTS
450 g/1 lb okra
2 tbsp corn oil
½ tsp onion seeds
3 medium fresh green chillies, chopped
1 medium onion, sliced
¼ tsp turmeric
2 tsp desiccated (shredded) coconut
½ tsp salt
1 tbsp natural (plain) low-fat yogurt
2 medium tomatoes, sliced
1 tbsp chopped fresh coriander (cilantro)

NUTRITIONAL VALUES (per portion)

Total fat	8.44 g
Saturated fat	2.09 g
Cholesterol	0.15 mg
Energy (kcals/kj)	119/501

1 ▲ Wash, top and tail the okra, cut into 1 cm/½ in pieces and set aside.

2 ▲ Heat the oil in a medium frying pan (skillet), add the onion seeds, green chillies and onion and fry for about 5 minutes until the onion has turned golden brown.

3 ▲ Lower the heat and add the turmeric, desiccated (shredded) coconut and salt and fry for about 1 minute.

4 ▲ Next add the okra, turn the heat to medium-high and quickly stir-fry for a few minutes until lightly golden.

5 ▲ Add the yogurt, tomatoes and finally the fresh coriander (cilantro). Cook for a further 2 minutes.

6 Transfer onto a serving dish and serve immediately.

Bombay Potatoes

This authentic dish belongs to the Gujerati, a totally vegetarian sect and the largest population in Bombay.

SERVES 4–6

INGREDIENTS
450 g/1 lb new potatoes
salt, to taste
1 tsp turmeric
4 tbsp vegetable oil
2 dried red chillies
6–8 curry leaves
2 onions, finely chopped
2 fresh green chillies, finely chopped
50 g/2 oz/2 cups fresh coriander (cilantro), coarsely chopped
¼ tsp asafoetida
½ tsp each, cumin, mustard, onion, fennel and nigella seeds
lemon juice, to taste

1 Scrub the potatoes under cold running water and cut them into small pieces. Boil the potatoes in water with a little salt and ½ tsp of the turmeric for 10–15 minutes, or until tender. Drain the potatoes well then mash. Put aside.

2 ▲ Heat the oil in a frying pan (skillet) and fry the dried chillies and curry leaves until the chillies are nearly burnt. Add the onions, green chillies, fresh coriander (cilantro), remaining turmeric and spice seeds and cook until the onions are soft.

3 ▲ Fold in the potatoes and add a few drops of water. Cook over a low heat for about 10 minutes, stirring well to ensure the spices are evenly mixed. Add lemon juice to taste, and serve.

Curried Cauliflower

In this dish the creamy coconut sauce complements the flavour of the spiced cauliflower.

SERVES 4–6

INGREDIENTS
1 tbsp gram flour (besan)
120 ml/4 fl oz/½ cup water
1 tsp chilli powder
1 tbsp ground coriander
1 tsp ground cumin
1 tsp mustard powder
1 tsp turmeric
salt, to taste
4 tbsp vegetable oil
6–8 curry leaves
1 tsp cumin seeds
1 cauliflower, broken into florets (flowerets)
175 ml/6 fl oz/¾ cup thick coconut milk

juice of 2 lemons
lime wedges, to serve

1 ▲ Mix the gram flour with a little of the water to make a smooth paste. Add the chilli, coriander, cumin, mustard, turmeric and salt. Add the remaining water and keep mixing to blend all the ingredients well.

2 Heat the oil in a frying pan (skillet), add the curry leaves and cumin seeds. Add the spice paste and simmer for about 5 minutes. If the sauce has become too thick, add a little hot water.

3 ▲ Add the cauliflower and coconut milk. Bring to the boil, reduce the heat, cover and cook until the cauliflower is tender but crunchy. Cook longer if you prefer. Add the lemon juice, mix well and serve hot with the lime wedges.

Bombay Potatoes (top) and Curried Cauliflower

Courgettes (Zucchini) with Mushrooms in a Creamy Sauce

LOW-FAT RECIPE

When cream and mushrooms are cooked together they complement each other beautifully. Though this dish sounds very rich, by using single (light) cream and very little oil you can keep the fat content to a minimum.

SERVES 4

INGREDIENTS

2 tbsp vegetable oil
1 medium onion, roughly chopped
1 tsp ground coriander
1 tsp ground cumin
1 tsp salt
1/2 tsp chilli powder
225 g/8 oz/3 cups mushrooms, sliced
2 medium courgettes (zucchini), sliced
3 tbsp single (light) cream
1 tbsp chopped fresh coriander (cilantro)

NUTRITIONAL VALUES (per portion)	
Total fat	7.73 g
Saturated fat	1.80 g
Cholesterol	4.50 mg
Energy (kcals/kj)	95/400

1 ▲ Heat the oil and fry the chopped onions until golden brown. Lower the heat to medium, add the ground coriander, cumin, salt and chilli powder and stir together well.

2 ▲ Once the onions and the spices are well blended, add the mushrooms and courgettes (zucchini) and stir-fry gently for about 5 minutes until soft. If the mixture is too dry just add a little water to loosen.

3 ▲ Finally pour in the cream and mix it well into the vegetables.

4 Garnish with fresh chopped coriander (cilantro), if wished, and serve immediately.

Potatoes with Red Chillies

LOW-FAT RECIPE

The quantity of red chillies used here may be too fiery for some palates. For a milder version, either seed the chillies, use fewer or substitute them with 1 roughly chopped red (bell) pepper.

SERVES 4

INGREDIENTS
12–14 baby new potatoes, peeled and halved
2 tbsp vegetable oil
½ tsp crushed dried red chillies
½ tsp white cumin seeds
½ tsp fennel seeds
½ tsp crushed coriander seeds
1 tbsp salt
1 medium onion, sliced
1–4 fresh red chillies, chopped
1 tbsp chopped fresh coriander (cilantro)

NUTRITIONAL VALUES (per portion)	
Total fat	6.31 g
Saturated fat	0.75 g
Cholesterol	0.00 mg
Energy (kcals/kj)	151/634

I ▲ Boil the baby potatoes in salted water until soft but still firm. Remove from the heat and drain off the water.

2 ▲ In a deep frying pan (skillet), heat the oil, then turn down the heat to medium. Then add the crushed chillies, cumin, fennel and coriander seeds and salt and fry for 30–40 seconds.

3 ▼ Add the sliced onion and fry until golden brown. Then add the potatoes, red chillies and fresh coriander (cilantro).

4 Cover and cook for 5–7 minutes over a very low heat. Serve hot.

Balti Baby Vegetables

There is a wide and wonderful selection of baby vegetables available in supermarkets these days, and this simple recipe does full justice to their delicate flavour and attractive appearance. Serve as part of a main meal or even as a light appetizer.

SERVES 4–6

INGREDIENTS

10 new potatoes, halved
12–14 baby carrots
12–14 baby courgettes (zucchini)
2 tbsp corn oil
15 baby onions
2 tbsp chilli sauce
1 tsp garlic pulp
1 tsp ginger pulp
1 tsp salt
400 g/14 oz/2 cups canned chick-peas (garbanzos), drained
10 cherry tomatoes
1 tsp crushed dried red chillies
2 tbsp sesame seeds

1 ▲ Bring a medium pan of salted water to the boil and add the potatoes and carrots. After about 12–15 minutes, add the courgettes (zucchini) and boil for a further 5 minutes or until all the vegetables are just tender.

2 ▲ Drain the vegetables well and set to one side.

3 ▲ Heat the oil in a deep round-bottomed frying pan (skillet) or a karahi and add the baby onions. Fry until the onions turn golden brown. Lower the heat and add the chilli sauce, garlic, ginger and salt, taking care not to burn the mixture.

4 ▲ Add the chick-peas (garbanzos) and stir-fry over a medium heat until the moisture has been absorbed.

5 ▲ Add the cooked vegetables and cherry tomatoes and stir over the heat with a slotted spoon for about 2 minutes.

6 Add the crushed red chillies and sesame seeds as a garnish and serve.

VARIATION

By varying the vegetables chosen and experimenting with different combinations, this recipe can form the basis for a wide variety of vegetable accompaniments. Try baby corn cobs, French (green) beans, mange-tout (snow peas), okra and cauliflower florets (flowerets), too.

Stuffed Okra

A delicious accompaniment to any dish, this can also be served on a bed of strained yogurt which gives an excellent contrast in flavour.

SERVES 4–6

INGREDIENTS
225 g/8 oz large okra
1 tbsp mango powder
¹/2 tsp ground ginger
¹/2 tsp ground cumin
¹/2 tsp chilli powder (optional)
¹/2 tsp turmeric
salt, to taste
a few drops of vegetable oil
2 tbsp cornflour (cornstarch), placed in a plastic bag
vegetable oil, for frying

2 ▲ In a bowl, mix the mango powder, ginger, cumin, chilli if using, turmeric and salt with a few drops of oil. Leave the mixture to rest for 1–2 hours.

3 ▲ Using your fingers, part the slit of each okra carefully and fill each with as much of the spice filling as possible.

4 Put all the okra into the plastic bag with the cornflour (cornstarch) and shake the bag carefully to cover the okra evenly.

5 ▲ Fill the frying pan (skillet) with enough oil to sit 2.5 cm/1 in deep, heat it and fry the okra in small batches for about 5–8 minutes or until they are brown and slightly crisp. Serve hot.

I ▲ Wash the okra and dry on kitchen paper (paper towel). Carefully trim off the tops without making a hole. Using a sharp knife, make a slit lengthways in the centre of each okra but do not cut all the way through.

Mixed Vegetable Curry

This is a very delicately spiced vegetable dish that makes an appetizing snack when served with plain yogurt. It is also a good accompaniment to a main meal of heavily spiced curries.

SERVES 4–6

INGREDIENTS

350 g/12 oz mixed vegetables, eg beans, peas, potatoes, cauliflower, carrots, cabbage, mange-touts (snow peas) and button mushrooms
2 tbsp vegetable oil
1 tsp cumin seeds, freshly roasted
½ tsp mustard seeds
½ tsp onion seeds
1 tsp turmeric
2 cloves garlic, crushed
6–8 curry leaves
1 dried red chilli
salt, to taste
1 tsp sugar
150 ml/¼ pint/⅔ cup natural (plain) yogurt mixed with 1 tsp cornflour (cornstarch)

1 ▲ Prepare all the vegetables you have chosen: string the beans; thaw the peas, if frozen; cube the potatoes; cut the cauliflower into florets (flowerets); dice the carrots; shred the cabbage; top and tail the mange-touts (snow peas); wash the mushrooms and leave whole.

2 ▲ Heat a large pan with enough water to cook all the vegetables and bring to the boil. First add the potatoes and carrots and cook until nearly tender then add all the other vegetables and cook until still firm. All the vegetables should be crunchy except the potatoes. Drain well.

3 ▲ Heat the oil in a frying pan (skillet) and fry the cumin, mustard and onion seeds, the turmeric, garlic, curry leaves and dried chilli gently until the garlic is golden brown and the chilli nearly burnt. Reduce the heat.

4 ▲ Fold in the drained vegetables, add the sugar and salt and gradually add the yogurt mixed with the cornflour (cornstarch). Heat to serving temperature and serve immediately.

Potatoes in a Yogurt Sauce

LOW-FAT RECIPE

It is nice to use tiny new potatoes with the skins on for this recipe. The yogurt adds a tangy flavour to this fairly spicy dish, which is delicious served with Wholemeal (Whole-Wheat) Chapatis.

SERVES 4

INGREDIENTS

12 new potatoes, halved
275 g/10 oz/1¼ cups natural (plain) low-fat yogurt
300 ml/½ pint/1¼ cups water
¼ tsp turmeric
1 tsp chilli powder
1 tsp ground coriander
½ tsp ground cumin
1 tsp salt
1 tsp soft brown sugar
2 tbsp vegetable oil
1 tsp white cumin seeds
1 tbsp chopped fresh coriander (cilantro)
2 fresh green chillies, sliced
1 fresh coriander sprig (optional)

NUTRITIONAL VALUES (per portion)	
Total fat	6.84 g
Saturated fat	1.11 g
Cholesterol	2.80 mg
Energy (kcals/kj)	184/774

1 ▲ Boil the potatoes in salted water with their skins on until they are just tender, then drain and set aside.

2 ▲ Mix together the yogurt, water, turmeric, chilli powder, ground coriander, ground cumin, salt and sugar in a bowl. Set aside.

3 ▲ Heat the oil in a medium saucepan and add the white cumin seeds.

4 ▲ Reduce the heat, stir in the yogurt mixture and cook for about 3 minutes over a medium heat.

5 ▲ Add the fresh coriander (cilantro), green chillies and cooked potatoes. Blend everything together and cook for a further 5–7 minutes, stirring occasionally.

6 Transfer to a serving dish and garnish with the coriander sprig, if wished.

COOK'S TIP

If new potatoes are unavailable, use 450 g/2 lb ordinary potatoes instead. Peel them and cut into large chunks, then cook as described above.

Spinach and Potatoes

India is blessed with over 18 varieties of spinach. If you have access to an Indian or Chinese grocer, look out for some of the more unusual varieties.

SERVES 4–6

INGREDIENTS

4 tbsp vegetable oil
225 g/8 oz potatoes
1 piece fresh ginger, 2.5 cm/1 in long, crushed
4 cloves garlic, crushed
1 onion, coarsely chopped
2 fresh green chillies, chopped
2 dried red chillies, coarsely broken
1 tsp cumin seeds
salt, to taste
225 g/8 oz fresh spinach, trimmed, washed and chopped or 225 g/8 oz frozen spinach, thawed and drained
2 firm tomatoes, coarsely chopped, to garnish

1 ▲ Wash the potatoes and cut into quarters. If using small new potatoes, leave them whole. Heat the oil in a frying pan (skillet) and fry the potatoes until brown on all sides. Remove and put aside.

2 ▲ Remove the excess oil leaving about 1 tbsp in the pan. Fry the ginger, garlic, onion, green chillies, dried chillies and cumin seeds until the onion is golden brown.

3 ▲ Add the potatoes and salt and stir well. Cover the pan and cook over a medium heat, stirring occasionally, until the potatoes are tender when pierced with a sharp knife.

4 ▲ Add the spinach and stir well. Cook with the pan uncovered until the spinach is tender and all the excess fluids have evaporated. Garnish with the chopped tomatoes and serve hot.

Mushrooms, Peas and Paneer

Paneer is a traditional cheese made from rich milk and is most popular with northern Indians. Rajasthani farmers eat this dish for lunch with thick parathas as they work in the fields.

SERVES 4–6

INGREDIENTS
6 tbsp ghee or vegetable oil
225 g/8 oz paneer, cubed
1 onion, finely chopped
few mint leaves, chopped
50 g/2 oz/2 cups fresh coriander (cilantro), chopped
3 fresh green chillies, chopped
3 cloves garlic
1 piece fresh ginger, 2.5 cm/1 in long, sliced
1 tsp turmeric
1 tsp chilli powder (optional)
1 tsp garam masala
salt, to taste
225 g/8 oz/3 cups tiny button mushrooms, washed and left whole
225 g/8 oz/1½ cups frozen peas, thawed and drained
175 ml/6 fl oz/¾ cup natural (plain) yogurt, mixed with 1 tsp cornflour (cornstarch)
mint sprig, to garnish

2 ▲ Grind the onion, mint, coriander (cilantro), chillies, garlic and ginger in a pestle and mortar or food processor to a fairly smooth paste. Remove and mix in the turmeric, chilli powder if using, garam masala and salt.

3 ▲ Remove excess ghee or oil from the pan leaving about 1 tbsp. Heat and fry the paste until the raw onion smell disappears and the oil separates.

4 ▲ Add the mushrooms, peas and paneer. Mix well. Cool the mixture and gradually fold in the yogurt. Simmer for about 10 minutes. Garnish with a sprig of mint and serve hot.

1 ▲ Heat the ghee or oil in a frying pan (skillet) and fry the paneer cubes until they are golden brown on all sides. Remove and drain on kitchen paper (paper towel).

Masala Mashed Potatoes

LOW-FAT RECIPE

These potatoes are very versatile and will perk up any meal.

SERVES 4

INGREDIENTS
3 medium potatoes
1 tbsp chopped fresh mint and coriander (cilantro), mixed
1 tsp mango powder
1 tsp salt
1 tsp crushed black peppercorns
1 fresh red chilli, chopped
1 fresh green chilli, chopped
50 g/2 oz/4 tbsp low-fat margarine

NUTRITIONAL VALUES (per portion)	
Total fat	5.80 g
Saturated fat	1.25 g
Cholesterol	0.84 mg
Energy (kcals/kj)	94/394

1 Boil the potatoes until soft enough to be mashed. Mash these down using a masher.

2 ▲ Blend together the remaining ingredients in a small bowl.

3 ▲ Stir the mixture into the mashed potatoes and mix together thoroughly with a fork.

4 Serve warm as an accompaniment.

Spicy Cabbage

LOW-FAT RECIPE

An excellent vegetable accompaniment, this is very versatile and can be served even as a warm side salad.

SERVES 4

INGREDIENTS
50 g/2 oz/4 tbsp low-fat margarine
1/2 tsp white cumin seeds
3–8 dried red chillies, to taste
1 small onion, sliced
225 g/8 oz/2 1/2 cups cabbage, shredded
2 medium carrots, grated
1/2 tsp salt
2 tbsp lemon juice

NUTRITIONAL VALUES (per portion)	
Total fat	6.06 g
Saturated fat	1.28 g
Cholesterol	0.84 mg
Energy (kcals/kj)	92/384

2 ▲ Add the sliced onion and fry for about 2 minutes. Add the cabbage and carrots and stir-fry for a further 5 minutes or until the cabbage is soft.

3 Finally, stir in the salt and lemon juice and serve.

1 ▲ Melt the low-fat margarine in a medium saucepan and fry the white cumin seeds and dried red chillies for about 30 seconds.

Masala Mashed Potatoes (top) and Spicy Cabbage

Spiced Potatoes and Carrots Parisienne

Ready prepared "parisienne" vegetables have recently become available in many supermarkets. These are simply root vegetables that have been peeled and cut into perfectly spherical shapes. This dish looks extremely fresh and appetizing and is equally delicious.

SERVES 4

INGREDIENTS

175 g/6 oz carrots parisienne
175 g/6 oz potatoes parisienne
115 g/4 oz runner beans, sliced
75 g/3 oz/6 tbsp butter
1 tbsp corn oil
1/4 tsp onion seeds
1/4 tsp fenugreek seeds
4 dried red chillies
1/2 tsp mustard seeds
6 curry leaves
1 medium onion, sliced
1 tsp salt
4 garlic cloves, sliced
4 fresh red chillies
1 tbsp chopped fresh coriander (cilantro)
1 tbsp chopped fresh mint
mint sprig

1 ▲ Drop the carrots, potatoes and runner beans into a pan of boiling water, and cook for about 7 minutes, or until they are just tender but not overcooked. Drain and set to one side.

2 ▲ Heat the butter and oil in a deep round-bottomed frying pan (skillet) or a large karahi and add the onion seeds, fenugreek seeds, dried red chillies, mustard seeds and curry leaves. When these have sizzled for a few seconds, add the onion and fry for 3–5 minutes.

3 ▲ Add the salt, garlic and fresh chillies, followed by the cooked vegetables, and stir gently for about 5 minutes, over a medium heat.

4 Add the fresh coriander (cilantro) and mint and serve hot garnished with a sprig of mint.

Karahi Shredded Cabbage with Cumin

This cabbage dish is only lightly spiced and makes a good accompaniment to most other dishes.

SERVES 4

INGREDIENTS
1 tbsp corn oil
50 g/2 oz/4 tbsp butter
1/2 tsp crushed coriander seeds
1/2 tsp white cumin seeds
6 dried red chillies
1 small savoy cabbage, shredded
12 mange-tout (snow peas)
3 fresh red chillies, seeded and sliced
12 baby corn cobs
salt, to taste
25 g/1 oz/1/4 cup flaked (slivered)
   almonds, toasted
1 tbsp chopped fresh coriander (cilantro)

1 Heat the oil and butter in a deep round-bottomed frying pan (skillet) or a karahi and add the crushed coriander seeds, white cumin seeds and dried red chillies.

2 ▲ Add the shredded cabbage and mange-tout (snow peas) and stir-fry for about 5 minutes.

3 ▲ Finally add the fresh red chillies, baby corn cobs and salt, and fry for a further 3 minutes.

4 Garnish with the toasted almonds and fresh coriander (cilantro), and serve hot.

Potatoes in a Hot Red Sauce

This dish should be hot and sour but, if you wish, reduce the chillies and add extra tomato purée (paste) instead.

SERVES 4–6

INGREDIENTS

450 g/1 lb small new potatoes
25 g/1 oz dried red chillies, preferably kashmiri
1 1/2 tsp cumin seeds
4 cloves garlic
6 tbsp vegetable oil
4 tbsp thick tamarind juice
2 tbsp tomato purée (paste)
4 curry leaves
salt, to taste
1 tsp sugar
1/4 tsp asafoetida
coriander (cilantro) sprig, to garnish

1 ▲ Boil the potatoes until they are fully cooked, ensuring they do not break. To test, insert a thin sharp knife into the potatoes. It should come out clean when the potatoes are fully cooked. Drain well.

2 Soak the chillies for 5 minutes in warm water. Drain and grind with the cumin seeds and garlic to a coarse paste using a pestle and mortar or food processor.

3 ▲ Heat the oil in a frying pan (skillet). Fry the paste, tamarind juice, tomato purée (paste), curry leaves, salt, sugar and asafoetida until the oil separates. Add the potatoes. Reduce the heat, cover and simmer for about 5 minutes. Garnish and serve.

Cucumber Curry

This makes a pleasant accompaniment to fish dishes and may be served cold with cooked meats.

SERVES 4–6

INGREDIENTS

120 ml/4 fl oz/1/2 cup water
115 g/4 oz creamed coconut
1/2 tsp turmeric
salt, to taste
1 tsp sugar
1 large cucumber, cut into small pieces
1 large red (bell) pepper, cut into small pieces
50 g/2 oz salted peanuts, coarsely crushed
4 tbsp vegetable oil
2 dried red chillies
1 tsp cumin seeds
1 tsp mustard seeds
4–6 curry leaves
4 cloves garlic, crushed
a few whole salted peanuts, to garnish

1 ▲ Bring the water to the boil in a heavy pan and add the creamed coconut, turmeric, salt and sugar. Simmer until the coconut dissolves to obtain smooth, thick sauce.

2 Add the cucumber, red (bell) pepper and crushed peanuts and simmer for about 5 minutes. Transfer to a heatproof serving dish and keep warm.

3 ▲ Heat the oil in a frying pan (skillet). Fry the chillies and cumin with the mustard seeds until they start to pop. Reduce the heat, add the curry leaves and garlic and fry. Pour over the cucumber mixture and stir well. Garnish and serve hot.

Potatoes in a Hot Red Sauce (top) and Cucumber Curry

Sweet-and-Sour Vegetables with Paneer

LOW-FAT RECIPE

This is one of my favourite grilled (broiled) vegetable selections. The cheese used in this recipe is Indian paneer, which can be bought at some Asian stores; tofu can be used in its place.

SERVES 4

INGREDIENTS

1 green pepper, cut into squares
1 yellow pepper, cut into squares
8 cherry, or 4 salad, tomatoes
8 cauliflower florets (flowerets)
8 pineapple chunks
8 cubes paneer (see Introduction)

Seasoned oil

1 tbsp soya oil
2 tbsp lemon juice
1 tsp salt
1 tsp crushed black peppercorns
1 tbsp clear honey
2 tbsp chilli sauce

NUTRITIONAL VALUES (per portion)	
Total fat	9.80 g
Saturated fat	4.43 g
Cholesterol	20.00 mg
Energy (kcals/kj)	171/718

1 ▲ Preheat the grill (broiler) to hot. Thread the prepared vegetables, pineapple and the paneer onto 4 skewers, alternating the ingredients. Set the skewers on a flameproof dish or grill tray.

2 In a small mixing bowl, mix all the ingredients for the seasoned oil. If the mixture is a little too thick, add 1 tbsp of water to loosen it.

3 ▲ Using a pastry brush, baste the vegetables with the seasoned oil. Grill (broil) under the preheated grill for about 10 minutes until the vegetables begin to darken slightly, turning the skewers to cook evenly.

4 Serve on a bed of plain boiled rice.

Vegetables and Beans with Curry Leaves

LOW-FAT RECIPE

Fresh curry leaves are extremely aromatic and there is no substitute for them. Fresh curry leaves also freeze well, but if necessary you can use dried ones. This is quite a dry curry.

SERVES 4

INGREDIENTS

2 tbsp vegetable oil
6 curry leaves
3 garlic cloves, sliced
3 dried red chillies
1/4 tsp onion seeds
1/4 tsp fenugreek seeds
3 fresh green chillies, chopped
2 tsp desiccated (shredded) coconut
115 g/4 oz/1/2 cup canned red kidney beans, drained

1 medium carrot, cut into strips
50 g/2 oz French beans, diagonally sliced
1 medium red (bell) pepper, cut into strips
1 tsp salt
2 tbsp lemon juice

NUTRITIONAL VALUES (per portion)	
Total fat	8.27 g
Saturated fat	2.47 g
Cholesterol	0.00 mg
Energy (kcals/kj)	130/548

1 Heat the oil in a medium deep frying pan (skillet). Add the curry leaves, garlic cloves, dried chillies, and onion and fenugreek seeds.

2 ▲ When these turn a shade darker, add the remaining ingredients, stirring constantly. Lower the heat, cover and cook for about 5 minutes.

3 Transfer to a serving dish and serve with extra coconut, if wished.

Sweet-and-Sour Vegetables with Paneer (top) and Vegetables and Beans with Curry Leaves

Corn Cob Curry

Corn-cobs are roasted on charcoal and rubbed with lemon juice, salt and chilli powder in India. In season, vendors fill the atmosphere with these delicious aromas. Corn is also a popular curry ingredient.

SERVES 4–6

INGREDIENTS
4 whole corn-cobs, fresh, canned or frozen
vegetable oil, for frying
1 large onion, finely chopped
2 cloves garlic, crushed
1 piece fresh ginger, 5 cm/2 in long, crushed
1/2 tsp turmeric
1/2 tsp onion seeds
1/2 tsp cumin seeds
1/2 tsp five-spice powder
chilli powder, to taste
6–8 curry leaves
1/2 tsp sugar
200 ml/7 fl oz/scant 1 cup natural (plain) yogurt

I ▲ Cut each corn-cob in half, using a sharp, heavy knife or cleaver to make clean cuts and prevent damaging the kernels. Heat the oil in a large frying pan (skillet) and fry the corn pieces until golden brown on all sides. Remove the corn-cobs and set aside.

2 ▲ Remove any excess oil leaving about 2 tbsp in the pan. Grind the onion, garlic and ginger to a paste using a pestle and mortar or food processor. Remove and mix in all the spices, curry leaves and sugar.

3 ▲ Reheat the oil gently and fry the onion mixture until all the spices have blended well and the oil separates from the paste.

4 ▲ Cool the mixture and gradually fold in the yogurt. Mix well until you have a smooth sauce. Add the corn to the mixture and mix well so all the pieces are evenly covered with the sauce. Gently reheat for about 10 minutes. Serve hot.

Curried Stuffed (Bell) Peppers

This is one of the most famous dishes of Deccan. Hot, spicy and extremely delicious, it is often prepared for weddings. It is made with extra oil several days in advance to allow the spices to mature.

SERVES 4–6

INGREDIENTS

1 tbsp sesame seeds
1 tbsp white poppy seeds
1 tsp coriander seeds
4 tbsp desiccated (shredded) coconut
½ onion, sliced
1 piece fresh ginger, 2.5 cm/1 in long, sliced
4 cloves garlic, sliced
handful of fresh coriander (cilantro)
2 fresh green chillies
4 tbsp vegetable oil
2 potatoes, boiled and coarsely mashed
salt, to taste
2 each, green, red and yellow (bell) peppers
2 tbsp sesame oil
1 tsp cumin seeds
4 fresh green chillies, slit
4 tbsp tamarind juice

2 ▲ Heat 2 tbsp of the vegetable oil in a frying pan and fry the ground paste for 4–5 minutes. Add the potatoes and salt and stir well until the spices have blended evenly into the potatoes.

3 ▲ Trim the bases of the peppers so they stand, then slice off the tops and reserve. Remove the seeds and any white pith. Fill the peppers with equal amounts of the potato mixture and replace the tops.

4 ▲ Heat the sesame oil and remaining vegetable oil in a frying pan and fry the cumin seeds and the slit green chillies. When the chillies turn white, add the tamarind juice and bring to the boil. Place the peppers over the mixture, cover the pan and cook until the peppers are nearly done.

1 ▲ In a frying pan (skillet), dry-fry the sesame, poppy and coriander seeds, then add the desiccated (shredded) coconut and continue to roast until the coconut turns golden brown. Add the onion, ginger, garlic, coriander (cilantro), and chillies and roast for a further 5 minutes. Cool, and grind to a paste using a pestle and mortar or food processor. Put aside.

Spicy Balti Potatoes

SERVES 4

INGREDIENTS
3 tbsp corn oil
1/2 tsp white cumin seeds
3 curry leaves
1 tsp crushed dried red chillies
1/2 tsp mixed onion, mustard and fenugreek seeds
1/2 tsp fennel seeds
3 garlic cloves
1/2 tsp shredded ginger
2 medium onions, sliced
6 new potatoes, cut into 5 mm/1/4 in slices
1 tbsp chopped fresh coriander (cilantro)
1 fresh red chilli, seeded and sliced
1 fresh green chilli, seeded and sliced

1 ▲ Heat the oil in a deep round-bottomed frying pan (skillet) or a karahi. Lower the heat slightly and add the cumin seeds, curry leaves, dried red chillies, mixed onion, mustard and fenugreek seeds, fennel seeds, garlic cloves and ginger. Fry for about 1 minute, then add the onions and fry for 5 minutes or until the onions are golden brown.

2 ▲ Add the potatoes, fresh coriander (cilantro) and fresh red and green chillies and mix well. Cover the pan tightly with a lid or foil, making sure the foil does not touch the food. Cook over a very low heat for about 7 minutes or until the potatoes are tender.

3 Remove the foil and serve hot.

Okra with Green Mango and Lentils

If you like okra, you'll love this spicy and tangy dish.

SERVES 4

INGREDIENTS
115 g/4 oz/2/3 cup yellow lentils (toor dhal)
3 tbsp corn oil
1/2 tsp onion seeds
2 medium onions, sliced
1/2 tsp ground fenugreek
1 tsp ginger pulp
1 tsp garlic pulp
1 1/2 tsp chilli powder
1/4 tsp turmeric
1 tsp ground coriander
1 green (unripe) mango, peeled and sliced
450 g/1 lb okra, cut into 1 cm/1/2 in pieces
1 1/2 tsp salt
2 fresh red chillies, seeded and sliced
2 tbsp chopped fresh coriander (cilantro)
1 tomato, sliced

1 ▲ Wash the lentils thoroughly and put in a saucepan with enough water to cover. Bring to the boil and cook until soft but not mushy. Drain and set to one side.

2 Heat the oil in a deep round-bottomed frying pan (skillet) or a karahi and fry the onion seeds until they begin to pop. Add the onions and fry until golden brown. Lower the heat and add the ground fenugreek, ginger, garlic, chilli powder, turmeric and ground coriander.

3 ▲ Throw in the mango slices and the okra. Stir well and add the salt, red chillies and fresh coriander (cilantro). Stir-fry for about 3 minutes or until the okra is well cooked.

4 Finally, add the cooked lentils and sliced tomato and cook for a further 3 minutes. Serve hot.

Spicy Balti Potatoes (top) and Okra with Green Mango and Lentils

Masala Beans with Fenugreek

LOW-FAT RECIPE

"Masala" means spice and this vegetarian dish is spicy, though not necessarily hot.

SERVES 4

INGREDIENTS
1 medium onion
1 tsp ground cumin
1 tsp ground coriander
1 tsp sesame seeds
1 tsp chilli powder
1/2 tsp garlic pulp
1/4 tsp turmeric
1 tsp salt
2 tbsp vegetable oil
1 tomato, quartered
225 g/8 oz French (green) beans
1 bunch fresh fenugreek leaves, stems discarded
4 tbsp chopped fresh coriander (cilantro)
1 tbsp lemon juice

NUTRITIONAL VALUES (per portion)	
Total fat	7.11 g
Saturated fat	0.88 g
Cholesterol	0.00 mg
Energy (kcals/kj)	100/419

1 Roughly chop the onion. Mix together the ground cumin and coriander, sesame seeds, chilli powder, garlic, turmeric and salt.

2 ▲ Place all of these ingredients, including the onion, in a food processor and process for 30–45 seconds.

3 ▲ In a medium saucepan, heat the oil and fry the spice mixture for about 5 minutes, stirring occasionally.

4 ▲ Add the tomato, French (green) beans, fresh fenugreek and fresh coriander (cilantro).

5 ▲ Stir-fry for about 5 minutes, sprinkle in the lemon juice and serve.

Vegetables with Almonds

Natural (plain) yogurt is added to the vegetables towards the end of the cooking time, which not only gives this dish a tangy note but also makes it creamy.

SERVES 4

INGREDIENTS

2 tbsp vegetable oil
2 medium onions, sliced
5 cm/2 in piece fresh ginger, shredded
1 tsp crushed black peppercorns
1 bay leaf
1/4 tsp turmeric
1 tsp ground coriander
1 tsp salt
1/2 tsp garam masala
175 g/6 oz/2 1/2 cups mushrooms, thickly sliced
1 medium courgette (zucchini), thickly sliced
50 g/2 oz French beans, sliced into 2.5 cm/1 in pieces
1 tbsp roughly chopped fresh mint
150 ml/1/4 pint/2/3 cup water
2 tbsp natural (plain) low-fat yogurt
25 g/1 oz/1/4 cup flaked (slivered) almonds

NUTRITIONAL VALUES (per portion)	
Total fat	10.11 g
Saturated fat	1.14 g
Cholesterol	0.30 mg
Energy (kcals/kj)	136/569

2 ▲ Lower the heat and add the turmeric, ground coriander, salt and garam masala, stirring occasionally. Gradually add the mushrooms, courgette (zucchini), French beans and the mint. Stir gently so that the vegetables retain their shapes.

3 Pour in the water and bring to a simmer, then lower the heat and cook until the water has been absorbed by the vegetables.

4 ▲ Beat the yogurt with a fork, then pour onto the vegetables and mix together well.

5 Cook for a further 2–3 minutes, stirring occasionally. Serve garnished with the flaked (slivered) almonds.

1 ▲ In a medium deep frying pan (skillet), heat the oil and fry the sliced onions with the shredded ginger, crushed black peppercorns and bay leaf for 3–5 minutes.

Pulses

Widely eaten in India, spicy pulses are both nutritious and tasty. Even everyday pulses, such as lentils and black-eyed beans, are transformed into delectable dishes by flavouring with blends of spices, and chick-peas are often curried to serve with tasty potato cakes. Less familiar pulses are worth searching for – Black Gram in a Spicy Cream Sauce is particularly tasty.

Lentils Seasoned with Fried Spices

Dhal is cooked in every house in India in one form or another. This recipe is a simplified version.

SERVES 4–6

INGREDIENTS

115 g/4 oz/¹/₂ cup red gram
50 g/2 oz/¹/₄ cup bengal gram
350 ml/12 fl oz/1¹/₂ cups water
4 fresh green chillies
1 tsp turmeric
1 large onion, sliced
salt, to taste
400 g/14 oz canned plum tomatoes, crushed
4 tbsp vegetable oil
¹/₂ tsp mustard seeds
¹/₂ tsp cumin seeds
1 clove garlic, crushed
6 curry leaves
2 dried red chillies
¹/₄ tsp asafoetida
deep-fried onions and fresh coriander (cilantro), to garnish

1 ▲ Place the first 6 ingredients in a heavy pan and bring to the boil. Simmer, covered, until the lentils are soft and the water has evaporated.

2 ▲ Mash the lentils with the back of a spoon. When nearly smooth, add the salt and tomatoes and mix well. If necessary, thin the mixture with hot water.

3 Fry the remaining ingredients until the garlic browns. Pour the oil and spices over the lentils and cover. After 5 minutes, mix well, garnish, and serve.

South Indian Lentils and Vegetables

Sambhar is a favourite south Indian dish served for breakfast with dosai (Indian pancakes) or idli (rice dumplings).

SERVES 4–6

INGREDIENTS

4 tbsp vegetable oil
¹/₂ tsp mustard seeds
¹/₂ tsp cumin seeds
2 dried red chillies
¹/₄ tsp asafoetida
6–8 curry leaves
2 cloves garlic, crushed
2 tbsp desiccated (shredded) coconut
225 g/8 oz/1 cup split red lentils (masoor dhal)
2 tsp sambhar masala
¹/₂ tsp turmeric
450 ml/³/₄ pint/scant 2 cups water
450 g/1 lb mixed vegetables, eg okra, courgettes (zucchini), cauliflower, shallots and (bell) peppers
4 tbsp tamarind juice
4 firm tomatoes, quartered
4 tbsp vegetable oil
2 cloves garlic, finely sliced
handful fresh coriander (cilantro), chopped

1 ▲ Heat the oil in a heavy saucepan. Fry the next 7 ingredients until the coconut browns. Mix in the lentils, sambhar masala, turmeric and water.

2 Simmer until the lentils are mushy. Add the vegetables, tamarind juice and tomatoes. Cook so the vegetables are crunchy.

3 ▲ Fry the garlic slices and fresh coriander (cilantro). Pour over the lentils and vegetables. Mix at the table before serving.

Lentils Seasoned with Fried Spices (top) and South Indian Lentils and Vegetables

Curried Chick-Peas (Garbanzos) with Potato Cakes

No other city in India is quite like Bombay. Its cuisine is typical of food you can buy right off the streets, which is the way the Bombayites like it – spicy, quick and nutritious.

SERVES 4–6

INGREDIENTS
2 tbsp vegetable oil
2 tbsp ground coriander
2 tbsp ground cumin
½ tsp turmeric
½ tsp salt
½ tsp sugar
2 tbsp flour paste
450 g/1 lb chick-peas (garbanzos), cooked and drained
2 fresh green chillies, chopped
1 piece fresh ginger, 5 cm/2 in long, finely crushed
75 g/3 oz/3 cups fresh coriander (cilantro), chopped
2 firm tomatoes, chopped

Potato Cakes
450 g/1 lb potatoes, boiled and coarsely mashed
4 fresh green chillies, finely chopped
50 g/2 oz/2 cups fresh coriander (cilantro), finely chopped
1½ tsp cumin powder
1 tsp mango powder
salt, to taste
vegetable oil, for shallow-frying

1 ▲ For the curry, heat the oil in a large saucepan and fry the coriander, cumin, turmeric, salt, sugar and flour paste, stirring frequently, until the water has evaporated and the oil separated out from the mixture.

2 ▲ Add the chick-peas (garbanzos), chillies, ginger, fresh coriander (cilantro) and tomatoes. Toss well and simmer for about 5 minutes. Remove to a serving dish and keep warm.

3 ▲ To make the potato cakes, in a large mixing bowl mix the mashed potato with the green chillies, ground coriander and cumin, mango powder and salt. Mix until all the ingredients are well blended.

4 ▲ Using your hands, shape the potato mixture into little cakes. Heat the oil in a shallow frying pan (skillet) or griddle and fry the cakes on both sides until golden brown. Transfer to a serving dish and serve with the curried chick-peas.

Black Gram in a Spicy Cream Sauce

Dhabas – highway cafes – are very lively eating places serving a variety of dishes. This recipe is commonly served, and is one of the most popular.

SERVES 4–6

INGREDIENTS

*175 g/6 oz/²/₃ cup black gram (urid dhal),
     soaked overnight*
50 g/2 oz/¹/₄ cup red gram
120ml/4 fl oz/¹/₂ cup double (heavy) cream
*120 ml/4 fl oz/¹/₂ cup natural (plain)
     yogurt*
1 tsp cornflour (cornstarch)
3 tbsp ghee
1 onion, finely chopped
*1 piece fresh ginger, 5 cm/2 in long,
     crushed*
4 fresh green chillies, chopped
1 tomato, chopped
¹/₂ tsp chilli powder
¹/₂ tsp turmeric
¹/₂ tsp ground cumin
salt, to taste
2 cloves garlic, sliced

1 ▲ Drain the black gram and place in a heavy pan with the red gram. Cover with water and bring to the boil. Reduce the heat, cover the pan and simmer until the gram are tender. The black gram will remain whole but the red gram will be mushy. Gently mash with a spoon. Allow to cool.

2 ▲ In a bowl, mix together the cream, yogurt and cornflour (cornstarch). Mix the cream mixture into the gram without damaging the whole black gram grains.

3 ▲ Heat 1 tbsp of the ghee in a frying pan (skillet) and fry the onion, ginger, 2 of the green chillies and the tomato until the onion is soft. Add the spices and salt and fry for a further 2 minutes. Add it all to the gram mixture and mix well. Reheat and transfer to a heatproof serving dish and keep warm.

4 ▲ Heat the remaining ghee in a frying pan and fry the garlic slices and remaining chillies until the garlic slices are golden brown. Pour over the gram and serve, folding the garlic and chilli into the gram just before serving.

Black-Eyed Peas and Potato Curry

Black-eyed peas are beige and kidney-shaped with a distinctive dark dot. This can be served as an appetizer or snack.

SERVES 4–6

INGREDIENTS
225 g/8 oz/1¹/₃ cups black-eyed peas, soaked overnight and drained
¹/₄ tsp bicarbonate of soda (baking soda)
1 tsp five-spice powder
¹/₄ tsp asafoetida
2 onions, finely chopped
1 piece fresh ginger, 2.5 cm/1 in long, crushed
few fresh mint leaves
450 ml/³/₄ pint/scant 1¹/₂ cups water
4 tbsp vegetable oil
¹/₂ tsp each, turmeric, ground coriander, ground cumin and chilli powder
4 fresh green chillies, chopped

75 ml/5 tbsp tamarind juice
2 potatoes, cubed and boiled
115 g/4 oz/4 cups fresh coriander (cilantro), chopped
2 firm tomatoes, chopped
salt, to taste

I ▲ Place the black-eyed peas with the first 7 ingredients in a heavy pan. Simmer until the beans are soft. Remove any excess water and reserve.

2 ▲ Heat the oil in a frying pan (skillet). Gently fry the spices, chillies and tamarind juice, until they are well blended. Pour over the black-eyed peas and mix.

3 Add the potatoes, fresh coriander (cilantro), tomatoes and salt. Mix well, and if necessary add a little reserved water. Reheat and serve.

Bengal Gram and Bottle Gourd Curry

This is an Anglo-Indian version of dhal, which is characteristically hot, and with the dhals left whole.

SERVES 4–6

INGREDIENTS
175 g/6 oz/²/₃ cup bengal gram
450 ml/³/₄ pint/1¹/₂ cups water
4 tbsp vegetable oil
2 fresh green chillies, chopped
1 onion, chopped
2 cloves garlic, crushed
1 piece fresh ginger, 5 cm/2 in long, crushed
6–8 curry leaves
1 tsp chilli powder
1 tsp turmeric
salt, to taste
450 g/1 lb bottle gourd or marrow (squash), courgettes (zucchini) or pumpkin, peeled, pithed and sliced

4 tbsp tamarind juice
2 tomatoes, chopped
handful fresh coriander (cilantro), chopped

I ▲ In a saucepan, cook the lentils in the water until the grains are tender but not mushy. Put aside without draining away any excess water.

2 ▲ Heat the oil in a deep saucepan. Fry the chillies, onion, garlic, ginger, curry leaves, chilli powder, turmeric and salt. Add the gourd pieces and mix. Cover and cook until the gourd is soft.

3 Add the lentils and water and bring to the boil. Add the tamarind juice, tomatoes and fresh coriander (cilantro). Simmer gently until the gourd is cooked. Serve hot with a dry meat curry.

Black-Eyed Peas and Potato Curry (top) and Bengal Gram and Bottle Gourd Curry

Green Gram and Rice

The whole spices are edible, but it is advisable to warn the diners about them.

SERVES 4–6

INGREDIENTS

4 tbsp ghee
1 onion, finely chopped
2 cloves garlic, crushed
1 piece ginger, 2.5 cm/1 in long, shredded
4 fresh green chillies, chopped
4 cloves
1 piece cinnamon stick, 2.5 cm/1 in long
4 green cardamom pods
1 tsp turmeric
salt, to taste
350 g/12 oz/1³/₄ cups patna rice, washed and soaked for 20 minutes

175 g/6 oz/²/₃ cup split green gram, washed and soaked for 20 minutes
600 ml/1 pint/2¹/₂ cups water

I ▲ Gently heat the ghee in a large heavy pan with a tight-fitting cover and fry the onion, garlic, ginger, chillies, cloves, cinnamon, cardamoms, turmeric and salt until the onion is soft and translucent.

2 ▲ Drain the rice and gram, add to the spices and sauté for 2–3 minutes. Add the water and bring to the boil. Reduce the heat, cover and cook for about 20–25 minutes or until all the water is absorbed.

3 Take the pan off the heat and leave to rest for 5 minutes. Just before serving gently toss the mixture with a flat spatula.

Split Lentils with Courgettes (Zucchini)

Most dhal dishes are runny but this one provides texture with the addition of the courgettes (zucchini).

SERVES 4–6

INGREDIENTS

175 g/6 oz/²/₃ cup small split yellow lentils (moong dhal)
¹/₂ tsp turmeric
300 ml/¹/₂ pint/1¹/₄ cups water
4 tbsp vegetable oil
1 large onion, finely sliced
2 cloves garlic, crushed
2 fresh green chillies, chopped
¹/₂ tsp mustard seeds
¹/₂ tsp cumin seeds
¹/₄ tsp asafoetida
few fresh coriander (cilantro) and mint leaves, chopped
6–8 curry leaves
salt, to taste
¹/₂ tsp sugar
200 g/7 oz canned tomatoes, chopped

225 g/8 oz courgettes (zucchini), cut into small pieces
4 tbsp lemon juice

I ▲ In a saucepan, boil the lentils and turmeric in the water and then simmer until the dhal is cooked but not mushy. Drain and reserve both the liquid and the dhal.

2 ▲ Heat the oil in a frying pan (skillet) and fry the remaining ingredients except the lemon juice. Cover and cook until the courgettes (zucchini) are nearly tender but still crunchy.

3 Fold in the drained dhal and the lemon juice. If the dish is too dry, add a small amount of the reserved water. Reheat and serve.

Green Gram and Rice (top) and Split Lentils with Courgettes (Zucchini)

Tarka Dhal

Tarka dhal is probably the most popular of lentil dishes and is found in most Indian/Pakistani restaurants.

SERVES 4

INGREDIENTS
115 g/4 oz/¹/2 cup masoor dhal (split red lentils)
50 g/2 oz/¹/4 cup moong dhal (small split yellow lentils)
600 ml/1 pint/2¹/2 cups water
1 tsp ginger pulp
1 tsp garlic pulp
¹/4 tsp turmeric
2 fresh green chillies, chopped
1¹/2 tsp salt

Tarka
2 tbsp vegetable oil
1 onion, sliced
¹/4 tsp mixed mustard and onion seeds
4 dried red chillies
1 tomato, sliced

Garnish
1 tbsp chopped fresh coriander (cilantro)
1–2 fresh green chillies, seeded and sliced
1 tbsp chopped fresh mint

NUTRITIONAL VALUES (per portion)

Total fat	6.61 g
Saturated fat	0.90 g
Cholesterol	0.00 mg
Energy (kcals/kj)	179/752

1 Pick over the lentils for any stones before washing them.

2 ▲ Boil the lentils in the water with the ginger, garlic, turmeric and chopped green chillies for 15–20 minutes or until soft.

3 ▲ Mash the lentil mixture down. The consistency of the mashed lentils should be similar to a creamy chicken soup.

4 ▲ If the mixture looks too dry, add more water. Season with the salt.

5 ▲ To prepare the tarka, heat the oil and fry the onion with the mustard and onion seeds, dried red chillies and sliced tomato for 2 minutes.

6 ▲ Pour the tarka over the dhal and garnish with fresh coriander (cilantro), green chillies and mint.

COOK'S TIP

Dried red chillies are available in many different sizes. If the ones you have are large, or if you want a less spicy flavour, reduce the quantity specified to 1–2.

Breads & Rice Dishes

Indian dishes are often served with breads and you'll find that Naan, Chapati and the deliciously flaky Paratha are surprisingly easy to make at home. Rice can be as plain or as exotic as you like — simply boiled, delicately spiced, or mixed with refreshing fruits as an accompaniment. It can also be layered with chicken and potatoes to make a tasty main meal.

Plain Boiled Rice

In India, rice is consumed in great quantities by all members of society. There are numerous ways in which it can be prepared, but plain boiled rice is the most common.

SERVES 4–6

INGREDIENTS
1 tbsp ghee, unsalted (sweet) butter or olive oil
350 g/12 oz/1¾ cups basmati rice, washed and drained
450 ml/¾ pint/scant 2 cups water
salt, to taste

1 ▲ Heat the ghee, butter or oil in a saucepan and sauté the drained rice thoroughly for about 2–3 minutes.

COOK'S TIP

To make a fragrantly spiced version, sauté 4–6 green cardamom pods, 4 cloves, 5 cm/2 in piece cinnamon stick, ½ tsp black cumin seeds and 2 bay leaves. Add 350 g/

2 ▲ Add the water and salt and bring to the boil. Reduce the heat to low, cover and cook gently for 15–20 minutes. To serve, fluff the grains gently with a fork.

12 oz/1¾ cups drained basmati rice and proceed as for plain boiled rice. For an even more luxurious rice, add 6–8 strands of saffron and sauté with the spices.

Fragrant Meat Pullao

This rice dish acquires its delicious taste not only from the spices but the richly flavoured meat stock.

SERVES 4–6

INGREDIENTS
900 g/2 lb chicken pieces, or lean lamb, cubed
600 ml/1 pint/2½ cups water
4 green cardamom pods
2 black cardamom pods
10 black peppercorns
4 cloves
1 medium onion, sliced
salt, to taste
450 g/1 lb/2¼ cups basmati rice, washed and drained
8–10 saffron strands
2 cloves garlic, crushed
1 piece fresh ginger, 5 cm/2 in long, crushed

1 piece cinnamon stick, 5 cm/2 in long
175 g/6 oz/1 cup sultanas (golden raisins) and blanched almonds, sautéed, to garnish

1 ▲ In a large saucepan, cook the chicken or lamb in the water with the cardamom pods, peppercorns, cloves, onion and salt until the meat is cooked. Remove the meat with a slotted spoon and keep warm. Strain the stock if you wish, and return to the saucepan.

2 ▼ Add the rice, saffron, garlic, ginger and cinnamon to the stock and bring the contents to the boil.

3 Quickly add the meat and stir well. Bring back to the boil, reduce the heat and cover. Cook covered for about 15–20 minutes. Remove from the heat and leave to stand for 5 minutes. Garnish with sultanas (golden raisins) and almonds and serve.

Plain Boiled Rice (top) and Fragrant Meat Pullao

Saffron and Cardamom Flavoured Rice

LOW-FAT RECIPE

There are two main ways of cooking rice: one is total absorption of water and the other is where you drain the water, which gets rid of any starch from the rice. For this recipe I have chosen the latter for obvious reasons.

SERVES 6

INGREDIENTS
450 g/1 lb/2¼ cups basmati rice
750 ml/1¼ pints/good 3 cups water
3 green cardamom pods
2 cloves
1 tsp salt
½ tsp crushed saffron strands
3 tbsp semi-skimmed (2%) milk

NUTRITIONAL VALUES (per portion)

Total fat	0.79 g
Saturated fat	0.19 g
Cholesterol	1.31 mg
Energy (kcals/kj)	264/1108

1 ▲ Wash the rice at least twice and place it in a medium saucepan with the water.

2 ▲ Toss all the whole spices into the saucepan along with the salt. Bring to the boil, cover and simmer for about 10 minutes.

3 Meanwhile, place the saffron and semi-skimmed (2%) milk in a small pan and warm. Alternatively, put the ingredients in a cup and warm for 1 minute in the microwave.

4 ▲ Now return to the rice to see if it is fully cooked. Use a slotted spoon to lift out a few grains and press the rice between your index finger and thumb. It should feel soft on the outside but still a little hard in the middle.

5 Remove the pan from the heat and carefully drain the rice through a sieve (strainer).

6 ▲ Transfer the rice back into the pan and pour the saffron and milk over the top of the rice.

7 ▲ Cover with a tight-fitting lid and place the pan back on a medium heat for 7–10 minutes.

8 After cooking, remove the pan from the heat and leave the rice to stand for a further 5 minutes before serving.

COOK'S TIP

Basmati rice is unequalled in flavour and texture and is the best variety to choose for Indian rice dishes. It is available from large supermarkets and Asian stores.

Rice Layered with Lentils

Bhori Muslims in India have their own special style of cooking and have adapted many of the traditional dishes from other Indian communities. This rice and lentil dish is served with a gourd curry, or Palida, which is prominently flavoured with fenugreek and soured with dried mangosteen (kokum). Lemon juice will provide the same effect.

SERVES 4–6

INGREDIENTS

175 g/6 oz/²/₃ cup bengal gram
600 ml/1 pint/2¹/₂ cups water
¹/₂ tsp turmeric
50 g/2 oz deep-fried onions, crushed
3 tbsp green masala paste
few fresh mint and coriander leaves, chopped
salt, to taste
350 g/12 oz/1³/₄ cups basmati rice, cooked
2 tbsp ghee
a little water

Curry

4 tbsp vegetable oil
¹/₄ tsp fenugreek seeds
15 g/¹/₂ oz dried fenugreek leaves
2 cloves garlic, crushed
1 tsp ground coriander
1 tsp cumin seeds
1 tsp chilli powder
4 tbsp gram flour mixed with 4 tbsp water
450 g/1 lb bottle gourd, peeled, pith and seeds removed and cut into bite-size pieces, or marrow (squash) or firm courgettes (zucchini) prepared in same way
175 ml/6 fl oz/³/₄ cup tomato juice
6 dried mangosteen (kokum), or juice of 3 lemons
salt, to taste

1 ▲ For the rice, boil the bengal gram in the water with the turmeric until the grains are soft but not mushy. Drain and reserve the water for the curry.

2 ▲ Toss the bengal gram gently with the deep-fried onions, green masala paste, chopped fresh mint and coriander, and salt.

3 ▲ Grease a heavy pan and place a layer of rice in the bottom. Add the bengal gram mixture and another layer of the remaining rice. Place small knobs of ghee on top, sprinkle with a little water and gently heat until steam gathers in the pan.

4 ▲ To make the curry, heat the oil in a pan and fry the fenugreek seeds and leaves and garlic until the garlic turns golden brown.

5 ▲ Mix the ground coriander, cumin and chilli powder to a paste with a little water. Add to the pan and simmer until all the water evaporates.

6 ▲ Add the remaining ingredients, and cook until the gourd is soft and transparent. Serve hot with the rice.

Colourful Pullao Rice

This lightly spiced rice makes an extremely attractive accompaniment to many Balti dishes, and is easily made.

SERVES 4–6

INGREDIENTS
450 g/1 lb/2⅓ cups basmati rice
75 g/3 oz/6 tbsp unsalted butter
4 cloves
4 green cardamom pods
1 bay leaf
1 tsp salt
1 litre/1¾ pints/4 cups water
a few drops each of yellow, green and red food colouring

I Wash the rice twice, drain and set aside in a sieve (strainer).

2 ▲ Melt the butter in a medium saucepan, and throw in the cloves, cardamoms, bay leaf and salt. Lower the heat and add the rice. Fry for about 1 minute, stirring constantly.

3 Add the water and bring to the boil. As soon as it has boiled, cover the pan and reduce the heat. Cook for 15–20 minutes.

4 ▲ Just before you are ready to serve the rice, pour a few drops of each colouring at different sides of the pan. Leave to stand for 5 minutes, mix gently and serve.

Fruity Pullao

SERVES 4–6

INGREDIENTS
450 g/1 lb/2⅓ cups basmati rice
75 g/3 oz/6 tbsp unsalted butter
1 tbsp corn oil
1 bay leaf
6 black peppercorns
4 green cardamom pods
1 tsp salt
75 g/3 oz/½ cup sultanas (golden raisins)
50 g/2 oz/½ cup flaked (slivered) almonds
1 litre/1¾ pints/4 cups water

I Wash the rice twice, drain and set aside in a sieve (strainer).

2 ▲ Heat the butter and oil in a medium saucepan. Lower the heat and throw in the bay leaf, peppercorns and cardamoms, and fry for about 30 seconds.

3 ▲ Add the rice, salt, sultanas (golden raisins) and flaked (slivered) almonds. Stir-fry for about 1 minute, then pour in the water. Bring to the boil, then cover with a tightly-fitting lid and lower the heat. Cook for 15–20 minutes.

4 Turn off the heat and leave the rice to stand, still covered, for about 5 minutes before serving.

Colourful Pullao Rice (top) and Fruity Pullao

Tomato Rice

This is delicious and can be eaten as a complete meal on its own.

SERVES 4

INGREDIENTS
2 tbsp corn oil
1/2 tsp onion seeds
1 medium onion, sliced
2 medium tomatoes, sliced
1 orange or yellow (bell) pepper, sliced
1 tsp ginger pulp
1 tsp garlic pulp
1 tsp chilli powder
2 tbsp chopped fresh coriander (cilantro)
1 medium potato, diced
1 1/2 tsp salt
50 g/2 oz/1/3 cup frozen peas
400 g/14 oz/2 cups basmati rice, washed
700 ml/24 fl oz/3 cups water

NUTRITIONAL VALUES (per portion)	
Total fat	6.48 g
Saturated fat	0.86 g
Cholesterol	0.00 mg
Energy (kcals/kj)	351/1475

1 ▲ Heat the oil and fry the onion seeds for about 30 seconds. Add the sliced onion and fry for about 5 minutes.

2 ▲ Start adding the sliced tomatoes, (bell) pepper, ginger, garlic, chilli powder, fresh coriander (cilantro), potatoes, salt and peas and stir-fry over a medium heat for a further 5 minutes.

3 Add the rice and stir for about 1 minute.

4 Pour in the water and bring to the boil, then lower the heat to medium. Cover and cook for 12–15 minutes. Leave the rice to stand for 5 minutes and then serve.

Pea and Mushroom Pullao

It is best to use button mushrooms and petit pois for this delectable rice dish as they make the pullao look truly attractive and appetizing.

SERVES 6

INGREDIENTS
2 tbsp vegetable oil
1/2 tsp black cumin seeds
2 black cardamom pods
2 cinnamon sticks
3 garlic cloves, sliced
1 tsp salt
1 medium tomato, sliced
50 g/2 oz/2/3 cup button mushrooms
450 g/1 lb/2 1/4 cups basmati rice
75 g/3 oz/heaped 1/3 cup petit pois
750 ml/1 1/4 pints/good 3 cups water

NUTRITIONAL VALUES (per portion)	
Total fat	4.34 g
Saturated fat	0.49 g
Cholesterol	0.00 mg
Energy (kcals/kj)	297/1246

1 Wash the rice at least twice and set aside in a sieve (strainer).

2 ▲ In a medium saucepan, heat the oil and add the spices, garlic and salt.

3 ▲ Add the sliced tomato and button mushrooms and stir-fry for 2–3 minutes.

4 Now add the rice and peas and gently stir around, making sure you do not break the rice.

5 Add the water and bring the mixture to the boil. Lower the heat, cover and continue to cook for 15–20 minutes.

Tomato Rice (top) and Pea and Mushroom Pullao

Rice Layered with Chicken and Potatoes

This dish, Murgh Biryani, is mainly prepared for important occasions, and is truly fit for royalty. Every cook in India has a subtle variation which is kept a closely guarded secret.

SERVES 4–6

INGREDIENTS

1.5 kg/3 lb chicken breast fillet, skinned and cut into large pieces
4 tbsp biryani masala paste
2 fresh green chillies, chopped
1 tbsp ginger pulp
1 tbsp garlic pulp
50 g/2 oz/2 cups fresh coriander (cilantro), chopped
6–8 fresh mint leaves, chopped, or 1 tsp mint sauce
150 ml/¼ pint/⅔ cup natural (plain) yogurt, beaten
2 tbsp tomato purée (paste)
4 onions, finely sliced, deep-fried and crushed
salt, to taste
450 g/1 lb/2¼ cups basmati rice, washed and drained
1 tsp black cumin seeds
1 piece cinnamon stick, 5 cm/2 in long
4 green cardamom pods
2 black cardamom pods
vegetable oil, for shallow-frying
4 large potatoes, peeled and quartered
175 ml/6 fl oz/¾ cup milk, mixed with 6 tbsp water
1 sachet saffron powder, mixed with 6 tbsp milk
2 tbsp ghee or unsalted (sweet) butter

Garnish

ghee or unsalted (sweet) butter, for shallow-frying
50 g/2 oz/⅓ cup cashew nuts
50 g/2 oz/⅓ cup sultanas (golden raisins)

1 ▲ Mix the chicken pieces with the next 10 ingredients in a large bowl and allow to marinate in a cool place for about 2 hours. Place in a large heavy pan and cook over a low heat for about 10 minutes. Set aside.

2 ▲ Boil a large pan of water and soak the rice with the cumin seeds, cinnamon stick and green and black cardamom pods for about 5 minutes. Drain well. If you prefer, some of the whole spices may be removed at this stage and discarded.

3 ▲ Heat the oil for shallow-frying and fry the potatoes until they are evenly browned on all sides. Drain the potatoes and set aside.

4 ▲ Place half the rice on top of the chicken in the pan in an even layer. Then make an even layer with the potatoes. Put the remaining rice on top of the potatoes and spread to make an even layer.

5 ▲ Sprinkle the water mixed with milk all over the rice. Make random holes through the rice with the handle of a spoon and pour into each a little saffron milk. Place a few knobs of ghee or butter on the surface, cover and cook over a low heat for 35–45 minutes.

6 ▲ While the biryani is cooking, make the garnish. Heat a little ghee or butter and fry the cashew nuts and sultanas (golden raisins) until they swell. Drain and set aside. When the biryani is ready, gently toss the rice, chicken and potatoes together, garnish with the nut mixture and serve hot.

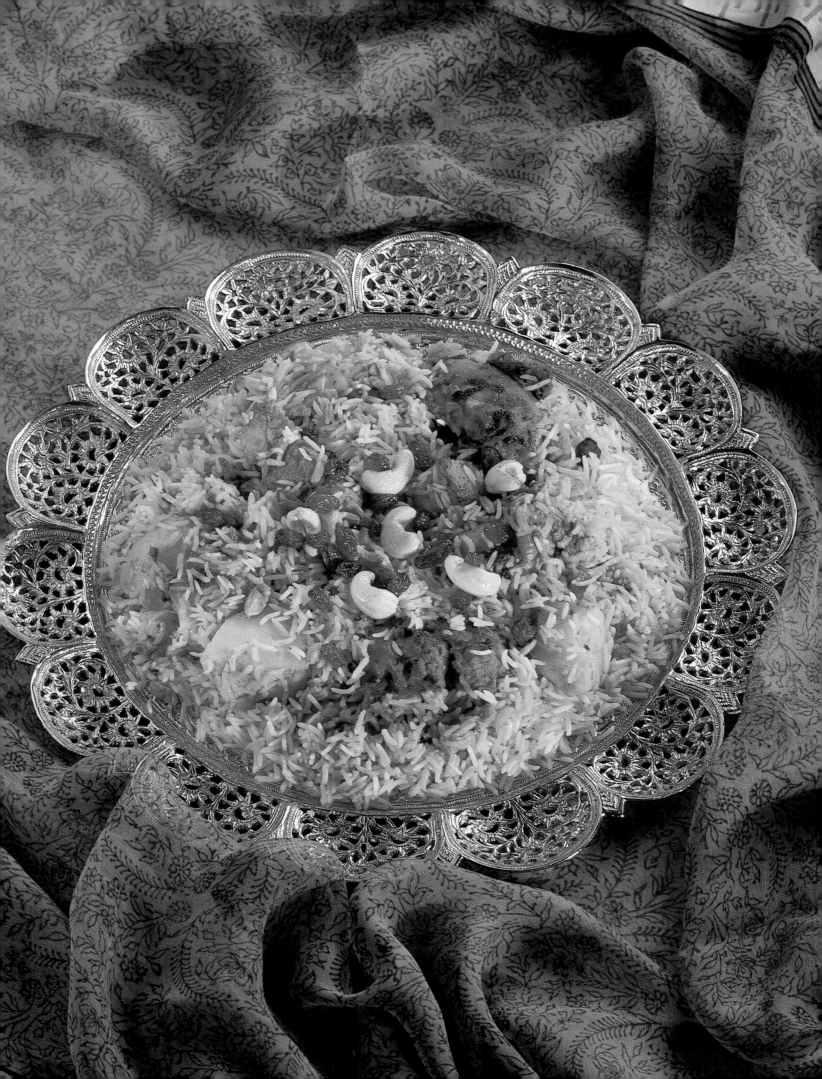

Chicken Pullao

This dish is a complete meal on its own, but is also delicious served with a lentil dish such as Tarka Dhal.

SERVES 4

INGREDIENTS

75 g/3 oz/6 tbsp low-fat margarine
1 medium onion, sliced
¹/4 tsp mixed onion and mustard seeds
3 curry leaves
1 tsp ginger pulp
1 tsp garlic pulp
1 tsp ground coriander
1 tsp chilli powder
1¹/2 tsp salt
2 tomatoes, sliced
1 medium potato, cubed
50 g/2 oz/¹/3 cup frozen peas
175 g/6 oz/1¹/4 cups chicken, skinned, boned and cubed
400 g/14 oz/2 cups basmati rice
4 tbsp chopped fresh coriander (cilantro)
2 fresh green chillies, chopped
700 ml/24 fl oz/3 cups water

NUTRITIONAL VALUES (per portion)	
Total fat	8.50 g
Saturated fat	1.96 g
Cholesterol	25.06 mg
Energy (kcals/kj)	406/1707

I Wash and soak the rice for 30 minutes, then set aside in a sieve (strainer).

2 ▲ In a medium saucepan, melt the low-fat margarine and fry the sliced onion until golden.

3 ▲ Add the onion and mustard seeds, the curry leaves, ginger, garlic, ground coriander, chilli powder and salt. Stir-fry for about 2 minutes.

4 ▲ Add the sliced tomatoes, cubed potato, peas and chicken and mix everything together well.

5 ▲ Add the rice and stir gently to combine with the other ingredients.

6 ▲ Finally, add the fresh coriander (cilantro) and chopped green chillies. Mix and stir-fry for a further 1 minute. Pour in the water.

7 Bring to the boil and lower the heat. Cover and cook for about 20 minutes.

Lamb Pullao

A pullao is a rice dish containing whole spices, which can either be plain or combined with meat, chicken or vegetables. Here it is made with minced (ground) lamb cooked in yogurt with a variety of spices. It makes a complete meal served on its own or served with Raita.

SERVES 4–6

INGREDIENTS
2 tbsp corn oil
1 tbsp unsalted butter or ghee
2 medium onions, sliced
1 tsp garlic pulp
1 tsp chilli powder
1/4 tsp ginger pulp
1/4 tsp turmeric
1 tsp garam masala
1 tsp salt
2 tbsp natural (plain) yogurt
2 medium tomatoes, sliced
450 g/1 lb lean minced (ground) lamb
2 tbsp chopped fresh coriander (cilantro)
2 medium fresh chillies, chopped
tomato slices (optional)

Rice
450 g/1 lb/2 1/4 cups basmati rice
1.2 litres/2 pints/5 cups water
4 cloves
4 green cardamom pods
1/2 tsp black cumin seeds
6 black peppercorns
1 1/2 tsp salt
1 tbsp chopped fresh coriander
2 fresh green chillies, chopped
1 tbsp lime juice
1/2 tsp saffron strands soaked in 2 tbsp milk
(optional)

1 Wash the rice twice, drain and set aside in a sieve (strainer).

2 Heat the oil and ghee in a deep round-bottomed frying pan (skillet) or a large karahi. Add the onions and fry until golden brown.

3 ▲ Lower the heat to medium and add the garlic, chilli powder, ginger, turmeric, garam masala, salt, yogurt and tomatoes and stir-fry gently for about 1 minute.

4 ▲ Add the minced (ground) lamb and turn up the heat to high. Use a slotted spoon to fry the lamb, scraping the bottom of the pan to prevent it from burning.

5 ▲ Add the fresh coriander (cilantro) and chillies, and continue to stir, breaking up any lumps in the meat as you work. Once the lamb is throughly cooked, set it to one side.

6 Put the rice into a large saucepan with the water, cloves, cardamoms, cumin seeds, peppercorns and salt, and bring to boil. When the rice has boiled for 2 minutes, drain off the water along with half the rice, leaving the rest in the saucepan.

7 ▲ Spread the cooked lamb over the rice in the saucepan and cover with the rice left in the strainer.

8 ▲ Add the fresh coriander, green chillies, lime juice and saffron in milk if using.

9 Cover the saucepan with a tight-fitting lid and cook over a very low heat for 15–20 minutes.

10 ▲ Check that the rice is cooked through and mix gently with a slotted spoon before serving. Garnish with slices of tomato if wished.

Rice Layered with Prawns (Shrimp)

This dish makes a meal in itself, requiring only pickles or Raita as an accompaniment. If serving for a party, complete your table with Boiled Egg Curry and Potatoes in a Red Hot Sauce.

SERVES 4–6

INGREDIENTS

2 large onions, finely sliced and deep-fried
300 ml/½ pint/1¼ cups natural (plain) yogurt
2 tbsp tomato purée (paste)
4 tbsp green masala paste
2 tbsp lemon juice
salt, to taste
1 tsp black cumin seeds
1 piece cinnamon stick, 5 cm/2 in long, or ¼ tsp ground cinnamon
4 green cardamom pods
450 g/1 lb fresh king prawns (jumbo shrimp), peeled and deveined
225 g/8 oz/2⅔ cups small whole button mushrooms
225 g/8 oz/1⅓ cups frozen peas, thawed and drained
450 g/1 lb/2¼ cups basmati rice soaked for 5 minutes in boiled water and drained
300 ml/½ pint/1¼ cups water
1 sachet saffron powder mixed with 6 tbsp milk
2 tbsp ghee or unsalted (sweet) butter

1 ▲ Mix the first 9 ingredients together in a large bowl. Fold the prawns (shrimp), mushrooms and peas into the marinade and set aside in a cool place for about 2 hours.

2 ▲ Grease the base of a heavy pan and add the prawns, vegetables and any marinade juices. Cover with the drained rice and smooth the surface gently until you have an even layer.

3 ▲ Pour the water all over the surface of the rice. Make random holes through the rice with the handle of a spoon and pour a little saffron milk into each hole.

4 ▲ Place a few knobs of ghee or butter on the surface and place a circular piece of foil directly on top of the rice. Cover and cook over a low heat for 45–50 minutes. Gently toss the rice, prawns and vegetables together and serve hot.

Paratha

A richer, softer and flakier variation on chapatis, Parathas require a longer preparation time so plan your menu well ahead. Like chapatis, Parathas can be kept warm wrapped in foil.

MAKES 12–15

INGREDIENTS
350 g/12 oz/2¼ cups chapati (ata) flour, or use wholemeal (whole-wheat) flour, plus extra for dusting
50 g/2 oz/½ cup plain (all-purpose) flour
salt, to taste
about 2 tbsp ghee, melted
water, to mix

1 ▲ Sift the flours and salt into a large mixing bowl. Make a well in the centre and add 2 tsp of the ghee and rub into the flour to make a crumbly texture. Very gradually add enough water to make a soft but pliable dough. Cover and leave to rest for 1 hour.

2 ▲ Divide the dough into 12–15 equal portions and keep covered. Take one portion at a time and roll out on a lightly floured surface into a circle about 10 cm/4 in in diameter. Brush with a little of the melted ghee and sprinkle with flour. With a sharp knife, make a straight cut from the centre to the edge.

3 ▲ Lift a cut edge and roll the dough into a cone shape.

4 Lift it and flatten it again into a ball. Roll the dough again on a floured surface into a circle about 17.5 cm/7 in in diameter.

5 ▲ Heat a griddle and cook one paratha at a time, placing a little of the remaining ghee along the edges. Cook the parathas on each side until golden brown. Serve hot.

Wholemeal (Whole-Wheat) Chapatis

Chapatis are prepared daily in most Indian homes. They are best eaten as soon as they are cooked although they can be kept warm, wrapped in foil and placed in a warm oven.

MAKES 10–12

INGREDIENTS
350 g/12 oz/2¼ cups chapati (ata) flour, or use wholemeal (whole-wheat) flour, plus extra for dusting
1 tsp salt
water, to mix
few drops of vegetable oil, for brushing
ghee or unsalted (sweet) butter, for spreading

1 ▲ Sift the flour and salt into a large bowl. Make a well in the centre and slowly add small quantities of water until you have a smooth but pliable dough. Grease the palms of your hands and knead the dough well. Keep covered until you are ready to use.

2 Divide the dough into 10–12 equal portions, using one portion at a time and keeping the rest covered. Knead each portion into a ball.

3 Flatten the ball with your hands and place on a floured surface. Roll out until you have a circle about 17.5 cm/ 7 in in diameter.

4 ▲ Heat a heavy griddle and, when hot, roast the chapatis on each side, pressing the edges down gently. When both sides are ready, brush the first side lightly with ghee or butter.

Naan

Traditionally, Naans are baked in a tandoor or clay oven, although these naans cooked in a conventional oven look just as authentic.

MAKES 6–8

INGREDIENTS
2 tsp dried (active dry) yeast
4 tbsp warm milk
2 tsp sugar
450 g/1 lb/4 cups plain (all-purpose) flour
1 tsp baking powder
½ tsp salt
150 ml/¼ pint/⅔ cup milk
150 ml/¼ pint/⅔ cup natural (plain) yogurt, beaten
1 egg, beaten
2 tbsp ghee, melted
flour, for dusting
ghee, for greasing
chopped fresh coriander (cilantro) and onion seeds, to sprinkle

1 ▲ Mix the yeast, warm milk and sugar and leave to become frothy. Sift together the flour, baking powder and salt. Make a well in the centre and add the yeast mixture, milk, yogurt, egg and ghee. Fold in all the ingredients.

2 Knead the dough well. Tightly cover the bowl and keep in a warm place until the dough doubles in size. To test, push a finger into the dough – it should spring back. Preheat the oven to 200°C/400°F/Gas 6. Roll out the dough on a floured surface.

3 ▲ Make each naan slipper-shaped, about 25 cm/10 in long and about 15 cm/6 in wide, tapering to 5 cm/2 in. Sprinkle with the coriander and onion seeds, Place on greased trays and bake in the preheated oven for 10–12 minutes.

Wholemeal (Whole-Wheat) Chapatis (top) and Naan

Side Dishes

Part of the charm of eating an Indian meal is the rich assortment of taste sensations. Cool and tangy Spiced Yogurt or Raita make a refreshing contrast to a fiery curry, while Mango Chutney and Fresh Coriander Relish add a piquant touch. Salads are often served as side dishes and a simple Tomato Salad or Avocado Salad are perfect to serve with many curried foods.

Sweet Potato and Carrot Salad

LOW-FAT RECIPE

This salad has a sweet-and-sour taste, and can be served warm as part of a meal or eaten in a larger quantity as a main course.

SERVES 4

INGREDIENTS
1 medium sweet potato
2 carrots, cut into thick diagonal slices
3 medium tomatoes
8–10 iceberg lettuce leaves
75 g/3 oz/½ cup canned chick-peas (garbanzos), drained

Dressing
1 tbsp clear honey
6 tbsp natural (plain) low-fat yogurt
½ tsp salt
1 tsp coarsely ground black pepper

Garnish
1 tbsp walnuts
1 tbsp sultanas (golden raisins)
1 small onion, cut into rings

NUTRITIONAL VALUES (per portion)	
Total fat	4.85 g
Saturated fat	0.58 g
Cholesterol	0.85 mg
Energy (kcals/kj)	176/741

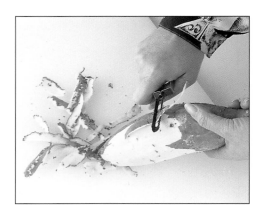

1 ▲ Peel the sweet potato and roughly dice. Boil until soft but not mushy, cover the pan and set aside.

2 Boil the carrots for a just a few minutes making sure they remain crunchy. Add the carrots to the sweet potatoes.

3 ▲ Drain the water from the sweet potatoes and carrots and place together in a bowl.

4 ▲ Slice the tops off the tomatoes, then scoop out and discard the seeds. Roughly chop the flesh.

5 ▲ Line a glass bowl with the lettuce leaves. Mix together the sweet potatoes, carrots, chick-peas (garbanzos) and tomatoes and place in the bowl.

6 ▲ Blend together all the dressing ingredients and beat using a fork.

7 ▲ Garnish with the walnuts, sultanas (golden raisins) and onion rings. Pour the dressing over the salad or serve it in a separate bowl, if wished.

Spiced Yogurt

Yogurt is always a welcome accompaniment to hot curries. This has been given a final fry with spices just to flavour the yogurt slightly.

MAKES 450 ML/¾ PINT/SCANT 2 CUPS

INGREDIENTS
450 ml/¾ pint/scant 2 cups plain yogurt
½ tsp freshly ground fennel seeds
salt, to taste
½ tsp sugar
4 tbsp vegetable oil
1 dried red chilli
¼ tsp mustard seeds
¼ tsp cumin seeds
4–6 curry leaves
pinch each, asafoetida and turmeric

1 ▲ In a heatproof serving dish, mix together the yogurt, fennel, salt and sugar and chill until you are nearly ready to serve.

2 ▲ Heat the oil in a frying pan (skillet) and fry the chilli, mustard and cumin seeds, curry leaves, asafoetida and turmeric. When the chilli turns dark, pour the oil and spices over the yogurt. Fold the yogurt together with the spices at the table before serving.

Raita

Raitas are served to cool the effect of hot curries. Cucumber and mint raita is most commonly served, so why not try a variation?

SERVES 4

INGREDIENTS
350 ml/12 fl oz/1½ cups natural (plain) yogurt
75 g/3 oz seedless grapes
50 g/2 oz shelled walnuts
2 firm bananas
1 tsp sugar
salt, to taste
1 tsp freshly ground cumin seeds
¼ tsp freshly roasted cumin seeds, chilli powder or paprika, to garnish

1 ▲ Place the yogurt in a chilled bowl and add the grapes and walnuts. Slice the bananas directly into the bowl and fold in gently before the bananas turn brown.

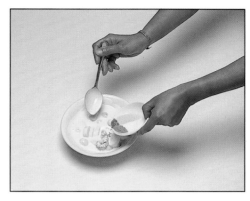

2 ▲ Add the sugar, salt and ground cumin, and gently mix together. Chill, and just before serving, sprinkle on the cumin seeds, chilli powder or paprika.

Spinach and Mushroom Salad

This salad is especially good served with the Glazed Garlic Prawns (Shrimp).

SERVES 4

INGREDIENTS
20 small spinach leaves
10 baby corn cobs
25 g/1 oz salad (garden) cress (optional)
115 g/4 oz/1½ cups mushrooms
8–10 onion rings
2 medium tomatoes
salt
crushed black peppercorns
2 fresh coriander (cilantro) sprigs
(optional)
3–4 lime slices (optional)

NUTRITIONAL VALUES (per portion)	
Total fat	0.93 g
Saturated fat	0.12 g
Cholesterol	0.00 mg
Energy (kcals/kj)	38/161

1 ▲ Halve the baby corn cobs, and slice the mushrooms and tomatoes.

2 ▲ Arrange all the salad ingredients in a bowl. Season with salt and pepper and garnish with fresh coriander (cilantro) and lime slices, if wished.

Nutty Salad

A delicious and filling salad which can be served as an accompaniment or as an appetizer.

SERVES 4

INGREDIENTS
1 medium onion, cut into 12 rings
115 g/4 oz/½ cup canned red kidney
*   beans, drained*
1 medium green courgette (zucchini),
*   sliced*
1 medium yellow courgette, sliced
50 g/2 oz/⅔ cup pasta shells, cooked
50 g/2 oz/½ cup cashew nuts
25 g/1 oz/¼ cup peanuts

Dressing
120 ml/4 fl oz/½ cup fromage frais
2 tbsp natural (plain) low-fat yogurt
1 fresh green chilli, chopped
1 tbsp chopped fresh coriander (cilantro)
½ tsp salt
½ tsp crushed black peppercorns

½ tsp crushed dried red chillies
1 tbsp lemon juice
lime wedges

NUTRITIONAL VALUES (per portion)	
Total fat	7.14 g
Saturated fat	1.09 g
Cholesterol	0.56 mg
Energy (kcals/kj)	153/642

1 Arrange the onion rings, red kidney beans, courgette (zucchini) slices and pasta in a salad dish and sprinkle the cashew nuts and peanuts over the top.

2 ▲ In a separate bowl, blend together the fromage frais, yogurt, green chilli, fresh coriander (cilantro) and salt and beat it well using a fork.

3 Sprinkle the black pepper, crushed red chillies and lemon juice over the dressing. Garnish the salad with the lime wedges and serve with the dressing in a separate bowl or poured over the salad.

Spinach and Mushroom Salad (top) and Nutty Salad

Tomato Salad

This is a simple relish served with most meals. It provides a contrast to hot curries, with its crunchy texture and refreshing ingredients.

SERVES 4–6

INGREDIENTS
2 limes
¹/₂ tsp sugar
salt and freshly ground black pepper,
*   to taste*
2 onions, finely chopped
4 firm tomatoes, finely chopped
¹/₂ cucumber, finely chopped
1 green chilli, finely chopped
few fresh coriander (cilantro) leaves,
*   chopped*
few fresh mint leaves, to garnish

1 ▲ Squeeze the juice of the limes into a glass bowl and add the sugar, salt and pepper. Allow to rest until the sugar and salt have dissolved, stirring occasionally. Mix together well.

2 ▲ Add the onions, tomatoes, cucumber, chilli and fresh coriander (cilantro) leaves. Chill, and garnish with mint before serving.

Fresh Coriander (Cilantro) Relish

Delicious as an accompaniment to kebabs, samosas and bhajias, this relish can also be used as a spread for cucumber or tomato sandwiches.

MAKES 400 G/14 OZ/1¾ CUPS

INGREDIENTS
2 tbsp vegetable oil
1 dried red chilli
¼ tsp each, cumin, fennel and onion seeds
¼ tsp asafoetida
4 curry leaves
115 g/4 oz/2 cups desiccated (shredded) coconut
2 tsp sugar
salt, to taste
3 fresh green chillies
175 g–225 g/6–8 oz fresh coriander (cilantro)
4 tbsp mint sauce
juice of 3 lemons

1 ▲ Heat the oil in a frying pan (skillet). Fry the dried chilli, the cumin, fennel and onion seeds, the asafoetida, curry leaves, desiccated (shredded) coconut, sugar and salt until the coconut turns golden brown. Cool.

2 ▲ Grind the spice mixture with the green chillies, fresh coriander (cilantro) and mint sauce. Moisten with lemon juice. Remove, and chill before serving.

Yogurt Salad

A delicious salad with a yogurt base, this is really an Eastern version of coleslaw.

SERVES 4

INGREDIENTS
350 ml/12 fl oz/1½ cups natural (plain) low-fat yogurt
2 tsp clear honey
2 medium carrots, thickly sliced
2 spring onions (scallions), roughly chopped
115 g/4 oz/1½ cups cabbage, finely shredded
50 g/2 oz/⅓ cup sultanas (golden raisins)
50 g/2 oz/½ cup cashew nuts
16 white grapes, halved
½ tsp salt
1 tsp chopped fresh mint
3–4 mint sprigs (optional)

NUTRITIONAL VALUES (per portion)	
Total fat	7.62 g
Saturated fat	1.20 g
Cholesterol	3.40 mg
Energy (kcals/kj)	201/846

I ▲ Using a fork, beat the yogurt in a bowl with the clear honey.

2 Mix together the carrots, spring onions (scallions), cabbage, sultanas (golden raisins), cashew nuts, grapes, salt and chopped mint.

3 ▲ Pour the yogurt mixture over the salad and blend everything together.

4 Transfer to a serving dish and garnish with the mint sprigs, if wished.

Spicy Baby Vegetable Salad

This warm vegetable salad makes an excellent accompaniment to almost any main course dish.

SERVES 6

INGREDIENTS
10 baby potatoes, halved
15 baby carrots
10 baby courgettes (zucchini)
115 g/4 oz/1½ cups button mushrooms

Dressing
3 tbsp lemon juice
1½ tbsp olive oil
1 tbsp chopped fresh coriander (cilantro)
1 tsp salt
2 small fresh green chillies, finely chopped

NUTRITIONAL VALUES (per portion)	
Total fat	3.54 g
Saturated fat	0.48 g
Cholesterol	0.00 mg
Energy (kcals/kj)	76/319

I Wash and boil all the baby vegetables until tender. Drain and place these in a serving dish.

2 ▲ In a separate bowl, mix together all the ingredients for the dressing.

3 Toss the vegetables in the dressing and serve.

Yogurt Salad (top) and Spicy Baby Vegetable Salad

Avocado Salad

In India, avocados are called butter fruit, reflecting their subtle taste. This delicate dish makes a good appetizer.

SERVES 4

INGREDIENTS
2 avocados
5 tbsp natural (plain) yogurt, beaten
115 g/4 oz/¹/₂ cup cottage cheese with chives
1 clove garlic, crushed
2 fresh green chillies, finely chopped
salt and pepper, to taste
lemon juice
mixed salad leaves, shredded
paprika and fresh mint leaves, to garnish

1 ▲ Halve the avocados and remove the stones (pits). Gently scoop out the flesh, reserving the skins, and cut into small cubes. In a bowl, mix the yogurt, cottage cheese, garlic, chillies and salt and pepper and fold in the avocado cubes. Chill in the refrigerator.

2 ▲ Rub the avocado skins with some lemon juice and line each cavity with some shredded salad leaves. Top with the chilled mixture, garnish with the paprika and mint leaves and serve immediately.

Indian Fruit Salad

This is a very appetizing and refreshing salad, with a typically Indian combination of citrus fruits seasoned with salt and pepper. It will provide the perfect ending to a heavy meal.

SERVES 6

INGREDIENTS
115 g/4 oz seedless green and black grapes
225 g/8 oz canned mandarin segments, drained
2 navel oranges, peeled and segmented
225 g/8 oz canned grapefruit segments, drained
1 honeydew melon cut into balls
¹/₂ watermelon cut into balls
1 fresh mango, peeled and sliced
juice of 1 lemon

salt and freshly ground black pepper, to taste
¹/₂ tsp sugar
¹/₄ tsp freshly ground cumin seeds

2 ▲ Mix together the remaining ingredients and sprinkle over the fruit. Gently toss, chill thoroughly and serve.

1 ▲ Place all the fruit in a large serving bowl and add the lemon juice. Toss gently to prevent damaging the fruit.

Avocado Salad (top) and Indian Fruit Salad

Tomato Chutney

This delicious relish is especially suited to lentil dishes. If kept refrigerated, it can be made a week before serving.

MAKES 450–500 G/16–18 OZ/2–2¼ CUPS

INGREDIENTS
6 tbsp vegetable oil
1 piece cinnamon stick, 5 cm/2 in long
4 cloves
1 tsp freshly roasted cumin seeds
1 tsp nigella seeds
4 bay leaves
1 tsp mustard seeds, crushed
4 cloves garlic, crushed
1 piece fresh ginger, 5 cm/2 in long, crushed
1 tsp chilli powder
1 tsp turmeric
4 tbsp brown sugar

800 g/1¾ lb canned, chopped tomatoes, drained (reserving juices)

1 ▲ Heat the oil over a medium heat and fry the cinnamon, cloves, cumin and nigella seeds, bay leaves and mustard seeds for about 5 minutes. Add the garlic and fry until golden.

2 ▲ Add the ginger, chilli powder, turmeric, sugar and the reserved tomato juices. Simmer until reduced, add the tomatoes and cook for 15–20 minutes. Cool and serve.

Mango Chutney

Chutneys are usually served as an accompaniment to curry but this one is particularly nice served in a cheese sandwich or as a dip with papadums.

MAKES 450 G/I LB/2 CUPS

INGREDIENTS
4 tbsp malt vinegar
1/2 tsp crushed dried chillies
6 cloves
6 peppercorns
1 tsp roasted cumin seeds
1/2 tsp onion seeds
salt, to taste
175 g/6 oz/3/4 cup sugar
450 g/1 lb green (unripe) mango, peeled and cubed
1 piece fresh ginger, 5 cm/2 in long, finely sliced

2 cloves garlic, crushed
thin peel of 1 orange or lemon (optional)

I ▲ In a saucepan, heat the vinegar with the chillies, cloves, peppercorns, cumin and onion seeds, salt and sugar. Simmer until the flavours of the spices infuse into the vinegar – about 15 minutes on a low heat.

2 ▲ Add the mango, ginger, garlic and peel, if using. Simmer until the mango is mushy and most of the vinegar has evaporated. When cool, pour into sterilized bottles. Leave for a few days before serving.

Hot Lime Pickle

A good lime pickle is not only delicious served with any meal, but it increases the appetite and aids digestion.

MAKES 450 G/1 LB/2 CUPS

INGREDIENTS
25 limes
225 g/8 oz salt
50 g/2 oz fenugreek powder
50 g/2 oz mustard powder
150 g/5 oz chilli powder
15 g/½ oz turmeric
600 ml/1 pint/2½ cups mustard oil
1 tsp asafoetida
25 g/1 oz yellow mustard seeds, crushed

1 ▲ Cut each lime into 8 pieces and remove the pips, if you wish. Place the limes in a large sterilized jar or glass bowl. Add the salt and toss with the limes. Cover and leave in a warm place for 1–2 weeks, until they become soft and dull brown in colour.

2 Mix together the fenugreek, mustard powder, chilli powder and turmeric and add to the limes.

3 Cover and leave to rest in a warm place for a further 2 or 3 days.

4 ▲ Heat the mustard oil in a frying pan and fry the asafoetida and mustard seeds. When the oil reaches smoking point, pour it over the limes. Mix well, cover with a clean cloth and leave in a warm place for about 1 week before serving.

Green Chilli Pickle

Southern India is the source of some of the hottest curries and pickles, which are said to cool the body.

MAKES 450–550 G/1–1¼ LB/2–2½ CUPS

INGREDIENTS
50 g/2 oz yellow mustard seeds, crushed
50 g/2 oz freshly ground cumin seeds
25 g/1 oz turmeric
50 g/2 oz garlic cloves, crushed
150 ml/¼ pint/⅔ cup white vinegar
75 g/3 oz/⅓ cup sugar
2 tsp salt
150 ml/¼ pint/⅔ cup mustard oil
20 small garlic cloves
450 g/1 lb small fresh green chillies, halved

1 ▲ Mix the mustard and cumin seeds, the turmeric, crushed garlic, vinegar, sugar and salt together in a sterilized glass bowl. Cover with a cloth and allow to rest for 24 hours. This enables the spices to infuse and the sugar and salt to melt.

2 Heat the mustard oil in a frying pan (skillet) and gently fry the spice mixture for about 5 minutes. (Keep a window open while cooking with mustard oil as it is pungent and the smoke may irritate the eyes.) Add the garlic cloves and fry for a further 5 minutes.

3 ▲ Add the chillies and cook gently until tender but still green in colour. This will take about 30 minutes on a low heat. Cool thoroughly and pour into sterilized bottles, ensuring the oil is evenly distributed if you are using more than one bottle. Leave to rest for a week before serving.

Hot Lime Pickle (top) and Green Chilli Pickle

Apricot Chutney

Chutneys can add zest to most meals, and in Pakistan you will usually find a selection of different kinds served in tiny bowls for people to choose from. Dried apricots are readily available from supermarkets or health food shops.

MAKES ABOUT 450 g/1 lb

INGREDIENTS

450 g/1 lb/3 cups dried apricots, finely diced
1 tsp garam masala
275 g/10 oz/1¼ cups soft light brown sugar
450 ml/¾ pint/scant 2 cups malt vinegar
1 tsp ginger pulp
1 tsp salt
75 g/3 oz/½ cup sultanas (golden raisins)
450 ml/¾ pint/scant 2 cups water

1 ▲ Put all the ingredients into a medium saucepan and mix together thoroughly.

2 ▲ Bring to the boil, then turn down the heat and simmer for 30–35 minutes, stirring occasionally.

3 When the chutney has thickened to a fairly stiff consistency, transfer into 2–3 clean jam jars and leave to cool. This chutney should be stored in the refrigerator.

Tasty Toasts

These crunchy toasts make an ideal snack or part of a brunch. They are especially delicious served with grilled (broiled) tomatoes and baked beans.

MAKES 4

INGREDIENTS

4 eggs
300 ml/½ pint/1¼ cups milk
2 fresh green chillies, finely chopped
2 tbsp chopped fresh coriander (cilantro)
75 g/3 oz/¾ cup Cheddar or mozzarella cheese, grated
½ tsp salt
¼ tsp freshly ground black pepper
4 slices bread
corn oil for frying

1 Break the eggs into a medium bowl and whisk together. Slowly add the milk and whisk again. Add the chillies, coriander (cilantro), cheese, salt and pepper.

2 Cut the bread slices in half diagonally, and soak them, one at a time, in the egg mixture.

3 ▼ Heat the oil in a medium frying pan (skillet) and fry the bread slices over a medium heat, turning them once or twice, until they are golden brown.

4 Drain off any excess oil as you remove the toasts from the pan and serve immediately.

Apricot Chutney (top) and Tasty Toasts

Desserts & Drinks

After a hot, spicy meal, Mango Sorbet with Sauce is a welcome, light dessert, while Light Vermicelli Pudding — delicately flavoured with saffron and tossed with coconut, almonds and pistachios — is ideal after a less substantial main course. On a hot day, or with hot food, there is no substitute for Sweet Lassi, a refreshing and delicious chilled yogurt drink.

Rich Rice Pudding

Both Muslim and Hindu communities prepare Kheer, which is traditionally served at mosques and temples.

SERVES 4–6

INGREDIENTS
1 tbsp ghee
1 piece cinnamon stick, 5 cm/2 in long
175 g/6 oz/³⁄4 cup soft brown sugar
115 g/4 oz/1 cup coarsely ground rice
1.2 litres/2 pints/5 cups full cream (whole) milk
1 tsp ground cardamom
50 g/2 oz/¹⁄3 cup sultanas (golden raisins)
25 g/1 oz/¹⁄4 cup flaked (slivered) almonds
¹⁄2 tsp freshly ground nutmeg, to serve

1 ▲ In a heavy pan, melt the ghee and fry the cinnamon and sugar. Keep frying until the sugar begins to caramelize. Reduce the heat immediately when this happens.

2 Add the rice and half the milk. Bring to the boil, stirring constantly to avoid the milk boiling over. Reduce the heat and simmer until the rice is cooked, stirring regularly.

3 ▲ Add the remaining milk, cardamom, sultanas (golden raisins) and almonds and leave to simmer, but keep stirring to prevent the kheer from sticking to the base of the pan. When the mixture has thickened, serve hot or cold, sprinkled with the nutmeg.

Classic Vermicelli Pudding

This sweet is prepared by Muslims very early in the morning of Id-ul-Fitr, the feast after the 30 days of Ramadan.

SERVES 4–6

INGREDIENTS
6 tbsp ghee
115 g/4 oz/1 cup vermicelli, coarsely broken
25 g/1 oz/¹⁄4 cup flaked (slivered) almonds
25 g/1 oz/¹⁄4 cup pistachios, slivered
25 g/1 oz cudapah nuts
50 g/2 oz/¹⁄3 cup sultanas (golden raisins)
50 g/2 oz dates, stoned (pitted) and slivered
1.2 litres/2 pints/5 cups full cream (whole) milk
4 tbsp dark brown sugar
1 sachet saffron powder

1 ▲ Heat 4 tbsp of the ghee in a frying pan (skillet) and sauté the vermicelli until golden brown. (If you are using the Italian variety, sauté it a little longer.) Remove and set aside.

2 Heat the remaining ghee and fry the nuts, sultanas (golden raisins) and dates until the sultanas swell. Add to the vermicelli.

3 ▲ Heat the milk in a large heavy pan and add the sugar. Bring to the boil, add the vermicelli mixture and boil, stirring constantly. Reduce the heat and simmer until the vermicelli is soft and you have a fairly thick pudding. Fold in the saffron powder and serve hot or cold.

Rich Rice Pudding (top) and Classic Vermicelli Pudding

Melon and Strawberry Salad

A beautiful and colourful fruit salad, this is suitable to serve as a refreshing appetizer or to round off a meal.

SERVES 4

INGREDIENTS
1 galia melon
1 honeydew melon
½ watermelon
225 g/8 oz fresh strawberries
1 tbsp lemon juice
1 tbsp clear honey
1 tbsp chopped fresh mint
1 mint sprig (optional)

NUTRITIONAL VALUES (per portion)	
Total fat	0.84 g
Saturated fat	0.00 g
Cholesterol	0.00 mg
Energy (kcals/kj)	139/584

1 ▲ Prepare the melons by cutting them in half and discarding the seeds. Use a melon baller to scoop out the flesh into balls or a knife to cut it into cubes. Place these in a fruit bowl.

2 Rinse and take the stems off the strawberries, cut these in half and add them to the fruit bowl.

3 ▲ Mix together the lemon juice and clear honey and add about 1 tbsp of water to make this easier to pour over the fruit. Mix into the fruit gently.

4 ▲ Sprinkle the chopped mint over the top of the fruit. Serve garnished with the mint sprig, if wished.

COOK'S TIP

Use whichever melons are available: replace galia with cantaloupe or watermelon with charentais, for example. Try to choose three melons with a variation in colour for an attractive effect.

Caramel with Fresh Fruit

LOW-FAT RECIPE

A creamy caramel dessert is a wonderful way to end a meal. It is light and delicious, and this recipe is very simple.

SERVES 6

INGREDIENTS
Caramel
2 tbsp sugar
2 tbsp water

Custard
6 medium eggs
4 drops vanilla essence (extract)
8–10 tbsp sugar
750 ml/1¼ pints/good 3 cups semi-skimmed (2%) milk
fresh fruit for serving

NUTRITIONAL VALUES (per portion)

Total fat	7.40 g
Saturated fat	2.77 g
Cholesterol	201.25 mg
Energy (kcals/kj)	229/964

1 To make the caramel, place the sugar and water in a heatproof dish and place in a microwave and cook for 4 minutes on high or until the sugar has caramelized. Or melt in a pan until pale gold in colour. Pour into a 1.2 litre/2 pint/5 cup soufflé dish. Leave to cool.

2 ▲ Preheat the oven to 180°C/350°F/Gas 4. To make the custard, break the eggs into a medium mixing bowl and whisk until frothy.

3 ▲ Stir in the vanilla essence (extract) and gradually add the sugar then the milk, whisking continuously.

4 ▲ Pour the custard over the top of the caramel.

5 Cook in the preheated oven for 35–40 minutes. Remove from the oven and leave to cool for about 30 minutes or until set.

6 Loosen the custard from the sides of the dish with a knife. Place a serving dish upside-down on top of the soufflé dish and invert, giving a gentle shake.

7 Arrange any fruit of your choice around the caramel and serve. Strawberries, blueberries, orange rings, banana slices and raspberries form the colourful array shown here.

Indian Ice Cream

Kulfi-wallahs (ice cream vendors) have always made kulfi, and continue to this day, without using modern freezers. Kulfi is packed into metal cones sealed with dough and then churned in clay pots until set. Try this method – it works extremely well in an ordinary freezer.

SERVES 4–6

INGREDIENTS

3 × 400 ml/14 fl oz cans evaporated milk
3 egg whites, whisked until peaks form
350 g/12 oz/3 cups icing (confectioners')
 sugar
1 tsp ground cardamom
1 tbsp rose water
175 g/6 oz/1 1/2 cups pistachios, chopped
75g/3oz/1/2 cup sultanas (golden raisins)
75 g/3 oz/3/4 cup flaked (slivered) almonds
25 g/1 oz/3 tbsp glacé (candied) cherries,
 halved

1 ▲ Remove the labels from the cans of evaporated milk and lay the cans down into a pan with a tight-fitting cover. Fill the pan with water to reach three-quarters up the cans. Bring to the boil, cover and simmer for 20 minutes. When cool, remove and chill the cans in the refrigerator for 24 hours.

2 ▲ Open the cans and empty the milk into a large, chilled bowl. Whisk until it doubles in quantity, then fold in the whisked egg whites and icing (confectioners') sugar.

3 ▲ Gently fold in the remaining ingredients, seal the bowl with cling film (plastic wrap) and leave in the freezer for 1 hour.

4 ▲ Remove the ice cream from the freezer and mix well with a fork. Transfer to a serving container and return to the freezer for a final setting. Remove from the freezer 10 minutes before serving.

Mango Sorbet (Sherbet) with Sauce

After a heavy meal, this makes a very refreshing dessert. Mango is said to be one of the oldest fruits cultivated in India, having been brought by Lord Shiva for his beautiful wife, Parvathi.

SERVES 4–6

INGREDIENTS
900 g/2 lb mango pulp
½ tsp lemon juice
grated rind of 1 orange and 1 lemon
4 egg whites, whisked until peaks form
50 g/2 oz/¼ cup caster (superfine) sugar
120 ml/4 fl oz/½ cup double (heavy) cream
50 g/2 oz/½ cup icing (confectioners') sugar

3 ▲ Remove and beat again. Transfer to an ice cream container, and freeze until fully set.

4 ▲ Whip the double (heavy) cream with the icing (confectioners') sugar and the remaining mango pulp. Chill the sauce for 24 hours. Remove the sorbet (sherbet) 10 minutes before serving. Scoop out individual servings and cover with a generous helping of mango sauce. Serve immediately.

I ▲ In a large, chilled bowl, mix half of the mango pulp, with the lemon juice and the grated rind.

2 ▲ Gently fold in the egg whites and caster (superfine) sugar. Cover with cling film (plastic wrap) and place in the freezer for at least 1 hour.

Ground Rice Pudding

LOW-FAT RECIPE

This delicious and light ground rice pudding is the perfect end to a spicy meal. It can be served hot or cold.

SERVES 4–6

INGREDIENTS
50 g/2 oz/¹/₂ cup coarsely ground rice
25 g/1 oz/2 tbsp ground almonds
4 green cardamom pods, crushed
900 ml/1¹/₂ pints/3³/₄ cups semi-skimmed (2%) milk
6 tbsp sugar
1 tbsp rose water

Garnish
1 tbsp crushed pistachio nuts
silver leaf (varq) (optional)

NUTRITIONAL VALUES (per portion)	
Total fat	8.78 g
Saturated fat	2.57 g
Cholesterol	14.70 mg
Energy (kcals/kj)	201/844

1 ▲ Place the ground rice and almonds in a saucepan with the green cardamoms. Add 600 ml/1 pint/2¹/₂ cups milk and bring to the boil over a medium heat, stirring occasionally.

2 ▲ Add the remaining milk and cook over a medium heat for about 10 minutes or until the rice mixture thickens to the consistency of a creamy chicken soup.

3 Stir in the sugar and rose water and continue to cook for a further 2 minutes. Serve garnished with pistachio nuts and silver leaf, if wished.

Vermicelli

LOW-FAT RECIPE

Indian vermicelli, made from wheat, is much finer than Italian vermicelli and is readily available from Asian stores.

SERVES 4

INGREDIENTS
115 g/4 oz/1 cup vermicelli
1.2 litres/2 pints/5 cups water
¹/₂ tsp saffron strands
1 tbsp sugar
4 tbsp low-fat fromage frais (optional)

Garnish
1 tbsp shredded fresh coconut, or desiccated (shredded) coconut
1 tbsp flaked (slivered) almonds
1 tbsp chopped pistachio nuts
1 tbsp sugar

NUTRITIONAL VALUES (per portion)	
Total fat	4.61 g
Saturated fat	1.66 g
Cholesterol	0.15 mg
Energy (kcals/kj)	319/1341

1 ▲ Crush the vermicelli in your hands and place in a saucepan. Pour in the water, add the saffron and bring to the boil. Boil for about 5 minutes.

2 ▲ Stir in the sugar and continue cooking until the water has evaporated. Strain through a sieve (strainer), if necessary, to remove any excess liquid.

3 Place the vermicelli in a serving dish and garnish with the shredded coconut, almonds, pistachio nuts and sugar. Serve with fromage frais, if wished.

Ground Rice Pudding (top) and Vermicelli

Tea and Fruit Punch

This delicious punch may be served hot or cold. White wine or brandy may be added to taste.

MAKES 875 ML/1¾ PINTS/3½ CUPS

INGREDIENTS
600 ml/1 pint/2½ cups water
1 cinnamon stick
4 cloves
2½ tsp Earl Grey tea leaves
175 g/6 oz/¾ cup sugar
450 ml/¾ pint/1½ cups tropical soft
 drink concentrate
1 lemon, sliced
1 small orange, sliced
½ cucumber, sliced

1 ▲ Bring the water to the boil in a saucepan with the cinnamon and cloves. Remove from the heat and add the tea leaves and allow to brew for 5 minutes. Stir and strain into a large chilled bowl.

2 ▲ Add the sugar and the soft drink concentrate and allow to rest until the sugar has dissolved and the mixture cooled. Place the fruit and cucumber in a chilled punch bowl and pour over the tea mix. Chill for 24 hours before serving.

Lassi

Lassi or buttermilk is prepared by churning yogurt with water and then removing the fat. To make this refreshing drink without churning, use low-fat natural (plain) yogurt.

SERVES 4

INGREDIENTS
450 ml/¾ pint/1½ cups natural (plain)
 yogurt
300 ml/½ pint/1¼ cups water
1 piece fresh ginger, 2.5 cm/1 in long,
 finely crushed
2 green chillies, finely chopped
½ tsp ground cumin
salt and freshly ground black pepper,
 to taste
few fresh coriander (cilantro) leaves,
 chopped, to garnish

1 ▲ In a bowl, whisk the yogurt and water until well blended. The consistency should be that of full cream (whole) milk. Adjust by adding more water if necessary.

2 ▲ Add the ginger, chillies and ground cumin, season with the salt and pepper and mix well. Divide into 4 serving glasses and chill. Garnish with coriander (cilantro) before serving.

Tea and Fruit Punch (top) and Lassi

Sweet Lassi

Lassi is a very popular drink both in India and Pakistan. It is available not only from roadside cafés but is also a great favourite in good restaurants and hotels. There is no substitute for this drink, especially on a hot day. It is ideal served with hot dishes as it helps the body to digest spicy food.

SERVES 4

INGREDIENTS
300 ml/½ pint/1¼ cups natural (plain) low-fat yogurt
1 tsp sugar, or to taste
300 ml/½ pint/1¼ cups water
2 tbsp puréed fruit (optional)
1 tbsp crushed pistachio nuts

NUTRITIONAL VALUES (per portion)	
Total fat	1.91 g
Saturated fat	0.52 g
Cholesterol	2.80 mg
Energy (kcals/kj)	60/251

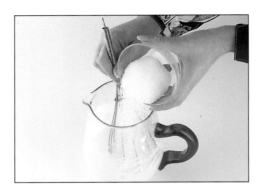

1 ▲ Place the yogurt in a jug and whisk it for about 2 minutes until frothy. Add the sugar to taste.

2 ▲ Pour in the water and the puréed fruit, if using, and continue to whisk for 2 minutes.

3 Pour the lassi into serving glasses. Serve chilled, decorated with crushed pistachio nuts.

Almond Sherbet

Traditionally this drink was always made in the month of Ramaden, when we used to break our fast. It should be served chilled. ·

SERVES 4

INGREDIENTS
50 g/2 oz/½ cup ground almonds
600 ml/1 pint/2½ cups semi-skimmed (2%) milk
2 tsp sugar, or to taste

NUTRITIONAL VALUES (per portion)	
Total fat	6.15 g
Saturated fat	1.70 g
Cholesterol	9.80 mg
Energy (kcals/kj)	117/492

2 ▲ Pour in the milk and sugar and stir to mix. Taste for sweetness and serve chilled.

1 ▲ Put the ground almonds into a jug.

Lassi flavoured with puréed raspberries (left) and Almond Sherbet

Stockists and Suppliers

United Kingdom

M. and S. Patel
372–382 Romford Road
London E7 8BS
(0181) 472-6201

Rafi's Spice Box
c/o 31 Schoolfield
Glemsford
Suffolk CO10 7RE
(mail order)

The Spice Shop
115–117 Drummond Street
London NW1 2HL
(0171) 387-4526

United States

Arizona

G&L Import-Export Corp.
4828 East 22nd Street
Tuscon
Arizona 85706
(602) 790-9016

Manila Oriental Foodmart
3557 West Dunlap Avenue
Phoenix
Arizona 85021
(602) 841-2977

California

Indian Food Mill
650 San Bruno Avenue East
San Bruno
California 94014
(415) 583-6559

Connecticut

India Spice & Gift Shop
3295 Fairfield Avenue
Fairfield
Connecticut 06605
(203) 384-0666

Florida

Grocery Mahat & Asian Spices
1026 South Military Trail
West Palm Beach
Florida 334436
(407) 433-3936

Illinois

Indian Groceries & Spices
7300 St Louis Avenue
Skokie
Illinois 60076
(708) 2480

Maryland

India Supermarket
8107 Fenton Street
Silver Springs
Maryland 20910
(301) 589-8423

Massachusetts

India Groceries
Oak Square
Boston
Massachusetts 02111
(617) 254-5540

New Jersey

Maharaja Indian Foods
130 Speedwell Avenue
Morristown
New Jersey 07960
(210) 829-0048

New York

Indian Groceries and Spices
61 Wythe Avenue
Brooklyn
New York 11211
(718) 963-0477

Ohio

Crestview Market
200 Crestview Road
Columbus
Ohio 43202
(614) 267-2723

Pennsylvania

Gourmail Inc.
Drawer 516
Berwyn
Pennsylvania 19312
(215) 296-4620

Texas

MGM Indian Foods
9200 Lamar Boulevard
Austin
Texas 78513
(512) 835 6937

Index

Almonds, 10
    almond sherbet, 250
    chicken and almond soup, 17
    vegetables with almonds, 183
Aniseed, 10
Apricot chutney, 236
Asafoetida, 10
Aubergines (eggplants): balti vegetables stuffed
    with lamb, 112
    stuffed aubergines with lamb, 108
Avocado salad, 230

Balti dishes, 6
    balti baby vegetables, 162
    balti baby chicken in tamarind sauce, 64
    balti butter chicken, 54
    balti chicken, 42
    balti chicken in saffron sauce, 50
    balti chicken pasanda, 77
    balti chicken with lentils, 58
    balti chicken with vegetables, 46
    balti chilli chicken, 47
    balti fish fillets in spicy coconut sauce, 131
    balti fried fish, 124
    balti lamb chops with potatoes, 31
    balti lamb tikka, 82
    balti minced (ground) lamb koftas with
        vegetables, 98
    balti minced (ground) lamb with potatoes and
        fenugreek, 83
    balti mini lamb kebabs (kabobs) with baby
        onions, 106
    balti prawns (shrimp) and vegetables in thick
        sauce, 142
    balti prawns (shrimp) in hot sauce, 134
    balti vegetables stuffed with lamb, 112
    chicken and pasta balti, 30
    chicken and tomato balti, 68
    chunky fish balti with peppers, 130
    karahi chicken with fresh fenugreek, 75
    karahi chicken with mint, 74
    khara masala balti chicken, 72
    paneer balti with prawns (shrimp), 138
    seafood balti with vegetables, 148
    spicy balti potatoes, 180
    sweet-and-sour balti chicken, 76
Bananas: raita, 222
Bay leaves, 10
Beef: beef Madras, 110
    beef with green beans, 114
    koftas, 96
    potato cakes with stuffing, 23
    spicy meat loaf, 96
    steak and kidney with spinach, 116
Bell peppers *see* Peppers
Bengal gram, 10
    Bengal gram and bottle gourd curry, 190
    lentils seasoned with fried spices, 186
Bhajias, onion, 14
Biryani: rice layered with chicken and
    potatoes, 208
Black-eyed peas, 10
    black-eyed peas and potato curry, 190
Black gram in a spicy cream sauce, 189
Bombay duck pickle, 152
Bombay potato, 158

Bomil: Bombay duck pickle, 152
Bottle gourds: Bengal gram and bottle gourd
    curry, 190
    rice layered with lentils, 202
Bread: naan, 216
    paratha, 215
    wholemeal (whole-wheat) chapatis, 216
Butter chicken, balti, 54

Cabbage: karahi shredded cabbage with cumin, 173
    spicy cabbage, 170
Caramel with fresh fruit, 243
Cardamom, 10
    saffron and cardamom flavoured rice, 200
Carrots: spiced potatoes and carrots parisienne, 172
    sweet potato and carrot salad, 220
Cashew nuts, 10
    chicken in a cashew nut sauce, 44
    nutty salad, 224
Cauliflower, curried, 158
Chana dhal, 10
    balti chicken with lentils, 58

    lentils with lamb and tomatoes, 118
Chapati flour, 10
Chapatis, wholemeal (whole-wheat), 216
Cheese: baked potato with spicy cottage cheese, 36
    mushrooms, peas and paneer, 169
    sweet-and-sour vegetables with paneer, 176
    tasty toasts, 236
Chick-peas (garbanzos), 10
    curried chick-peas (garbanzos) with potato
        cakes, 188
Chicken: balti baby chicken in tamarind sauce, 64
    balti butter chicken, 54
    balti chicken, 42
    balti chicken in saffron sauce, 50
    balti chicken pasanda, 77
    balti chicken with lentils, 58
    balti chicken with vegetables, 46
    balti chilli chicken, 47
    chicken and almond soup, 17
    chicken and pasta balti, 30
    chicken and tomato balti, 68
    chicken curry, 57
    chicken in a cashew nut sauce, 44
    chicken in a hot red sauce, 63
    chicken in spicy onions, 70
    chicken kofta balti with paneer, 26
    chicken Mulligatawny, 18
    chicken naan pockets, 24
    chicken pullao, 210

chicken tikka, 24
chicken with green mango, 66
chicken with pineapple, 28
classic tandoori chicken, 48
fragrant meat pullao, 198
hot chicken curry, 60
karahi chicken with fresh fenugreek, 75
karahi chicken with mint, 74
khara masala balti chicken, 72
Moghul-style chicken, 62
rice layered with chicken and potatoes, 208
spicy chicken and mushroom soup, 16
spicy masala chicken, 52
stuffed roast chicken, 56
sweet-and-sour balti chicken, 76
tandoori chicken, 53
Chilli powder, 10
Chillies: balti chilli chicken, 47
    balti prawns (shrimp) in hot sauce, 134
    dried chillies, 10
    fish fillets with a chilli sauce, 132
    fresh chillies, 10
    green chilli pickle, 234
    potatoes in a hot red sauce, 174
    potatoes with red chillies, 161
    prawns (shrimp) with okra, 136
    tasty toasts, 236
Chipsticks, eggs baked on, 78
Chutneys: apricot, 236
    mango, 233
    tomato, 232
    see also Pickles; Relishes
Cilantro *see* Coriander
Cinnamon, 10
Cloves, 10
Coconut, 10
    balti fish fillets in spicy coconut sauce, 131
Cod: balti fried fish, 124
    chunky fish balti with peppers, 130
    fish and vegetable kebabs (kabobs), 128
    seafood balti with vegetables, 148
Colourful pullao rice, 204
Coriander (cilantro), 8, 10
    fresh coriander (cilantro) relish, 227
    stuffed fish, 144
    tomato and coriander (cilantro) soup, 20
Coriander seeds, 10
Corn cob curry, 178
Courgettes (zucchini): courgettes with mushrooms
    in a creamy sauce, 160
    split lentils with courgettes, 192
Crêpes *see* Pancakes
Cucumber curry, 174
Cumin, 10
    karahi shredded cabbage with cumin, 173
Curries: beef Madras, 110
    Bengal gram and bottle gourd curry, 190
    black-eyed peas and potato curry, 190
    boiled egg cury, 78
    chicken curry, 57
    corn cob curry, 178
    cucumber curry, 174
    curried cauliflower, 158
    curried chick-peas (garbanzos) with potato
        cakes, 188
    curried stuffed (bell) peppers, 179
    hot-and-sour meat and lentil curry, 120
    hot chicken curry, 60

hot dry meat curry, 88
Kashmiri-style lamb, 88
khara masala lamb, 94
lamb korma, 110
mixed vegetable curry, 164
Moghul-style chicken, 62
Parsi prawn (shrimp) curry, 145
rice layered with lentils, 202
steak and kidney with spinach, 116
vegetables and beans with curry leaves, 176
see also Balti dishes
Curry leaves, 10

Drinks: almond sherbet, 250
lassi, 248
sweet lassi, 250
tea and fruit punch, 248
Duck casserole, hot sweet-and-sour, 71

Eggplants *see* Aubergines
Eggs: boiled egg curry, 78
eggs baked on chipsticks, 78
spicy omelette, 34
Equipment, 7

Fennel seeds, 10
Fenugreek, 10
balti minced (ground) lamb with potatoes and
fenugreek, 83
karahi chicken with fresh fenugreek, 75
karahi prawns (shrimp) and fenugreek, 135
masala beans with fenugreek, 182
Fenugreek seeds, 10
Fish: fish cakes, 152
pickled fish steaks, 127
see also individual types of fish
Five-star powder, 10
Fragrant meat pullao, 198
French (green) beans: beef with green beans, 114
masala beans with fenugreek, 182
Fruit: caramel with fresh fruit, 243
Indian fruit salad, 230
Fruity pullao, 204

Garam masala, 8, 10
Garlic, 10
garlic pulp, 8
Ghee, 10
Ginger, 10
ginger pulp, 8
Gourds *see* Bottle gourds
Grapes: raita, 223
Green beans *see* French beans
Green gram and rice, 192

Huss: prawns (shrimp) and fish in herb sauce, 126

Ice cream, Indian, 244
Indian fruit salad, 230
Indian ice cream, 244
Ingredients, 9-11

Kabobs *see* Kebabs
Karahi chicken with fresh fenugreek, 75
Karahi chicken with mint, 74
Karahi prawns (shrimp) and fenugreek, 135
Karahi shredded cabbage with cumin, 173
Kashmiri-style lamb, 88
Kebabs: balti minced (ground) lamb koftas with
vegetables, 98
balti mini lamb kebabs (kabobs) with baby
onions, 106
fish and vegetable kebabs (kabobs), 128
koftas, 96
mince kebabs, 104
Khara masala balti chicken, 72
Khara masala lamb, 94
Kidney beans *see* Red kidney beans
Kidneys: steak and kidney with spinach, 116
Koftas, 96
balti minced (ground) lamb koftas with
vegetables, 98

Lamb: balti lamb chops with potatoes, 31
balti lamb tikka, 82
balti minced (ground) lamb koftas with
vegetables, 98
balti minced (ground) lamb with potatoes and
fenugreek, 83
balti mini lamb kebabs (kabobs) with baby
onions, 106

balti vegetables stuffed with lamb, 112
hot-and-sour meat and lentil curry, 120
hot dry meat curry, 88
Kashmiri-style lamb, 88
khara masala lamb, 94
lamb chops Kashmiri-style, 102
lamb korma, 110
lamb pullao, 212
lamb with peas and mint, 92
lamb with spinach, 86
lentils with lamb and tomatoes, 118
mince kebabs, 104
Moghul-style roast lamb, 84
spicy lamb tikka, 90
spicy spring lamb roast, 100
stuffed aubergines (eggplants) with lamb, 108
tandoori masala spring lamb chops, 32
Lassi, 248
sweet lassi, 250
Lentils: balti chicken with lentils, 58
hot-and-sour meat and lentil curry, 120
lentil soup, 22
lentils seasoned with fried spices, 186
lentils with lamb and tomatoes, 118
okra with green mango and lentils, 180
rice layered with lentils, 202
South Indian lentils and vegetables, 186
split lentils with courgettes (zucchini), 192
tarka dhal, 194
Lime pickle, hot, 234

Mace, 10
Mango powder, 10
Mangoes, 10
chicken with green mango, 66
mango chutney, 233
mango sorbet (sherbet) with sauce, 245
okra with green mango and lentils, 180
Masala beans with fenugreek, 182
Masala chicken, spicy, 52
Masala mashed potatoes, 170
Masoor dhal, 10
tarka dhal, 194
Meat curry, hot dry, 88
Meat loaf, spicy, 96
Melon and strawberry salad, 242
Milk: classic vermicelli pudding, 240
ground rice pudding, 246
home-made paneer, 138
rich rice pudding, 240
Mince kebabs, 104
Mint, 10
karahi chicken with mint, 74
lamb with peas and mint, 92
Moghul-style chicken, 62
Moghul-style roast lamb, 84
Moong dhal, 10
tarka dhal, 194
Mullet *see* Red mullet
Mushrooms: courgettes (zucchini) with
mushrooms in a creamy sauce, 160
mushrooms, peas and paneer, 169
pea and mushroom pullao, 206
spicy chicken and mushroom soup, 16
spinach and mushroom salad, 224
Mustard seeds, 11

Naan, 216
chicken naan pockets, 24
Nigella, 11
Nutmeg, 11
Nutty salad, 224

Okra: okra in yogurt, 156
okra with green mango and lentils, 180
prawns (shrimp) with okra, 136
stuffed okra, 164
Omelette, spicy, 34
Onion seeds, 11
Onions, 8
balti mini lamb kebabs (kabobs) with baby
onions, 106
chicken in spicy onions, 70
onion bhajias, 14

Pancakes (crêpes): eggs baked on chipsticks, 78
prawn (shrimp) and spinach pancakes, 146
Paneer, 11
chicken kofta balti with paneer, 26
home-made paneer, 138
mushrooms, peas and paneer, 169
paneer balti with prawns (shrimp), 138
sweet-and-sour vegetables with paneer, 176
Papaya (paw-paw): spicy lamb tikka, 90
Paratha, 215
Parsi prawn (shrimp) curry, 145
Pasanda, balti chicken, 77
Pasta shells: chicken and pasta balti, 30

Peanuts: nutty salad, 224
Peas: lamb with peas and mint, 92
    mushrooms, peas and paneer, 169
    pea and mushroom pullao, 206
Pepper water, South Indian, 18
Peppercorns, 11
Peppers (bell): balti vegetables stuffed with
    lamb, 112
    chunky fish balti with peppers, 130
    curried stuffed (bell) peppers, 179
Pickled fish steaks, 127
Pickles: green chilli pickle, 234
    hot lime pickle, 234
    see also Chutneys; Relishes
Pineapple, chicken with, 28
Pistachios, 11
Plaice: balti fish fillets in spicy coconut sauce, 131
    fish fillets with a chilli sauce, 132
    grilled (broiled) fish fillets, 140
Pomegranate seeds, 11
    prawns (shrimp) with pomegranate seeds, 38
Pomfret: stuffed fish, 144
Poppy seeds, 11
Pork, Portuguese, 105
Portuguese pork, 105
Potatoes: baked potato with spicy cottage
    cheese, 36
    balti lamb chops with potatoes, 31
    balti minced (ground) lamb with potatoes and
      fenugreek, 83
    black-eyed peas and potato curry, 190
    Bombay potato, 158
    curried chick-peas (garbanzos) with potato
      cakes, 188
    fish cakes, 152
    masala mashed potatoes, 170
    potato cakes with stuffing, 23
    potatoes in a hot red sauce, 174
    potatoes in a yogurt sauce, 166
    potatoes with red chillies, 161
    rice layered with chicken and potatoes, 208
    spiced potatoes and carrots parisienne, 172
    spicy balti potatoes, 180
    spinach and potato, 168
Prawns (shrimp): balti prawns and vegetables in
    thick sauce, 142
    balti prawns in hot sauce, 134
    glazed garlic prawns, 141
    grilled (broiled) prawns, 38
    karahi prawns and fenugreek, 135
    paneer balti with prawns, 138
    Parsi prawn curry, 145
    prawn and spinach pancakes (crêpes), 146
    prawns and fish in herb sauce, 126
    prawns with okra, 136
    prawns with vegetables, 150
    rice layered with prawns, 213
    seafood balti with vegetables, 148
    prawns with pomegranate seeds, 38
Pullao: chicken pullao, 210
    colourful pullao rice, 204
    fragrant meat pullao, 198
    fruity pullao, 204
    lamb pullao, 212
    pea and mushroom pullao, 206
Punch, tea and fruit, 248

Raita, 223
Red gram, 11
    lentils seasoned with fried spices, 186
Red kidney beans: nutty salad, 224

vegetables and beans with curry leaves, 176
Red mullet: fried whole fish, 136
Relishes: fresh coriander (cilantro) relish, 227
    tomato salad, 226
    see also Chutneys; Pickles
Rice, 10
    chicken pullao, 210
    colourful pullao rice, 204
    fragrant meat pullao, 198
    fruity pullao, 204
    green gram and rice, 192
    ground rice pudding, 246
    lamb pullao, 212
    pea and mushroom pullao, 206
    plain boiled rice, 198
    rice layered with chicken and potatoes, 208
    rice layered with lentils, 202
    rice layered with prawns (shrimp), 213
    rich rice pudding, 240
    saffron and cardamom flavoured rice, 200
    tomato rice, 206

Saffron, 11
    balti chicken in saffron sauce, 50
    saffron and cardamom flavoured rice, 200
Salads: avocado, 230
    nutty, 224
    spicy baby vegetable, 228
    spinach and mushroom, 224
    sweet potato and carrot, 220
    tomato, 226
    yogurt, 228
Samosas, vegetable, 34
Seafood balti with vegetables, 148
Sesame seeds, 11
Sherbet, almond, 250
Sherbet *see* Sorbet
Shrimp *see* Prawns
Sorbet (sherbet), mango with sauce, 245
Soups: chicken and almond, 17
    chicken Mulligatawny, 18
    lentil, 22
    South Indian pepper water, 18
    spicy chicken and mushroom, 16
    tomato and coriander (cilantro), 20
    yogurt, 14
South Indian lentils and vegetables, 186
South Indian pepper water, 18
Spices, 8, 9
    garam masala, 8
Spinach: lamb with spinach, 86
    prawn (shrimp) and spinach pancakes
      (crêpes), 146
    spinach and mushroom salad, 224
    spinach and potato, 168
    steak and kidney with spinach, 116
Star anise, 11
Steak and kidney with spinach, 116
Strawberries: melon and strawberry salad, 242
Sweet-and-sour balti chicken, 76
Sweet-and-sour vegetables with paneer, 176
Sweet potato and carrot salad, 220

Tamarind, 11
    balti baby chicken in tamarind sauce, 64
Tandoori chicken: classic, 48
    low-fat, 53
Tandoori masala spring lamb chops, 32
Tarka dhal, 194

Tasty toasts, 236
Tea and fruit punch, 248
Toasts, tasty, 236
Tomatoes: chicken and tomato balti, 68
    lentils with lamb and tomatoes, 118
    tomato and coriander (cilantro) soup, 20
    tomato chutney, 232
    tomato rice, 206
    tomato salad, 226
Toor dhal, 11
Turmeric, 11

Urid dhal, 11

Vegetables: balti baby vegetables, 162
    balti chicken with vegetables, 46
    balti minced (ground) lamb koftas with
      vegetables, 98
    balti prawns (shrimp) and vegetables in thick
      sauce, 142
    balti vegetables stuffed with lamb, 112
    fish and vegetable kebabs (kabobs), 128
    mixed vegetable curry, 164
    prawns (shrimp) with vegetables, 150
    seafood balti with vegetables, 148
    South Indian lentils and vegetables, 186
    sweet-and-sour vegetables with paneer, 176
    vegetable samosas, 34
    vegetables and beans with curry leaves, 176
    vegetables with almonds, 183
    see also Salads *and individual types of vegetable*
Vermicelli, 11
    classic vermicelli pudding, 240
    light vermicelli pudding, 246

Walnuts, 11
    raita, 223
Wholemeal (whole-wheat) chapatis, 216

Yogurt, 8
    lassi, 248
    okra in yogurt, 156
    potatoes in a yogurt sauce, 166
    raita, 223
    spiced yogurt, 222
    sweet lassi, 250
    yogurt salad, 228
    yogurt soup, 14

Zucchini *see* Courgettes

ARMAMENT AND TECHNOLOGY

DESTROYER FRIGATES
AND CORVETTES

Illustrations: Lluis Adell i Jaumandreu, Camil Busquets, Douglas A. Cromby, Octavio Díez Cámara, Jorge Flethes Serrano, Santiago García Gaya, Hanny & Leo Van Ginderen, Jon Godsell, Antonio Moreno García, Marc Piché, Diego Quevedo Carmona, Chris Sattler, Harry M. Steele, Vicente Talón, Ralph Thorsteinson, Winter & Findler, Leonid Yakutin; Aerospatiale, Alenia, Alstom, Armada española, Empresa Nacional "Bazán", Daniel Bechennec, Blohm + Voss, Bofors/Celsius, Celsius/Kockums, Centre IMP/Helio DCN Cherbourg, Colebrand Defence, DCN International, Denel LIW/Vektor, Eurosam, Fincantieri, GEC Alsthom, GEIE Eurotorp, GE Marine & Industrial Engines, Jeumont Industrie, Kollmorgen/GE, Konsberg, Litton Ingalls, Lockheed Martin, Marina Militare, Marine Nationale, Matra Bae Dynamics, Mc Donnell Douglas, Meval, Nordic Defence Industries A/S, Oerlikon-Contraves, Studio Grafico Restani, Royal Navy, STN Atlas Elektronik, Swedish Navy, Thomson Marconi, US Navy, Voith Hydro.

Researcher: Albert Campanera i Rovira

Computer specialist: José Manuel Rojo Ara y Albert Rojo Mateu

Production: Ediciones Lema, S.L.
Editorial director: Josep M. Parramón Homs
Original text: Camil Busquets
Coordination: Eduardo Hernández
Translator: Mike Roberts

I.S.B.N. 84-95323-13-3

Photosetting and photomechanics: Novasis, S.A.L.
Barcelona (Spain)
Printed in Spain

DESTROYERS
FRIGATES
AND CORVETTES

LEMA
Publications

The post-war period

At the end of the war, many of the ships on order were cancelled. Of those that remained, many continued in service with the U.S. Navy. However, a large number were also transformed to allied and other friendly navies. By the 1970's some 300 were still in active service, though most of them had received improved weapons. During this period, several Sumner and Gearing, particularly the latter, were modernized through FRAM (Fleet Rehabilitation and Modernization) programs, which added a good ten years to their service life. A lot of these ended their service in countries with navies linked to the USA, such as Korea, Spain, Greece, Mexico, Taiwan and Turkey. Some are still being used today.

In the early 1950s, a considerably larger and different class of destroyers was planned, eventually coming into service between 1955 and 1959. These were the eighteen Forrest Sherman that survived up until the 1980s. They belonged to the same period as the four Mitscher DD 927 to 930, later re-classified as DL 2 to 5. DL 2 and 3 ended their days as DDG 35 and 36.

Nowadays, very few navies have destroyers in their fleets, and even fewer can boast of a particularly high number. Undoubtedly, the most modern and highest number, of ships of this class, belong to the US Navy.

Modern United States destroyers

Before the Second World War, the USA started establishing bases for its so-called Two Ocean Fleet, the most important and numerous fleet of destroyers that any country has ever possessed. The best known of the American war time destroyers are perhaps the Fletcher, Allen M. Summer and the Gearing class's. A total of 481 were built. The last the U.S.S. Meredith DD 890 being commisioned on the 31st of December 1945.

CHARLES ARLEIGH A.BURKE CLASS
The Burke class has a higher turning coefficient (0.14 to 0.10) than the Spruance, making it more stable platform.

THE KIDD'S SENSORS
The Kidd's electronic system is also different to that of the Spruance, as shown by this picture of the Callaghan. Only two of this class, the Scott and the Chandler, are still in service.

anti-aircraft missiles as Sea Sparrows, Harpoons and Tomahawks, and re-numbered DD. Anti-ship missiles were later added, and TASM/TLAM (Tomahawk Anti Ship Missile/Tomahawk Anti Land Missile) converted them into the only destroyers capable of attacking land targets. This was demonstrated during the Desert Storm operation, in which 112 Tomahawks (Caron/2, Fife/60, Leftwich/8, Paul F.Foster/40 and Spruance/2) were launched against Iraq. On January 17th 1993 the Caron, Hewitt and Stump launched a further 45, and on June 26th the Peterson launched another 14.

The DDG

The 23 ships of the Charles F. Adams class came into service during the early 1970's. They were the first class of destroyers to be almost totally armed with SAM anti-aircraft missiles.

Apart from their own ships, the USA also financed the construction of another six, three by Germany and three by Australia, under the credit system called "Off Shore Procurement". The original series starting going out of service from 1990 onwards, and three vessels were given to the Greek fleet in 1991 and 1992.

HARPOON MISSILES

Although, in principle, all Arleigh Burkes contain SSM Harpoon missiles, some of them have been removed. The Ross, in this photo taken at Norfolk base in September 1998, only has supports for them on the upper deck of the poop.

The Spruance

These ships were designed in the late seventies to replace the FRAM, although they ended up taking the place of the Forrest Sherman class as well.

The first came into service on September 20th 1975, and the last, on March 5th 1983. Two rather innovative methods for the time were used to construct these 31 ships. First, they were welded throughout, considerably speeding up the construction process. Second, they were all assigned to the same shipyard, Litton/Ingalls, which minimised costs and permitted mass production.

Combat operations

Although in principle these were high capacity 'all gun' and 'no missile' destroyers, they were eventually equipped with such

KIDD CLASS

The general appearance of the four Kidds, the Chandler is shown in the photo, was similar to the Spruance, but with two missile launchers, one on each aftercastle, instead of the ASROC, and one on the forecastle instead of the Sea Sparrow.

Armament

The original artillery was made up of two 127/54-mm Mk45 automatic single turret guns, an octuple ASROC anti-ship missile, and ASW torpedo launcher. Nevertheless, on entering service, they were supplied with CIWS anti-missile weapons and Sea Sparrow missiles.

Harpoons have always been carried in groups of four, usually in the waist. As for Tomahawks, from October 1982, some ships received two quadruple ABL (Armoured Boxed Launchers) in their poops, one on each side of an ASROC launcher. In June 1987, these were removed and replaced with a 61 VLS Mk 41. Some ships received another VLS in their poops, substituting the Sea Sparrow.

Propulsion

A large area of the space on these ships has been kept in reserve for future developments. This reserve space was later put to good use in the four ships of the Kidd class, and in the Aegis cruisers which used a similar hull. These ships are driven by four LM 2500 gas turbines that generate a maximum of 80,000 hp. These can take them up to speeds of 19 knots with one engine, 27 with two, and over 30 by using all four.

The Kidd

In December 1973, the Iranian government announced its intention to construct two AAW destroyers based on the Spruance class, in particular the AA version. On August 27th, it was revealed that four more would be built, although only four of the potential six were ever formally commissioned. They were going to be equipped with twin Mk 26 launchers with Standard ER missiles, though the bow launcher could be limited to 24 missiles, in order to make room for the 203/55 mm Mk 71 Major Calibre Light Weight Gun, that was being tested at the time. The kidd also had a different electronic sensor system.

The fall of the Shah Reza Pahlevi's re-

TOMAHAWKS ON BOARD

Before VLS were available, these vessels were equipped with launchers for four Tomahawk missiles, one on each side of the ASROC. Shown here is the Ingersoll with ABL/Tomahawk at the beginning of the 1980s.

THE CHARLES F.ADAMS

These were the first US Navy destroyers to carry missiles. Germany and Australia received three each, and later Greece received some that had been decommissioned by the Navy. The Australian Perth, shown here, is still in service.

gime in 1979 meant that the USA could not allow such modern and powerful ships to fall into the hands of Islamic fundamentalism, and so the vessels were instead sold to the US Navy. Only two kidd, the Scott and the Chandler, are still being used today.

The Arleigh A. Burke

These destroyers were planned as replacements for the Charles F. Adams and Coontz that were taken out of service in the late 1980s and early 1990s. There is also a very similar class, the Oscar Austin, which has a few distinctive features and very different armaments.

The return to steel

These are the first destroyers to go back to using steel as their base material in the superstructure, abandoning light aluminum alloys due to the danger of almost inextinguishable fires, constantly fed by the oxygen of the burning metal. The experience of the U.S.S. *Belknap* was enough to convince warship builders that steel was the more sensible material. Not only is it more resistant to missile blasts, fire and splintering, but it also protects against magnetic pulses. The most important zones of the Arleigh Burke class are protected by Kevlan armour plating, with a total of 130 tons being used per vessel. The vessels were also designed with a heavy emphasis on the latest developments in stealth technology.

A numerous series

A total of 49 Arleigh Burkes were originally programmed by the Carter Administration. This was raised to 63 in the Reagan era. However, the high cost of these ships (about 1,000 million dollars per unit) reduced the project, resulting in just 28 Flight I and II versions, and a further 21 Oscar Austin Flight IIA, coming into service from 2000 onwards.

The project did not lack in controversy, particularly when, for economic

RAM MISSILES

The Spruance started receiving RAM missiles in the late 1990s for defensive purposes. The Nicholson is shown here at Portsmouth in September 1998.

STEALTH

The Burke class has been designed taking into account the latest stealth technology. The superstructure is positively pitched while the dead work is negative.

reasons, the helicopter hangar was left out of all but the IIAs. For this reason, these ships operate with the indispensable Seahawk LAMPS III, which they can refuel and rearm, but cannot maintain.

Successful ships

Three very different factors contribute to the excellence of the Arleigh Burke class; the duke class of the royal navy were the first I.E. H.M.S. Norfolk; they are considerably shorter in relation to their breadth than other such ships; which results in a more stable platform from which to fire missiles and guns and are the first to employ NBC (Nuclear/Biological/Chemical) citadels. The latter are sealed air tight, and can be accessed through an airlocking hatch. All Arleigh Burkes were equipped with SSM Harpoon missiles, but they have since been wholly or partially removed from many vessels.

As for electronic sensors, they are the first destroyers to use a multi-purpose SPY-ID phase panel, comparable to that used by AEGIS cruisers.

SENSORS AND ARMAMENTS

The TACTAS Gould SQR-99 is on the stern, along with the Nixie SLQ-25 acoustic anti-torpedo decoys. In the poop there is a position for VERTREP and a 127-mm gun.

STERN MAST SENSORS

Two radar are positioned on the stern mast, the Lockheed SPS-40B/C/D for air surveillance is on the maintop and the Hughes Mk 23 Target Acquisition System is beneath. The latter automatically reacts to sea skimmer missiles at distances of up to 100 miles.

PURSUIT SENSORS

Some of these ships are equipped with infrared sensors to work nocturnally at close range.

ARMAMENTS ON THE STERN

The stern weapons are the Raytheon GMLS Mk 29 octuple Sea Sparrow launcher (with two reloads) and one of the two 127/54-mm guns, unchanged since the earliest days of this vessel.

VLS CRANE

A VLS Mk-41 is made up of eight groups of cells, but each one is only able to carry five missiles because the other three are used to transport the service crane used for emergency maintenance at sea.

MISSILE ILLUMINATORS

The illuminator and guider for the Raytheon Sea Sparrow Mk-91 are set above the hangar, along with I/J band radar, consisting of two different antennas, one receptive and the other for transmission.

COMPARISON OF CURRENT CHARACTERISTICS

CLASS	SPRUANCE (31)	KIDD (4)	BURKE (28)	AUSTIN (14+3)
YR. INTRODUCED	1975/1983	1981/1982	1991/1999	2000/2004
L'GTH/B'DTH/D'GHT	172 x 16.8 x 8.8	172 x 16,8 x 10	154 x 20.4 x 10	155 x 20.4 x 10
DISPLACEMENT	8,280	9,574	8,422	9,217
PROPULSION	Gas turbines	Gas turbines	Gas turbines	Gas turbines
ENGINES	LM 2500 (4)	LM 2500 (4)	LM 2500-30 (4)	LM 2500-30 (4)
HORSE POWER	86,000	86,000	105,000	105,000
SPEED/AUTON.	32.5-6,000/20	30-6,000/20	32-4,400/20	32-4,400/20
ARMAMENTS	Tomahawk/ASROC (61)/	Harpoon (8)	Tomahawk/ASROC/	NC
	VLS Sea Sparrow (8)	Standard SM-2MR (52)	Standard (90)	
	Harpoon (8) - RAM	ASROC (16)	Harpoon (8)	
	Two 127/54 mm guns	Two 127/54-mm guns	One 127/54-mm gun	
	2 CIWS Vulcan Phalanx	2 CIWS Vulcan Phalanx	ERGM	
	Four 12,7 mm	Four 12,7 mm	2 CIWS Vulcan Phalanx	
	machine guns	machine guns	Two 324 mm 2 x III LT/ASW	
	Two 324 mm III LT/ASW	Two 324 mm III LT/ASW		
	2 LAMPS III helicopters	One LAMPS III helicopter		

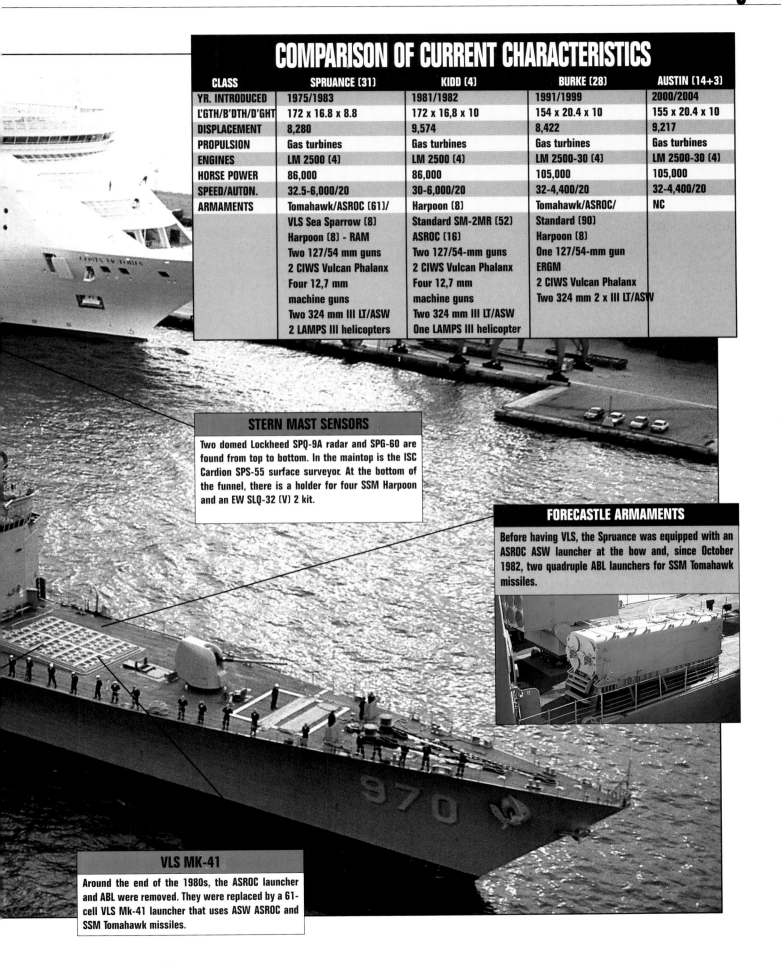

STERN MAST SENSORS

Two domed Lockheed SPQ-9A radar and SPG-60 are found from top to bottom. In the maintop is the ISC Cardion SPS-55 surface surveyor. At the bottom of the funnel, there is a holder for four SSM Harpoon and an EW SLQ-32 (V) 2 kit.

FORECASTLE ARMAMENTS

Before having VLS, the Spruance was equipped with an ASROC ASW launcher at the bow and, since October 1982, two quadruple ABL launchers for SSM Tomahawk missiles.

VLS MK-41

Around the end of the 1980s, the ASROC launcher and ABL were removed. They were replaced by a 61-cell VLS Mk-41 launcher that uses ASW ASROC and SSM Tomahawk missiles.

The destroyer has changed enormously since it was conceived by Fernando de Vilaamil in 1885. Although there are now less destroyers being used in Europe than two decades ago, it is still one of the most important components of the continent's naval forces.

A variety of names

The original design of the destroyer or torpedo boat destroyer, as they were originally known in the royal navy, was to protect the battleships of a hundred years ago from the small fast torpedo boats of the day.

The destroyer's name varies quite dramatically from country to country. NATO and English speaking countries may call them destroyers, but for Germans they are *Zerstörer,* for the Spanish *destructores,* while the Italians still call them *cacciatorpediniere* or simply *caccia,* and in French they progressed from being *contretorpilleurs* to being *escorteurs d'escadre* and now seem to have become *frégates.* Therefore, it seems easiers to make use of the internationally accepted initials DD (Destroyer) and DDG (Missile Destroyer)..

A long evolution

Of course, it is not just the destroyer's

name that has developed. The difference between the mere 380 tons and 58.7 meters of the first destroyer and the immense 9,000 tons and 155 meters of an Oscar Austin (Arleigh A.Burke flight IIA) is indicative of the effects of a century that has included two world wars and countless lesser conflicts. Thus, the capacity that was considered unique to cruisers half a century ago, is now more appropriate for a destroyer.

It would be impossible to detail the whole development process here, suffice to say that compared with the 206 European destroyers in 1998, there were 815 in 1956. However, we must remember that many of those had been built for use in the Second World War, and that their military value and technological capabilities were far inferior to the kind of ships that can be seen today.

The 42 Type

The 42 Type resulted from the requirements of the Royal Navy, when, following the cancellation in 1966 of a project to construct new aircraft carriers, it was considered imperative that the Navy should possess light escort craft with aerial defense capabilities.

The project suffered from heavy pressure to keep down costs, which meant that the finished product was not very autonomous when used at high speeds (it needed constant refuelling) and considerably shorter than expected (the give-away sign of cost cutting). Neither did it possess particularly impressive armaments (the 22 strong missile cargo of SAM Sea Dart is but half the number that were supplied to the Type 82 H.M.S. Bristol).

Three different sub-classes

Fourteen ships were completed (six in batch 1, four in batch 2 and four in batch 3), of which 12 are still in active service. Five of these ships served in the Falklands Conflict. Two, *H.M.S. Sheffield* and *Coventry* were lost, while a third, *Glasgow*, was seriously damaged. The ships of the third batch were considerably longer (141.1 m compared with 125 m) and are slightly wider (14.9 m compared with 14.3 m), this is a strengthing strip. The ships also have greater displacement. They are not unlike Broadsword class frigates in appearance, but are larger and heavier. They have a certain amount of anti-ship capabilities, and although they do not possess their propulsion system which is gas turbine, using a COGOG system (i.e. combined gas and gas SSM missiles) they do have a twin ramp that can be used against surface targets SAM launcher on the bow.

HEAVILY ARMED
Luigi Durand de la Penne destroyers are heavily armed, as can be seen in this photograph, along with the three funnels, one in the forward superstructure and two angled outwards in the after superstructure.

LONGER
The four ships of the batch 3 type h2 destroyers are 16 m longer. An extra 9 meters has been added to the forward section of the hull.

Propulsion and armaments

They are driven by COGOG gas turbines, and as well as the aforementioned Sea Darts, also have a 114/55 mm Mk-8 gun, a limited number of lighter guns (and two CIWS Vulcan Phalanx) and, on some of them, anti-submarine torpedos that are fired from 324 mm tubes. They can also carry a Lynx helicopter. H.M.S. Birmingham, D 86 the second vessel to be built, is about to be taken out of service. The others should eventually be replaced by the new DDG/FFG Horizon class in 2002.

1172

The superstructure on this ship is slanted to reduce their radar signature, though not as much as on some other ships (left photograph)

AERIAL RADAR
All type 42 ships have Marconi/Signaal Type 1022 aerial reconnaissance radar, operating on band D and reaching as far as 160 miles. (right photograph)

The Georges Leygues/Cassard

The French Armada's class F-70 destroyers were built as replacements for the class T-47 Surcouf and the class T-53 Duperré, which were taken out of service midway through the 1980s. The class is made up of two different types, one ASW and the other AAW. The former, the Georges Leygues class, are seven extraordinarily different ships. There are only two of the latter class, the Cassard, because the original plan for a series of four had to be reduced owing to financial problems.

Anti-submarine ships

The Georges Leygues are essentially ASW although, as is normal these days, they can be used for most other purposes. The class is formed by the Georges Leygues; Dupleix, Montcalm; Jean de Vienne; Primaguet; La Motte-Picquet and Latouche-Treville. They use CODOG propulsion (two RR Olympus TM3B engines and two SEMT-Pielstick 16 PA6 V280 diesel engines). They can reach speeds of 30 knots (21 with diesel engines), with a range of 8,500 miles at 18 knots (on diesel engines) or 2,500 at 28 (on gas turbines).

Modernization plan

They are currently undergoing the OP3A modernization plan (Opération Amélioration Autodéfense Antimissiles) under which each ship in turn will have its armaments improved (two sextuple SAM Matra Sadral launchers, Matra/Bae Milas ASW missiles and two 30 mm Breda-Mauser guns), and also their sensors and ESM/ECM elements. They

RADAR
In this picture of the Francesco Mimbelli one can see the radar and sensors on the masts and over parts of the superstructure. The SPS-768 for aerial reconnaissance is over the bridge, and the SPS 52 C 3D and SPS 774 are on the stern mast.

will also be fitted with a command position on top of the bridge. The rest of the weaponry will remain intact; this consists of four (or eight on the three later ships) SSM Exocet missiles, an octuple container for 26 SAM Crotale Naval supersonic missiles, a 100/55-mm mod. 68 CADAM automatic all-purpose gun, two 20 mm Oerlikon, four 12.7 mm machine guns, ASW torpedos and a Lynx helicopter.

Anti-aircraft ships

In 1988 and 1991, the French Marine Nationale received two AAW F 70 A/A class destroyers, the Cassard and Jean Bart. These were specially designed for anti-aircraft and anti-missile warfare, built on F-70 ASW hulls and with radically modified propulsion, by only using four special SEMT-Pielstick 18PA6 V 280 BTC diesel engines, making them highly independent and fast enough to serve as efficient escorts for aircraft carriers, even nuclear ones.

New weapons

Budget problems delayed production of these units, as did the doubts over the usefulness of SAM Standard SM-1 MR missiles, becoming somewhat obsolete after 30 years of use and about to be replaced by

RADAR

In this stern photo of H.M.S. Glasgow a type 42, Batch 1, you can see the fibre glass domes wich protect the two Marconi radars, these operate on the J and I wave band.

the new Aster 30. It has a collection of arms made up of four SSM Exocet missiles and several SAM, Mistral, Standard and the already mentioned Aster missiles.

The Luigi Durand de la Penne

In the mid 1980s, Italy ordered the production of two modern destroyers that were to be called *Animoso* and *Ardimentoso*, though they were eventually named after two war heroes, *Luigi Durand* de la Penne and *Francesco Mimbelli*. The Marina Militare doubted for a long time whether or not to accept the ships, owing to concern over the excessive noise they made.

Interesting features

These ships, when fully loaded, weigh a very useful 5,400 tons. It is said that they

COMPARISON OF TECHNICAL CHARACTERISTICS

CLASS/QUANT	YR. INTROD	LTH/BTH/HGT	DISPLACE.	PROPULSION	ENGINES	HP	SPEED/RANGE	ARMAMENTS
Tipo 42/III (4)	1982/1985	141 x 14.9 x 5.8	4,675	COGOG	Olympus TM3B (2)	43,000	30-4,000/18	22 SAM Sea Dart
					Tyne RM1C (2)	10,680		One 114/55 mm Mk8 gun
								Two VI CIWS Vulcan Phalanx
								Several 20 mm
								Six 324 mm TL ASW (2 x III)
								One Lynx helicopter
G. Leygues (7)	1979/1990	139 x 14 x 5.7	4,580	CODOG	Olympus TM3B (2)	46,200	30-2,500/28	8 SSM Exocet
					SEMT-Pielstick (2)	12,800	21-8,500/18	One SAM/CIWS Crotale Naval
								Two Simbad or Sadral CIWS
								One 100/55 mod. 8 gun
								Several 30 and /or 20 mm and 12.7 mm
								324 mm TL ASW
								Two Lynx helicopters
Cassard (2)	1988/1991	138 x 14 x 6.5	4,730	Diesel	SEMT-Pielstick (4)	43,200	29.5-4,800/24	Eight SSM Exocet 40 SAM Standard
								SM-1MR 2 CIWS Sadral
								1 gun of 100/55 mod. 8
								2 Oerlikon of 20 mm + 12.7 mm
								2 TL ASW of 324 mm
								1 helicopter AS 565 MA
								Panther

have been pushed to the utmost limit to provide space for all kinds of equipment. This does make them somewhat unstable and rather uncomfortable.

They are driven by CODOG, producing a total of 66,600 horsepower (54,000 from the gas turbines and 12,600 from the diesel engines), wich in turn are connected to variable pitch propellers. Their weaponry is made up of eight SSM Teseo Mk 2 missiles, ASW Milas missiles, forty SAM Standard SM-IMR, sixteen SAM Aspide, a 127/54 mm gun (from the Audace), three OTO-Melara 76/62 mm Super Rapid, six 324 mm ASW torpedo tubes and two AB-212 ASW helicopters. It is also capable of operating SH-3D Sea King and even the new EH-101 Merlin, that is currently being tested on board.

Peculiarities

They also have three funnels in a similar configuration to that of H.M.S. Bristol, that is one forward and side by side further aft. The crew totals 377 of which 32 are officers making a ratio of 0.0698 people per ton, rather high when compared to the french F-70 (0.0475), an Algonquin (0.0572), a Burke (0.0335) or even a Charles Adams (0.0704), a steamer designed 40 years ago.

SSM MISSILES

The eight SSM Exocet MM 40 missiles are located between the two main blocks of the superstructure. The two domes above house the Syracuse combat data satellite transmission system.

The Prairie

These ships, built with steel alloys, are protected by Kelvar at important points. The "Prairie" sound absorbing system has also been installed, this is made up of a thin layer of air bubbles that are blown through the hull at various points along its length. Bubbles are even blown though the propellers. The bubbles then form a cushion on which the ship rides, and this reduces the underwater noise from the ship.

Amongst the escort ships in modern fleets, there are many vessels that can be compared with one another, though there are also those that are rapidly becoming obsolete.

The canadian tribal class

As Canada is a member of the Commonwealth, it has in the past, tended to look to Great Britain for ships for the Royal Canadian Navy. Some of these ships were built in Great Britain but the majority were built in Canadian shipyards.

This was the case until 1950s, when they decided that they would design and build their own warships. It is also worth painting out that Canada does not use the Nato system for naming its ships.

An efficient design

In 1963 Canada cancelled a projected series of eight frigates wich, would have been fitted with the U.S. made "Tartar" missile system. In 1968 however, four destroyers were ordered. They were given four of the names that would have been used in the cancelled frigate project. These were Iruquois, Huron, Athabaskan and

Algoquin; they became the tribal class. The shape of the hull, size and general characteristics were relatively similar, though with improved anti-submarine capabilities. This was because at the time all the ships in the Nato fleets faced the potential threat from the powerful Soviet submarine fleet.

Before and after

The first version was armed with quadruple SAM Sea Sparrow launchers, rather unusually attached to the front superstructure of the bridge. An Italian 127/54 mm OTO-Melera gun, six triple mount 324 mm ASW tubes equipped with Honeywell Mk

46 torpedoes and a triple ASW Limbo Mk 10 launcher, along with two CH-124A Sea King helicopters. There was also a superior multiple sensor system, of British-American design. The ships were powered by a COGOG gas turbine system supplied by Pratt & Whitney rather than General Electric. The engines then turned two variable pitch five-bladed propellers.

The appearance of the ships went more or less in accordance with the fashion of the time, a large superstructure and enclosed bridge that extended across the whole of the ship, on top a lattice mast was fitted to carry radar and other communications aerials. The gun turret was positioned on the foredeck, and there was a large hanger at the aft end of the superstructure. This was capable of housing two Sea King helecopters. At the stern of the ship a limbo mortar and VDS system was fitted. They were also fitted with two funnels, side by side, and angled outwards.

The TRUMP update

Between 1987 and 1995, these four ships were radically modified by Litton

MILITARY STRENGTH
Kongos are the most powerful ships in the Japanese fleet, similar in appearance and features to the Burkes used by the US Navy.

DECOY LAUNCHERS
This craft has Russian PK 16 decoy launchers, with 16 rockets each, including infrared and anti-radar. They are situated on the stern above the deck of the superstructure.

Systems Canada Ltd, according to the Tribal class Update and Modernization Project (TRUMP). This in effect meant that the ships were completly re-built and re-armed, with another OTO-Melara, but this time the 76/62 mm was installed at the higher position of deck 02. They had a VLS Mk 41 with 29 cells (32 minus the three for the crane) with SAM Standard SM-2MR Block III missiles. A CIWS Vulcan Phalanx was positioned above on the hangar roof. Nothing was done to change the 324-mm TL ASW, but the obsolete Limbo mortar was removed.

The COGOG system was maintained as the form of propulsion, although its cruiser turbines were replaced by more powerful GM Allison versions.

The sensor system was replaced with a more modern, but essentially similar version made by Signaal, this included the large SPQ-502 search antenna on the roof of the bridge, instead of being on a ledge on the mast. The flight deck was equipped with a Beartrap emergency mooring system, and the NBC battle systems were updated and moved to the citadel. This way the control of the engines was automated, and centrally controlled from the bridge. Now there is only one funnel, with a filter system to cool the exhaust gas and so reduce the infrared.

COMPARISON OF CURRENT CHARACTERISTICS

CLASS/N°.	YEAR INTROD.	LTH/WTH/DTH	DISPLACE.	PROPULSION	ENGINES	HP	SPEED/RANGE	ARMAMENTS
Iroquois (4)	1972/1973	130 x 15,2 x 6,6	5,100	COGOG	Pratt & Whitney FT4 A2 (2) Allison 570-KF (2)	50,000 12,700	27 15-4,500/15	29 SAM Standard SM-2MR III One 76/62 mm OTO-Melara gun One CIWS Vulcan Phalanx Six 324 mm (2 x III) TL ASW Two CH-124 Sea King helicopters
Kongo (4)	1993/1998	161 x 21 x 10	9,485	COGAG	LM 2500 (4)	102,160	30-4,500/20	8 SSM Harpoon 90 SAM/ASW Standard/ASROC One 127/54 mm OTO Melara gun Two CIWS Vulcan Phalanx Six 324 mm (2 x III) TL ASW One helicopter (without hangar)

The Japanese MSDF

Japan was devastated by the Second World War, and had the dubious honor of being the only country to have ever suffered the effects of an atomic bomb. After the war, Japan was practically left without a fleet, and had the Korean War not broken out, it is difficult to know what would have come of it. That war converted Japan into a huge unsinkable aircraft carrier, and the departure point of numerous amphibian operations. Another important event, the spread of communism in Asia, reinforced Japan's international role. A country supposedly forbidden to have any kind of Navy for any purpose other than self-defense, though in recent years she has been able to build up its fleet to the extent that it was the most important in Asia, with some 150 very modern ships (19 SSK, 42 DD/DDG, 15 FF/FFG, 13 amphibian ships, 34 MCMV and 24 major auxiliary vessels). Another dozen will be added before 2002, and there are an additional 500 ships of different capacities that make up the Maritime Security Agency.

HANGAR AND VDS

The big double hangar on these large canadian ships allows simultaneous use of two Sea King helicopters. The active/passive VDS is given a specialised position on the stern.

The Kongos

Japan's most modern ships are the Kongo class destroyers, all of which entered service between 1993 and 1998. These four ships are the first outside of the US Navy to use the AEGIS system, proof in itself of Japan's military strength.

A clear similarity

They look remarkably similar to the American Arleigh Burkes, and their capacity and armaments are almost carbon copies. They are armed with two VLS silos (one forward on the superstructure with 24 cells and the other towards the stern with 61 cells), and a total of 90 SAM and ASW missiles. Eight SSM Harpoons guarantee its anti-ship capabilities, along with ASROC anti-submarine missiles contained in the VLS and ASW Honeywell Mk 46 mod. 5 Neartip torpedos and Seahawk SH-60 J helicopters. They are also fitted with a 127/54-mm OTO-Melara gun and two Vulcan Phalanx CIWS multi-tubes.

Electronics

They have first class electronic support equipment that includes TACTASS and hull sonar, along with ESM/ECM for electronic warfare and decoy launchers and Prairie

acoustic absorbers. They incorporate stealth technology and are COGAG driven by four LM 2500 gas turbines.

The Murasame

As well as these magnificent ships, Japan is also building another eleven of the large Murasame class, also known as mini-Kongos or Asagiris, which should all be ready by 2002.

They are 5000 ton vessels and when fully equipped they will be armed with 45 VLS, 8 Harpoon, one 76/62 gun, 2 CIWS Vulcan Phalanx and 324 mm TL ASW with Honeywell torpedos. They also have an SH-60 J helicopter with its hangar.

The Asagiri

These 8 vessels entered service between 1982 and 1991. They displace 4,200 tons when fully loaded; are 132 metres in length, 14.6 wide and have 4-5 metres of draught; they use COGAG propulsion with four RR Spey SMA jet engines; 53,300 hp of power and maximum speeds of over 30 knots; they are equipped with Harpoon missiles, Sea Sparrow and ASROC, a 76/62 mm^2 gun, Vulcan Phalanx anti-missile and 324 mm ASW Torpedos.

The *Marasesti*

You would not expect a country like

POOP

As with the Arleigh Burke class, the four Kongos do not have a hanger, dispite having a displacement of 9,485 tons. Aft of the superstructure there is a 61 cell VLS silo and aft of this is the flight deck.

THE MATSUYUKI

These 12 ships are almost all the same, although the newer ones have steel superstructures. They form the most homogenous and numerous group of the Japanese Navy, and are frequently used on training missions.

Romania, given all the problems it has had to overcome in the last ten years or so, to have a fleet of warships of any size or consequence. Indeed it does not, however it does have what by any standards must be an exceptional ship, the destroyer Maraseti.

The ship was built by the Mangalia shipyard, and it is widely believed that there was Russian assistance with the project. It was originally meant to be a multi-purpose destroyer using SSM and ASW rockets, with CODAG engines.

Inherited problems

Its keel was laid in 1979, and the hull was launched in 1981. But the project had

to be radically modified as a result of the economic crisis that swept across the Eastern bloc countries in the mid 1980s. The two gas turbines could not be completed in time, and instead a CODAD propulsion system had to be improvised on the spot.

Unusual engines

The ship is powered by four German locomotive engines. As the gearboxes for connecting two of the engines to each shaft could not be manufactured in Romania, she was fitted with four shafts and propellers instead. The two inner shafts are used when maneuvering, as these can be reversed, which is not the case with the outer pair. All the propellers are three bladed fixed pitch. The ship is steered by two semi balanced rudders, all of them with three blades.

FORECASTLE
The high forecastle of these canadian ships almost reaches nine metres, enough to confront the turbulent waters of the Atlantic and Pacific, where they are normally used.

SENSORS
On the bridge, on a high pedestal, is the Signaal SPG 502 (LW08) aerial surveillance radar. In front, on either side, are the Signaal SPG 501 (STIR 1.8) missile directors. On the gunwale is an ESM/ECM countermeasure.

Armaments and electronics

The main armament consists of eight SS-N-2 C Styx missiles, positioned one above the other in holders on deck 01, while the ASW mortars are placed on the forecastle. During trials, problems with stability arose, she had to return to her builders for modifications with the result that the missiles were taken down a deck, the mortars raised one and the masts were shortened.

The electronic systems are Russian, but could hardly be considered state of the art. The Styx missiles, with active infrared radar guidance, could easily be countermeasured by more modern ESM/ECM.

Lights and shadows

The ship finally entered service in 1992, and could be considered a fairly average destroyer, though rather precarious to work on, due to the insufficient air conditioning and the poor steering as a result of the stability problems. However, once these problems have been overcome, it is believed that the ship will be able to stay afloat in the most dangerous of sea conditions.

Without doubt, this attractive looking ship seems to have adequate military strength.

Russia, despite having so many internal problems, continues to have an important role in worldwide affairs. Therefore, the country needs a sizeable and capable fleet. In this chapter we shall explore the development of the Russian fleet since the Second World War, through the years of the Cold War and into the current period of post-communism. We shall pay particular attention to two classes that appeared in the 1980s, the Sovremenny and the Udaloy.

From the Skoryi to the Kashin

The history of Russian destroyers since the end of the Second World War has been a long and complex process. During the war, Stalin applied a considerable part of the nation's industrial strength to the construction of a fleet that could be better described as numerous rather than modern.

The first destroyer built in the Cold war period was the Skoryi, of which 72 units were completed between 1949 and 1954. It was an attractive ship, but rather antiquated, and certain limitations let it down. For example, its twin 130-mm guns could only be raised to 40°, somewhat disadvantageous at a time when most destroyers had anti-aircraft capabilities. It was also equipped with a few 37 mm A/A guns, 10 533 mm torpedo tubes mounted in sets of five, two mortars and dry docks with anti-submarine charges. It also carried 50 mines.

BESSTRASHNY DESTROYER

The Sovremenny has a very imposing presence, particularly due to the bulk of its bridge, flanked by two quadruple SSM missile batteries.

NASTOYCHEV DESTROYER

The silhouette of this ship shows off its two 130/77-mm turrets, a gun that forms part of the formidable Russian firepower. Also visible is the quadruple block of Raduga SS-N-22 (3M-80 Zubr) anti-ship missiles.

They were driven by low pressure turbines, hardly state of the art propulsion. It had electronic equipment for limited air surveillance, and its sonar would not have been particularly effective against the nuclear and second-generation submarines of the time. In retrospect, one asks oneself how on earth the USSR could have carried out any kind of large-scale naval attack against the West.

The Skoryi was followed by the Kotlin (25 ships with naval weaponry, including anti-aircraft and fire control radar); the Kildin class (4 ships, completed between 1959 and 1960, armed with SS-N-1 anti-ship missiles); the Krupny class (8 ships, completed between 1960 and 1961, with better missile weapons); the Kynda (officially cruisers); the Kanin (8 ships, completed between 1961 and 1963), and the Kashin (20 ships, completed between 1962 and 1973, with gas turbines). All these were intermediate displacement craft, none of which weighed more than 5000 tons when fully loaded. This, along with the shapes of their hulls, made them rather unstable platforms.

New ships

Some time around the early 1980s two

new, modern destroyers appeared, with greater capacity, which make up the backbone of the current Russian fleet. They are the Sovremenny class (12 ships, the last of which is about to be completed) and the Udaloy (8 ships completed between 1983 and 1995); the former has to be considered as a destroyer, but the latter is more like a frigate. The Sovremenny has anti-ship features while the Udaloy is more appropriate for anti-submarine warfare.

The Sovremenny

There is a very traditional design to these ships. Their large superstructure reaches as far as the bridge. Indeed there is something undoubtedly imposing about the Sovremenny's bulky presence. The first ships appeared in 1985 and measured 156 x 17.3 meters, and had a draught of 6.5 meters, displacing 7,940 kg. The main armaments are also in their traditional positions, with a twin 130/70-mm turret and a twin Gadfly missile launcher forward and aft. On either side, under the bridge, there are two quadruple ports for SSM Sunburn missiles.

The telescopic hangar for the helicopter

PROBLEMATIC STEALTH

The very presence of these ships, having very few adequately pitched surfaces, suggests a considerable radar signature that is not easily reduced. This could mean that they can use decoys very effectively.

EXCELLENT NAVIGATION

This ship's castle is almost nine metres high, guaranteeing effective maneuverability. The Bezboyaznnenny is shown here in 1991.

and its landing platform are in unusual positions for the Russian navy, imitating Western fleets by being located aft of the funnel and on to of the superstructure. As this area of the ship moves about less, take off and landing is easier and safer.

Armament

Its armament is made up of eight SS-N-22 Sunburn anti-ship missiles, forty SA-N-7 Gadfly anti-missile and aircraft (or SA-N-17 on later models), and 130/70 mm water cooled guns in twin turrets and AK-630 anti-aircraft-missiles. It also has torpedos

and anti-submarine weapons (four 533-mm tubes on two twin mounts and two RBU 1000 rocket launchers with 120 rockets). It carries 50 mines and a Ka-25 Hormone B helicopter with guided missiles.

Engines

It is driven, unlike the Udaloy, by the more traditional steam turbines: with four tubular pressurised KVN boilers and two interlocked GTZA-674 turbines, with two propellers and a bow truster at the bow.

Electronics

The electronic sensor system is made up of Top Plate 3D air surveillance radar, three Palm Frond surface surveillance systems, Six SA-N-7 Front Dome fire control radar, Kite Screech for 130-mm guns and Bass Tilt for CIWS AK-630 guns. It is equipped with IFF Salt Pot/High Pole/Long Head and two Tacan Light Bull. It also has Bull Horn and Whale Tongue hull sonar.

It has eight PK-10 and two PK-2 decoy launchers, four ESM/ECM Foot Ball and six Half Cup anti-laser alarms. It has an optronic visor and a SqueezeBox telemetric laser.

Additions

It seems that two more ships will be added to the series, probably for sale to China. One common characteristic is the wide radar signature that such bulky

BOW ARMAMENTS

The high castle makes for excellent sailing. It holds the two 100/59-mm artillery set-ups. In front of them is one of the eight octuple VLS with SAM SA-N-9 missiles.

BOW RADAR

At the front of the bridge are two Eye Bowl (for the SS-N-14). On a low pedestal is a Cross-Sword for SA-N-9 and on a higher pedestal, the Kite Screech for the 100-mm guns.

superstructures suppose, and the extensive variety of elements that make up the ships' interiors. The fact that no use has been made of any of the expected reduction systems seems to imply that the Russian navy either possesses highly efficient decoy systems, or does not consider stealth measures to be of importance.

The Udaloy

If the Sovremenny can be considered a destroyer with anti-submarine features, the Udaloy is the complete opposite, being an anti-submarine ship with anti-surface weapon features. Even the Russian navy classifies them differently: BPK Bolshoi Protivolodochny Korabl (heavy anti-submarine vessel) as opposed to Eskadrenny Minonosets (squadron destroyer). There are enormous differences between the two. They are somewhat larger than the Sovremenny, although at first sight you may think differently, being 164 meters long and 19.3 meters wide. It also displaces almost 1,000 kg more, 8,900 to be precise. They are driven by COGAG (125,000 hp) gas turbines engines with two propellers, and the break is nearer the stern, behind the second pair of funnels. The helicopter deck, like its hangar, is found in the usual Russian position, completely inside the stern and above the tracks that are used for launching mines and the VDS hatch.

Armament

Its armament and electronic equipment differ according to the role of the ship. For ASW it has eight SS-N-14 Silex missiles, two Ka-27 Helix A helicopters, two RBU-6000 rocket launchers and two quadruple 533 mm torpedo launch tubes. For anti-aircraft and missile warfare, it is armed with four groups of sixteen SA-N-9 missiles and four CIWS Ak-630 guns. For anti-aircraft and ship purposes, it has two 100/59-mm multi-purpose guns on simple mounts. It generally carries at least 30 mines.

MULTIPLE SENSORS

There is no shortage of electronic sensors. In this photograph of the Bespokoiny , one can see the raising and turning domes of the Front Dome (for SAM) and Bass Tilt (for AK-630), along with the BandStand on the bridge for SSM datalink.

Electronics

The electronic sensor system is made up of Top Plate 3D air surveillance radar (or sometimes Strut Pair), three Palm Frond surface surveyors, two Cross sword fire controls for SA-N-9, two Eye Bowls for SS-N-14, Kite Screech for 100 mm guns and two Bass Tilt for AK-630. It incorporates Horse Jaw hull sonar and HorseTail VDS. For electronic warfare it can use four Foot Ball, two Bell Shroud and two Bell Squat, and also has two PK-2 decoy launchers and eight PK-10, with in-built sound absorbance.

The 1155.1 Type

There is a second Udaloy with a considerably different weapon configuration. It has eight SSM SS-N-22 Sunburn missiles; 64 SA-N-9 Gauntlet; ASW SS-N-15 Starfish missiles; two CADS-N-1 combined missile/gun mounts; two ASW RBU 6000 mortars and eight 533 mm tubes on two quadruple mounts.

Although it seems that the original target was for three ships to be built, only the Admiral Chabanenko actually materialised. As regards to the other two, the Admiral Basisty was scrapped in 1994 before completion and the Admiral Kucherov was never even started.

STEAM ENGINES

The funnel of the Bespekoiny can be seen giving off clouds of smoke in this photograph. This is not a common image these days, as steam becomes less and less common as a means of propulsion.

HANGAR AND DECK

The Kamov Ka-27 Helix helicopter has a telescopic hangar and corresponding flight deck. This does not have any kind of anchorage system, maybe because this is the most stable part of the ship.

FIRE CONTROL RADAR

The 130-mm guns use Kite Screech fire control radar. They operate on H/1/K (K from 20 to 40 Ghz) and may use monopulse tracking.

ILLUMINATION RADAR

The front dome is the director and illuminator of the SAM SA-N-7 Gadfly missiles. It operates on H/I (6 to 8 and 8 to 10 Ghz).

AERIAL RADAR

Back to back type Top Plate radar is used for 3D reconnaissance and surveillance, operating on D/E (from 1 to 2 and from 2 to 3 Ghz).

SAM SA-N-7 MISSILES

The Gadfly was first used in 1981. It is a missile that uses solid fuel and reaches Mach 3 at 18 miles. The Front Dome radar allows for semi-active guidance.

130/70 MM GUNS

First used in 1981, these guns can be raised from 15 to over 85°, firing up to 30 rounds per minute. They reach 16 miles and each missile weighs some 35-kg. Their initial speed is 0.6 miles a second.

SSM SS-N-22 MISSILES

The Sunburn is a later development of the SS-N-9, and was first used in 1981. It uses a motor that consumes liquid fuel. It weighs 3,500 kg, with a warhead, possibly nuclear, of 500. It reaches a speed of 2.5 Mach, though in some phases of attack this can be boosted to 4.5. It can reach up to 66 miles, using either radar or active/passive infrared guidance.

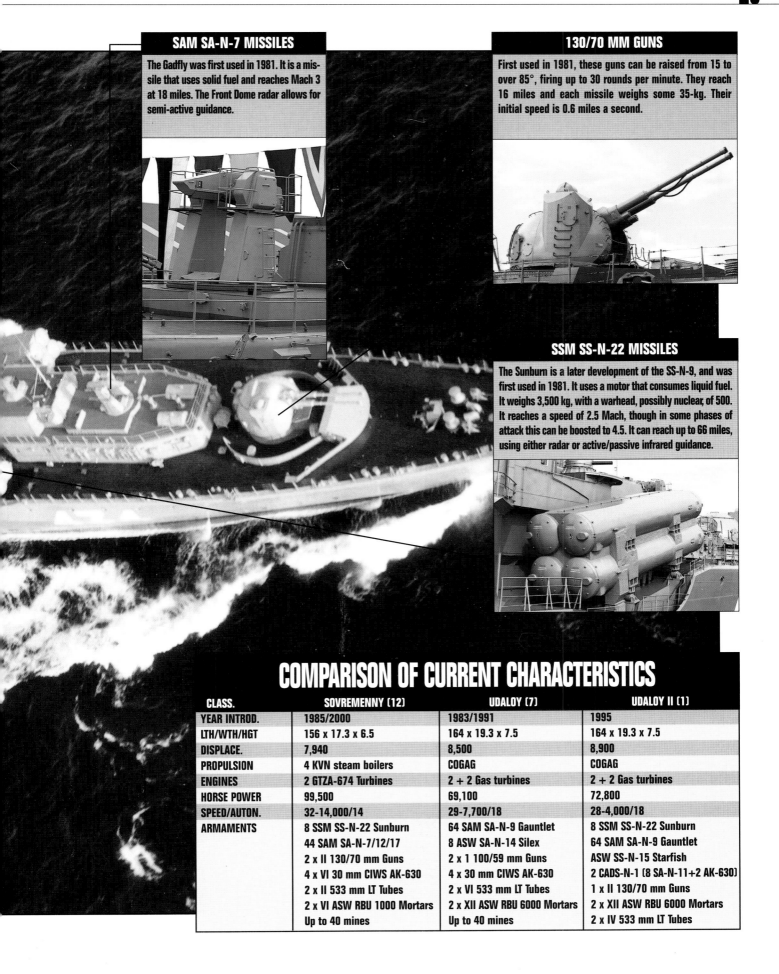

COMPARISON OF CURRENT CHARACTERISTICS

CLASS.	SOVREMENNY (12)	UDALOY (7)	UDALOY II (1)
YEAR INTROD.	1985/2000	1983/1991	1995
LTH/WTH/HGT	156 x 17.3 x 6.5	164 x 19.3 x 7.5	164 x 19.3 x 7.5
DISPLACE.	7,940	8,500	8,900
PROPULSION	4 KVN steam boilers	COGAG	COGAG
ENGINES	2 GTZA-674 Turbines	2 + 2 Gas turbines	2 + 2 Gas turbines
HORSE POWER	99,500	69,100	72,800
SPEED/AUTON.	32-14,000/14	29-7,700/18	28-4,000/18
ARMAMENTS	8 SSM SS-N-22 Sunburn	64 SAM SA-N-9 Gauntlet	8 SSM SS-N-22 Sunburn
	44 SAM SA-N-7/12/17	8 ASW SA-N-14 Silex	64 SAM SA-N-9 Gauntlet
	2 x II 130/70 mm Guns	2 x 1 100/59 mm Guns	ASW SS-N-15 Starfish
	4 x VI 30 mm CIWS AK-630	4 x 30 mm CIWS AK-630	2 CADS-N-1 (8 SA-N-11+2 AK-630)
	2 x II 533 mm LT Tubes	2 x VI 533 mm LT Tubes	1 x II 130/70 mm Guns
	2 x VI ASW RBU 1000 Mortars	2 x XII ASW RBU 6000 Mortars	2 x XII ASW RBU 6000 Mortars
	Up to 40 mines	Up to 40 mines	2 x IV 533 mm LT Tubes

The tactical and strategic revolution brought about by the invention of radar was as important to naval warfare as the invention of steam power. If anything, it was even more important, for radar is capable of locating any object, be it a missile, airplane or ship, at any time and in any circumstance.

A revolutionary discovery

In 1886, Heinrich Hertz found that radioelectrical waves reflect off metal surfaces. The first patents were granted in 1904 for devices that used radioelectrical waves to measure distances as navigational aids. However, none of the countries that took part in the First World War used such waves for any use other than radiocommunication, known then as wireless, and whose aerials soon became regular features on all sizeable warships.

In 1922, Marconi's discoveries brought the subject back into the public eye. At the same time, two North Americans, Hoyt Taylor and Leo Young, of the Naval Aircraft Radio Laboratory, observed that when destroyers passed near to a radio, they caused radioelectrical distortion to the equipment. In 1930, a technician at the Naval Research Laboratory, quite by

A LITTLE OF EVERYTHING
The island of an aircraft carrier, where the majority of electronic equipment is held, is like a display of all kinds of radar. Amongst those shown here are, on the bridge, an SPS-48, on the stern mast, an SPS-49/(V)5, on the gangways, two pairs of Mk 91 illuminators and an ESM/ECM SLQ-32(V)4.

3D AERIAL RADAR
One of the most widely used long distance air surveillance radar in the US Navy is ITT SPS-48. This particular one has IFF. It operates on E/F, has 2.2 MW of power, a range of 220 miles, an altitude of 33,000 m and is of vertical polarisation.

accident, detected an airplane with a 32.8 mc (9.1 m) telemetry aerial. He found that using higher frequencies (100 mc) his discovery could serve as a reliable detection system, and his theories held true when they were first adopted for military use in 1932. Both Great Britain and the USA produced improved systems, particularly the former, logically enough, as a result of the outbreak of the Second World War.

From the radio-telemetre to radar

During the war, the two different sides' electronic technology progressed differently. The Axis countries merely used it as a more efficient way of measuring distances than optical methods. The Allies, on the other hand, used it extensively for detecting airplanes and ships, as well as for range finding. The respective outcomes are only too well known: the Germans faced the ultimately fatal setback of losing the submarine war, while the Allies were able to totally dominate the seas and the skies.

Radar

Radar is, basically, a transmitter and receiver of very high frequency waves (between 2 and 100 GHz) that uses the echo of an object to measure its altitude, bearing and distance.

The shape of a radar beam is not unlike that of a drop of water; the transmitter/receiver is positioned at its apex and

the reflective lens on the blunt side. A radar beam travels in a straight line, regardless of the curvature of the earth, therefore the higher up it is, the more effective radar can be.

Dangerous radiation

High frequency transmissions or microwaves can be very dangerous to humans, so when radar is operating, people are advised to keep well away. On ships, this means getting below deck. If this is not possible, danger zones need to be adequately screened. It might be worth mentioning that although modern domestic microwave ovens are wonderful for heating and cooking food, they need to be shielded in a similar way. The oven automatically turns itself off as soon as you open the door, because if a human body is exposed to microwaves it will suffer, amongst other problems, serious burns.

Doppler radar

So called Doppler radar can detect any stationary or moving object, although only those that are moving appear on screen. This method of highlighting only those objects that are moving, is used on virtually

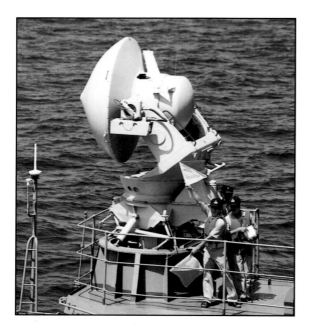

SELF STABILIZATION
All sensors systems on a ship need self-stabilisation systems to cope with the movements of the vessel. The hydraulic systems used for this purpose can be seen in this photo of a Signaal STIR.

all modern ships; and help to overcome the problems of background interference.

Phased arrays

Radar aerial rotation speed depends on the distance of the echo, at short distances this has to be extremely fast and when under attack from supersonic missiles it can become unbalanced. Therefore Phased Arrays were developed one of the most recent revelations in the use of radar. These panels record any echo within reach and send it to a screen without having to move. The North American SPY-1 of the AEGIS system and Russian Sky Watch belong to this group.

ARGO APECS II
Dutch Karel Doorman frigates use autochthonous production ESM/ECM like the Argo APECS II, set up in two groups, one at the starboard end of the bridge and the other at the port side of the hangar.

PHASED ARRAYS
The most recent revelation in the use of radar, are so-called phased arrays: a fixed antenna that sends updates of information concerning time and bearing onto large screens.

Aerial search radar

As radar was perfected and could send more defined and precise beams, its range also decreased because of the need for constant scanning together with oscillating movements of the antenna, causing an inconveniently long space of time between one scan and the next. 3D radar was to be the solution, simultaneously supplying information on each of the

three magnitudes.

The technology for doing this with only one radar is not particularly sophisticated, which is why Back to Back radar was designed. One antenna deals with orientation and the other with altitude, a system that does present certain imbalances, because of the discrepancy between one beam and the other. Therefore, the information needs to be equated on-screen so that the actual image corresponds to requirements.

Surface radar

Surface reconnaissance radar is designed exclusively for locating the danger of smaller boats and ships, that may pose a

threat. Their usual purpose is that of determining the position and the calculation of distance, given that these ships' echoes will always come from the surface.

Navigation radar

Ultimately, a warship is still a vessel that has to sail on the surface of the sea. Its navigational radar is no different to that of any normal merchant ship, used for simply identifying other traffic in the area it is travelling in.

That said, it is not unusual for some warships to use this kind of radar for the occasional military purpose.

Identification Friend or Foe

IFF are special sensors that can identify echoes and ascertain whether they come from enemies or friends. These signals follow secret codes that are standardised between allied countries. This caused a serious problem during the Falklands Conflict because British radar, until they changed their coding system, identified Argentine Exocet missiles as friendly, because they had originally been supplied by France.

TACAN

Tactical Aid to Navigation are radio beacons used for guiding aircraft, making

ESM/ECM

The components of electronic warfare are ESM, ECM and/or ECCM. They are made up of equipment that eliminates, minimises or interferes with the echoes that enemies receive. The Raytheon 32(V)3 is the model preferred by the US Navy, of which there are several versions.

it very easy for aircraft to locate allied ships equipped with the facility. TACAN should not be confused with landing radar that is used by aircraft to align themselves correctly for landing on an aircraft carrier.

Both systems are fundamental for the flight controllers of these airplanes, because there are moments when a plane needs to land on a ship in the shortest possible time.

SIGNAAL WM 25

Many frigates use Dutch WM 25 radar, including the Spanish Descubierta, the Dutch Kortenear and the German Bremen or 122 Type. These transport it on top of a peculiar cone-shaped structure in which some of the ESM counter measures are housed (left photograph).

SALAMANDRE

French Dassault manufacture the Salamandre ESM/ECM, used for protection against surveillance and missile radar, along with illuminators and electromagnetic missile detectors. In the photograph on the right, this equipment is shown assembled on a patrol ship in Qatar.

and white of one of the numerals on the side of a ship is a sufficient guide for a warhead to direct itself efficiently at its target. For this reason, some forces use low visibility numerals.

Electronic warfare

By Electronic Warfare, we mean all activity that attempts to confuse and disorientate enemy sensors, thus making them less effective. Most commonly used are ESM (Electronic Support/Surveillance Measures), ECM (Electronic Counter Measures) and/or ECCM (Electronic Counter-Counter Measures), along with other counter measures, in particular decoy launchers. The general idea is to confuse the enemy signal, causing them to receive unbalanced and erroneous information. Though technically different, those that generate interference, or 'jamming' produce similar results. Stealth technology behaves in a similar way, too, by reducing a ship's own own echo and limiting the return of enemy radar beams, but is not usually considered a component of electronic warfare. The US Navy tends to prefer using variants of the Raytheon 32 (v) 3.

Infrared sensors

Any source of heat generates infrared emissions. An engine's exhaust, even more so if we are talking about that of a gas turbine, produces more than enough infrared energy to be picked up by the sensitive sensors on modern missiles. The difference in contrast between the black

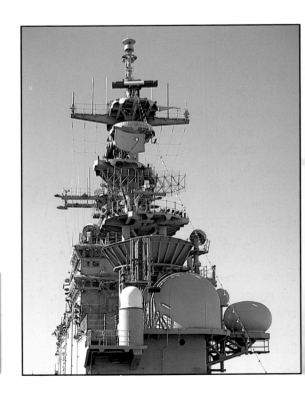

Since the Second World War, Russia has constructed a long line of frigates, leading up to the most recent addition, the Neustrashymy. On the following pages, we shall study some of its predecessors.

The domination of the seas

It has been said that there are two ways of dominating the seas: positive, practised by those who already control a zone and prevent enemy ships from entering it, and negative, preventing the enemy from taking advantage of a given zone, although without being able to use it oneself either. In the Second World War, there were examples of both, in the so-called battle for the Atlantic, in which the allies acted positively and the Germans negatively.

In the first case, the allies used merchant convoys along routes that they struggled to keep open, and prevented the Germans from doing likewise, except along the Norwegian coast and in the Baltic Sea. The Germans, meanwhile, sent submarines and surface ships (known as sur-

> **AIR CONDITIONING**
> The many openings in the hull and superstructure suggest an unsatisfactory air conditioning system, which would complicate NBC isolation.

> **CROSS SWORD RADAR**
> High on the bridge and on a raised pedestal is the radar for the SAM SA.N-9 Gauntlet missiles. Cross Sword operates on band K and is made up of the containers for the electronics, two upper antennas and one in front, leaning at 22.5° in relation to the vertical one.

face raiders) into the Atlantic, trying to prevent the movement of allied fleets.

The Cold War

After the Second World War, the USSR initiated the period of confrontation between the West and the East known as the Cold War. After closing the land border with Berlin, the Soviet Union, having learned the lesson that no matter how powerful one's land forces may be, you always have

to defend the seas around your coast line, started building a sizeable fleet. The Soviet Union had, and still has as Rusia, the largest area of coast to defend in the world, although many of these waters are not of the greatest strategic importance, such as the long and hostile North Siberian coast. The process began with the mass production of four classes: the Sverdlov class cruisers, first generation Whiskey class submarines, Skory destroyers and the Riga class frigates. The first of these appeared in the early 1950s, causing so much concern abroad that Western countries began investing even more in their own armaments.

From Rigas to Krestas

The Riga class, named after a Baltic port that is now the capital of the independent state of Latvia, were an intermediate size frigate (1,500 tons when fully loaded, nowadays they could be considered corvettes), committed to use in the rough waters of the North Sea. Like other Russian ships of the time, if they had ever needed to prove their worth in

SIZE

The ratio between length and breadth is 123/15.5 (0.126), suggesting that this ship should be able to sail very well.

TOP PLATE RADAR

At the top of the stern mast, some 24 metres above the waterline, is the 3D air and surface surveillance radar, operating on D/E bands. The two panels lag 30° to each other, with the IFF antenna in between.

direct combat with western ships, they would hardly have been considered dangerous rivals.

Antiquated technology

The 66 Rigas were ships that used technology that dated back to 1940, only armed with 100-mm guns, a few 37-mm anti-aircraft missiles, two or three torpedos and mortar rockets, A/S charges and 50 mines. Although they sailed very well, their size was a huge disadvantage in particularly violent seas, and they were somewhat unsafe for the sailors on board.

New ships

The 12 Kolas were larger ships than the

Riga class and carried better armaments, but production was stopped in favor of the Riga class, because they were easier to build on a large scale. Both the Riga class and Kolas class were powered by traditional and steam turbines.

New concepts

The Mirka, Grisha and Koni were similar ships which came into service in the late 1960s and the early 1970s. Some of them started using SAM SA-N-4 missiles and used combined CODAG/COGAG powering systems. These ships started establishing the differences between what we could consider to be frigates and those that are classified as corvettes, and heavy and/or missile patrol ships. Although some might say that Krestas class are actually cruisers (the Kresta II weighed 7,700 tons when fully loaded), the Russians classified it as a BPK or heavy anti-submarine ship. A total of four Kresta I and ten Kresta II were constructed between 1965 and 1977. Since the breakup of the Soviet Union, many of these vessels now belong to former members of the USSR such as the Baltic States and the Ukraine and this has, understandably, led to a great deal of controversy.

The Russian fleet also possessed some former destroyers that had been recon-

ASW MISSILES
Foreward of the bridge on the Krivak II is a quadruple battery of ASW SS-N-14 Silex missiles, which can have a 5-kiloton nuclear warhead or a conventional one, with type 40 or 53-72 torpedoes.

GRISHA FRIGATES
Grishas are ships that were built in the early 1980s, and there were five different classes. Some are still being used by countries that once belonged to the USSR, such as the Lithuanian *Aukstaitis* in this photograph.

verted into frigates (Kanin class etc.), making them even harder to classify satisfactorily.

The Krivak class

The next frigates, SKR Storozhevoy Korabl (patrol ships) were the Krivak class, of which 21 Krivak I, 11 Krivak II and 8 Krivak III were built between 1970 and 1990. Later, they too were considered BPKs. They are still being used today. It seems that India is going to acquire an as yet undetermined number of these vessels. They weigh between 3,575 and 3,900 tons, with a wide range of armaments: 76/60 and 100/59-mm guns, SAM SA-N-4 and SSM SS-N-25 missiles, ASW SS-N-14 anti-submarine missiles, RBU 6000 mortars and 533-mm torpedo launchers. They also carry up to 20 mines.

The Ka-25 or Ka-27 helicopter should also be considered an anti-submarine requisite as well as a long distance illuminator.

Electronics

The electronic systems are made up of Head Net or Top Plate aerial radar, Don Kay, Palm Frond, Don 2 or Spin trough surface radar and Eye Bowl, Pop Group, Owl Screech, Kite Screech, Bass Tilt and/or Plank Shave for missile guidance. They use ESM/ECM Bell Shroud or Bell Squat and Half Cup laser alarms. They have Bull Nose and VDS Mare Tail or Steer Hide hull sonar.

Propulsion

All Krivaks are powered COGAG, with two gas turbines for cruising and maneuvering and two more for sailing at full power. The crew numbers 200, 18 of which are officials.

The Neustrashimy class

This is the latest model that Russia has come up with. At the time of writing, one is already in service and another one could be making its appearance shortly. The constructors at Yantar in Kaliningrad scrapped a third hull. This ship could well provide competition for the Udaloy in guns actions. It would probably be very successful should Russia decide to export it, as it is comparable to western frigates, not unlike a small sized Udaloy.

The only unit being used so far was launched in 1993, and visited Kiel in 1995 as part of the Kielerwoche Naval Week

CADS-N-1

On either side of the helicopter hangar are the CADS-N-1 point defense mounts. On the starboard side is the primary helicopter flight control system.

RAISED BOW

The shape of the bow also indicates that there is a large bow mounted sonar dome beneath the waterline.

that celebrated the 50th anniversary of the end of the Second World War.

Platform

The hull has some typical russian characteristics, although there are some obvious western influences. These include the negative sheer forward to enable the gun to fire at-0. The upper deck extends for almost the whole length of the ship. This gives enough space for a flight deck and hanger. There is an extention from the middle of the flight deck to the stern, this extension appears to house a VDS or towed array system. There also appears to be deck rails for mines.

Associated sensors

The straight stem and raised bow indicate the almost undoubtable presence of a large bulb that contains Ox Yoke and Whale Tongue medium frequency active/ passive surveillance sonars. The configuration of the large hatch at the stern is probably used for an Ox Tail VDS, and even though the doors for an acoustic rast do not seem to be visible, it's possible that one does exist and that it uses the same hatchway as an exit.

Engine power

They are driven by COGAG, with four turbines, and can reach a speed of 30 knots and have a range of 4,500 miles at 16 knots. The funnels are positioned in such a way that one/I supposes that there are two engine rooms. The forward one for the port shaft, and the aft one for the starboard shaft. It probably uses turbo generators to produce the electrical power.

Stealth technology

It is interesting that this is the first time that Russia has built a ship that uses stealth technology that can evade enemy sensors. It relies on the usual inwardly slanted bulkheads, probably to avoid having to overstretch the higher decks, in a unique way that gives the ship a strange bellow-like appearance.

Armaments

The armaments consist of SAM SA-N-9 Gauntlet missiles with two CIWS CADS-N-1 mounts (two multitube guns and two quadruple sets of SA-N-11 missiles). Although the clamps are already in place, the SSM SS-N-25 has not yet been installed. It could use SS-CX-5 Sapless from its torpedo launchers. For ASW it has SS-N-15 or 16 missiles, launched by TL, six 533-mm tubes combined with launchers and a ten-tube RBU 12000 mortar. It has a 100/59 multi-purpose gun, positioned in the bow turret, just in front of the VLS SA-N-9 battery.

Sensors

The electronic sensor systems are as would be expected on such a ship: Top Plate and Palm Frond reconnaissance/ sur-

MAIN ARTILLERY

The single 100/59-mm gun, quite small for such a ship, even more so considering the fact that it only fires 16 kg missiles once a second.

KRIVAK FRIGATES

21 Krivak I frigates were completed between 1970 and 1982, followed by the modified Krivak II and III versions. These were built from 1989, and some of them will eventually be destined for India.

veillance/ vigilance radar, Cross Sword for fire control SA-N-9, Kite Screech for the SSM 100-mm gun and Hot Flash for the CADS-N-1. It is also equipped with Salt Pot and Box Bar IFF, weapons controls, Bell Crown datalinking, ESM/ECM electronic warfare, Foot Ball, Half Hat and Half Cup interception laser, along with PK 10 and PK 16 counter measures and decoy launchers.

THE CONCEPT OF THE FFG

The most successful frigate in recent years is the Oliver Hazard Perry, the result of Admiral Elmo Zumwait's naval programs.

The ships of this class were the first ships in the U.S. Navy to implement a "design to cost" concept.

Between 1977 and 1988 the US Navy constructed a frigate that was considered at the time to be the best in the world. It was so efficient that it was built under license by other countries.

The frigate in the modern US Navy

The US fleet did not have any frigates until the mid 1950s, when it received the first DL. In the Second World War, it had used escort destroyers (DE), a name that has little to do with that of DDE.

At the outset of the war, the United States Bureau of Ships ordered the construction of over a thousand DE, and several hundred of those went into service from 1943 onwards.

The Post War period

In the ten years that followed the war, many of these ships returned to the USA after having been lent to other countries. Most of them were immediately scrapped, though some were converted into DER or DEC, and then passed on to other navies.

TRANSFERED SHIPS

The Knox has turned out to be a very satisfactory ship, and not surprisingly the USA has transferred several of them to allied navies, such as the greek Epirus (formerly Connole), shown here.

In the mid 1950s, the Navy built new escort ships, and financed similar off-shore projects for navies in other NATO countries (France and Italy). This was the first 'pure' combat ship, and more than a thousand were completed.

New types

The first type was the Dealey class, of which 13 were built. These were followed by two Bronstein class and ten García class, using a new type of high-pressure steam tur-

bines which caused several problems. The four Cloud Jones got over those difficulties by using Fairbanks diesel engines. Six Brooke class frigates were also built at the same time as the Garcia class. Though they carried SAM "Tartar" missiles.

A successful ship

The next class, the Knox, was highly successful, so much so that many, albeit in different countries (Greece and Turkey, for example), are still being used 30 years later. They were originally classed as DE, but on the 30th June 1975, the US Navy renamed them as FF, or frigates. A version of these ships was built in Spain (the Baleares class), equipped with Standard SM1 MR missiles.

Anti-SLOC strategy

In the early 1970s, at the height of the Vietnam War, it was decided that a large number of escort ships was needed to pro-

BETTER CAREENING
The Spanish F-84 and F-85 (Navarra and Canarias) have perfected the shape of the hull, including a natural deflector at the stern end that improves consumption and, consequently, autonomy.

tect the fleets of oil tankers that transported the world's supply of that precious liquid out of the Middle East.

This was known as anti-SLOC (Sea Line Of Communications) warfare, and a special escort and fleet convoy ship was built for the purpose. The FFG frigate, or Oliver Hazard Perry, was considered the best anti-submarine escort ship that had ever existed, and the USA constructed the second largest series ever built in peacetime.

SIX AUSTRALIAN SHIPS
The RAN ordered the construction of six ships between 1980 and 1993, the first of which were built by Todd in the USA. The first Australian-built unit was the Melbourne, shown here.

Damage without war

The emergence of ASM missiles that could be launched from the air, as used in the Falklands Conflict and the Iran-Iraq War, was considered a serious threat. The U.S.S. Stark provided proof of that when, on the 17th of May 1987, she was struck by two Exocet missiles fired by an Iraqi Mirage F-1. One of them did not explode, but the other badly damaged the forward section of the hull, however there was at least one positive side to the experience: it showed that those ships, despite having been mass-produced for minimum cost, were extraordinarily robust. Further proof of this came when, on the 14th of April of the following year, the Samuel B. Roberts struck a mine, but was not so badly damaged that it could not return to port.

The Oliver H. Perry

FFGs are powered by two LM 2500 gas turbines, connected to a single shaft and a single variable pitch five bladed propeller. This obliges the use of two 350 horsepower retractable electric auxiliary engines to help the ship maneuver in port. These are the first US Navy anti-submarine ships in over 40 years not to use ASROC missile and torpedo systems. Because they do not have the usual octuple launcher and their Mk 13 mod. 4 launcher cannot use them either, launching instead SSM Harpoon and SAM Standard.

Armament

The only anti-submarine armament is the two triple mounts 324-mm tubes for Honeywell Mk 46 and/or Alliant/Westinghouse Mk 50, that can also be launched from SH-60 B LAMPS III helicopters. These helicopters, in constant contact with the ship via data-link, provide the ship with a range and reliability that any ASROC system would find difficult to match. So that operation can be possible in all weather conditions, what is known as RAST has been included, a special system of guidance that uses a pulley attachment that allows the helicopter to be pulled onto the deck by means of a cable. The RAST assembly means that the ship has to be slightly longer and the bow higher, with a step above the TACTASS compartment.

A high price

The very sophistication of these ships has hindered their construction. The complete unit cost, including the hull,

weapons, sensors and helicopters is far more expensive than was originally calculated.

The price shot through the roof when the original electronics and armament systems had to be considerably updated in view of the advanced threats that it had to confront. At the moment, some of the more conventional ships have RAM, and more modern ones have RAM/Phalanx.

Reduced series

Of the original 75 ships that were planned, only 51 have been completed. However, the many ups and downs of recent years were greatly influenced by doubts over the Naval Reserve Force, who eventually received some Knox and Perry class ships as substitutes for their Gearing class training ships.

The Adelaide

Midway through the 1970s, the Royal Australian Navy saw the need to replace their six Leander and Rothesay class frigates. This led to a debate not unlike that over the Charles F. Adams class destroyers a few years earlier (a fairly clear decision, really), that had also created quite a political stir.

However, the decision was made considerably easier when the Oliver Hazard

Mk 3000 Neptune; on F-85 and F-86 there is a natural deflector at the stern for greater range, better fuel consumption and speed; and a Prairie sound absorbency system.

The Cheng Kung

Meanwhile Thailand built seven ships at its own Kaoshiung yard. The main difference is in the armament and corresponding support systems. Unlike the original Oliver Hazard Perry, it has eight SSM Hsiung Fenh II missiles, contained in quadruple ports, and 40/70-mm guns in turrets positioned on either side of the hangar and at the same height as the 76/62-mm OTO-Melara. Some also have three 20-mm guns on the roof of the han-

Perry class was suggested, the best anti-submarine frigate of the time, and the project, received the go-ahead. The first units were built in the USA, and they were numbered as per the Perry class (FFG-17, 18, 35 and 44).

Two more were constructed later in Australia itself, more or less identical to the others.

The Santa Maria

Spain needed escort ships for its aircraft carrier called Principe de Asturias, and therefore built six FFG, each with its own particular characteristic.

Three similar groups

The Santa Maria, F-18, Victoria, F-82 and Numancia, F-83 were the first set. The Reina Sofia, F-84, was built separately and the two corvettes, F-37 and F-38, were sold to Egypt. The Navarra, F-85, and Canarias, F-86, were the last to be built, with electronic systems designed specifically for Spain. The combat systems were all installed in Spain.

Different to the originals

The six Spanish FFG include several modifications of the original idea, the more important changes being: a breadth extended from 13.7 m to 14.3 m, with a larger buoyoncy; a set of computerised stabilising fins; a CIWS Meroka mount instead of Phalanx; Selenia RAN 30L/X radar for CIWS; ESM/ECM Nettunel or

SIX SPANIARDS
Spain built six FFG at the Bazán/Ferrol shipyard. The Reina Sofia was the fourth of the series, built to take over from the two corvettes that were sold to Egypt.

SONAR DOME
Not one Perry has a bow dome, their hull domes are positioned under the bridge. The Santa Maria has a medium frequency Raytheon SQS-56, used for surveillance and attack.

gar. The roof of the bridge, between the two masts, has been reinforced to bear the weight of the Hsiung Feng II.

MISSILE LAUNCHER

On the forecastle there is an all-purpose Mk 13 mod. 4 launcher for SSM Harpoon and SAM Standard SM-1MR missiles. The launcher is assembled as on the Reina Sofia F-84.

OTHER SENSORS

The Raytheon SPS-55 radar is on the mast of the Santa Maria, used for surface surveillance. Also here is the Selenis RAN 30L/X that controls the CIWS Meroka. Part of the EW Nettunel/Mk 300 Neptune equipment is also positioned here.

SENSORS AND EW

The RCA Mk 92 mod. 2/6 illuminator is situated on the bridge, on I/J bands and characteristically dome shaped. Also here are the elements of the ESM/ECM Nettunel system.

DECOY LAUNCHER

The sextuple Loral Hycor SBROC Mk 37 mod. 1-2 decoy launchers use radar and infrared decoys that can reach up to two and a half miles.

DEFLECTOR AT THE STERN

The Navarra F-85 and the Canarias F-86 have a deflector fitted to the underwater section of the stern. This improves the water flow and results in improved fuel comsumtion and range.

TACASS PASSIVE SONAR

On the port side of the stern is the TACASS system, a passive sonar rastra that is more than 2 km long and can pick up echoes from over 60 miles away.

FLIGHT DECK

The large flight deck has Rast, a very reliable system that pulls the helicopter down to the deck by means of a pulley and a cable that is attached to the helicopter.

NIXIE DECOYS

The Nixie decoy launchers are situated at the stern, used for confusing enemy torpedos. They are attached to the ship by an umbilical chord that both tows it and transmits sounds.

PROPELLER AND RUDDER

The Santa Maria uses a five-blade propeller, specially designed to reduce acoustic noise, and it also has a highly effective semicompensated rudder.

O ver the next quarter of a century, new frigates will come into service with cha- racteristics and features that are being developed today. They should all include phased array radar and, quite possibly, new laser weapons.

SEA WRAITH II
The Vosper Thornycroft stealth friga- te weighs 3,000 tons. It uses CODLAG propulsion with quiet electric motors. It can reach speed of 28 to 30 knots, and its maximum length is 138 metres.

EMPAR RADAR
European Phased Array Radar ope- rates on band G. It has been designed specifically for 3D detection, capable of multiple pursuit and missile guidance. It will be used on frigates and larger ships as the main sensor for combat purposes.

The NFR 90

At the end of the 1980s, due to the fact that several countries felt the need to replace some or all of their frigates, the so-called NFR 90 or NATO Frigate Replacement was introduced in prepara- tion for the 1990s.

At first, the countries interested in the NFR 90 project were Germany, Canada, Spain, the USA, France, Holland and the UK, and they first planned to construct about 50 ships. This would considerably reduce costs by combining the economic strengths of each country, yet at the time trying to find ways for each nation to per- sonalise their own part of the project in accordance with their specific needs.

However, it was impossible to find a way of satisfying all of the different coun- tries. The needs and ideas of the North European countries were very different to those of the other participants, particu- larly in the case of the USA, who were already deeply involved in construction of their own Arleigh Burkes. Canada had already ordered their first batch of six Halifax class in 1983, and made a second identical order in 1987. Then, in September 1989, in light of an extensive revision of requirements for the ship, Great Britain pulled out of NFR 90 project, shortly followed by France and Italy. Only Spain, Holland and Germany remained, this not surprisingly almost caused the project to be dropped completely, as it was now completely uneconomic for the remaining three countries to continue by themselves.

The CNGF and TFC

However, the NFR 90 project did serve to show that there were at least some common interests, and two new projects came into existence, the CNGF (Common New Generation Frigates) and TFC (Trilateral Frigate Co-operation). The first unified France, Italy and Great Britain and the second involved Germany, Spain and Holland.

Both projects shared in the development of a European phased array radar, the APAR (Active Phased Array), along with MFR (Multi-Function Radar) and datalink systems, projects that took a long time in coming about, not forgetting that simply building a platform (i.e. the hull and ship) was pointless if it did not also have the whole range of electronics

FRIGATE

This 4,000 ton ship will be driven by CODOG gas turbines at speeds up to 30 knots, with variable pitch propellers. It has SSM, SAM/PDMS missiles and ASW armaments.

F-100 FRIGATE

The first of this series is already being made at the E.N.Bazán shipyard in El Ferrol. It should be completed before the year 2000, launched in 2001, and handed over to its users in 2002.

and armaments too.

The fact that there were reservations over the reliability and timing of the APAR project even before it had started, particularly when the already tried and tested AEGIS system had twenty years of service behind it, proved to be a constant bugbear. Spain, for example, had no desire to wait so many years when the replacement of its fleet was such an urgent issue. Some of the Spanish fleet, the modernized american world war 2 destroyers, had already been removed from service and there was no indication of how they were going to be replaced, now that the NFR 90 fracas had put them at least a decade behind schedule.

Three different projects

Therefore, Spain decided to use AEGIS/SPY-1 on a newer and lighter version of the F-100 frigates, called the D, though without ignoring the progress of APAR, which would be used on their F-110 frigates. Consequently, Germany opted for its F-124 project, as did Holland with their De Zeven Provincien.

Meanwhile, CNGF continued as planned, but adopting the new name of Horizon, shared between France, Italy and Great Britain. At the time of writing, the project seems to be progressing smoothly.

It is worth remembering that stealth technology is a must these days, so therefore, despite seeming relatively compatible, there is a possibility that any of the new projects could cross over and interfere with the development of the other, especially considering that there are so many parallel projects going on. Amongst the most attractive, feasible and novel are the German MEKO A-200 and the Sea Wraith II, Demonstrator and Cougar —the first two by Vosper Thornycroft and the third by BAeSEMA. The Demonstrator is particularly outstanding, a futuristic trimaran that may or may not result in an actual ship, but is impressively innovative all the same.

The De Zeven Provincien

Of all the aforementioned frigates, the ones that will go into service first are the Dutch De Zeven Provincien, scheduled for 2001, 2003, 2004 and 2005.

Platform

The three earlier ones (the others are the F-100 and F-124 class) will be of greater displacement, on the same hull length.

The angled form of the bow and superstructure reduces the radar signature of the ship: the upper deck extends from the bow to the hanger.

The funnels have been divided into two pairs, both pairs angle outwards. The forward pair are higher than the after pair, giving the ship a unique appearance.

DCN FRIGATE
This is the DCN project for a super anti-aircraft frigate called La Fayette. It will have SSM, SAM/PDMS missiles and a 100-mm gun plus a helicopter deck and hangar. No figures have been released yet.

LIGHT COUGAR FRIGATE
With a displacement of 2,800 tons and a maximum length of 118 metres, this ship is equipped with CODAG propulsion that uses two extremely powerful water jets. It can reach speeds of up to 30 knots and has acoustic and infrared stealth radar.

Armaments

They are armed with SSM Harpoon and SAM Standard SM2-MR weapons in a 40-cell VLS silo, which at the same time uses the new quadruple ESSM, greatly increasing its missile capabilities. The gun is a 127/54-mm gun (OTO-Breda) on the forecastle and two CIWS Goalkeeper higher up on the bridge and hangar and complemented by two 20-mm Oerlikon. For ASW there are Mk 46 torpedos that are launched from 324-mm tubes or a Lynx helicopter.

Sensors

The sensor system is primarily made up of the aforementioned APAR for air and surface surveillance, as well as fire control; a SMART L 3D for air surveillance and a Scout for navigation and surface observation.

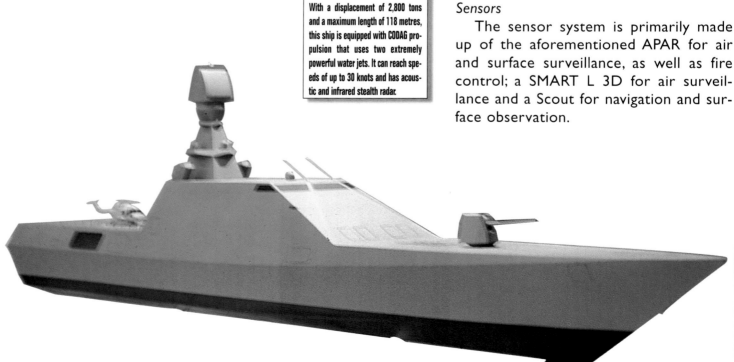

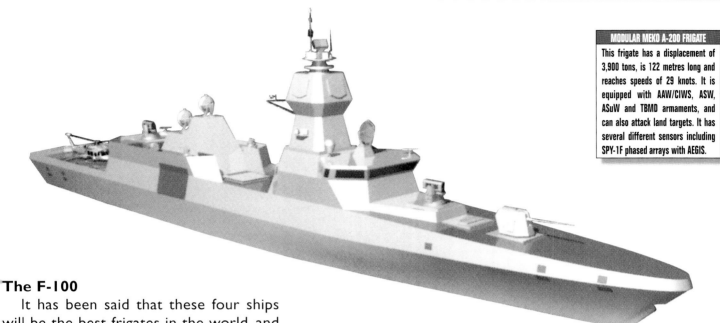

MODULAR MEKO A-200 FRIGATE

This frigate has a displacement of 3,900 tons, is 122 metres long and reaches speeds of 29 knots. It is equipped with AAW/CIWS, ASW, ASuW and TBMD armaments, and can also attack land targets. It has several different sensors including SPY-1F phased arrays with AEGIS.

The F-100

It has been said that these four ships will be the best frigates in the world, and they will come into service in September 2002, November 2003, December 2004 and February 2006.

Project and design

The project is one hundred per cent Spanish, carried out by the Empresa Nacional Brezán at their shipyard in El Ferrol. The first unit should be ready in September 1999, the construction process having already started some time ago.

The hull is shaped well enough to keep it seaworthy in seas up to force 8, fully operational on those of force 6, although they

FRENCH-NORWEGIAN NSM

Programmed for completion in 2004, and conceived originally for use on frigates, this anti-ship missile will also be used from the air. It has a 120-kg HE warhead.

will not be able to use helicopter or refuelling systems on seas rougher than force 5.

Platform

The main platform, hull and superstructure, will be made of high tension AH-36 steel, and at certain points DH-55 steel will be used. The hull will be reinforced in places, most importantly between frames 0 and 44 with 01 between 44 and 164.

The structure of these ships is based on a refined, curved shaped hull designed for stealth, with a main deck that covers the whole length of the ship, including the flight deck: under this is deck 2, deck 1 and the bilge deck. Deck 01 covers the whole length of the superstructure.

The phased arrays are on a raised structure above the bridge, with octagonal sections and prismatic edges, thus avoiding the need of Mack shaped structures such those used on the De Zeven Provincien and 124 frigates.

The F-124 class

These frigates are the planned substitutes for the Charles F. Adams class of destroyers of the German Bundesmarine, which are already being taken out of service.

The philosophy of the project

They, like all ships of the type, are consi-

F-100 E.N.BAZÁN FRIGATE
With a displacement of 5,761, a length of 147 metres, a maximum speed of 28 knots, this ship also has AAW/CIWS, ASW, and ASuW weapons and can attack onto land. It has stealth capabilities using radar, acoustics and infrared.

dered ships for aerial defense, capable of discovering and identifying any kind of air target, and also being able to deal with them appropriately. For the moment, three have been ordered, with a fourth under discussion. They will probably be built at four different yards, Blohm und Voss in Hamburg, Howaldswerke in Kiel, Thyssen Nordseewerke in Emden and Lürssen in Bremen. Basically, they are a continuation of the 123 type Brandenburg class with more complex database distribution technology, multifunction phased array radar and a comprehensive arsenal of ESSM, RAM and SM-2 missiles.

A PROVEN TRIMARAN
COGAG/COGOG gas turbines would drive this ship, but with powerful water jet propulsion. It could reach speeds of up to 25-30 knots.

Platform

Outwardly they look similar to the Dutch De Zeven Provincien, but with just one 76/62-mm gun (OTO-Breda) instead of a 127 model, and just one pair of angled funnels instead of two. They share similar characteristics, such as CODAG propulsion instead of CODOG, and the 124 has just one gas turbine as opposed to the Zeven's two, and their levels of speed and autonomy are slightly different too.

There are more frigates than any other kind of ship in the naval fleets of the world, several hundred are currently being used. Over the next few years, more of these ships will be built than any other type.

From the Atlantic to the Mediterranean

The frigates that are currently in service can be divided into two general groups: frigates known as 'Atlantic', with their own particular features and characteristics; and what are known as 'Mediterranean' these mainly Italian, which, though not entirely different to the former, are sufficiently different to be considered separately.

Specific needs

It is well worth remembering that the sea conditions in the North Atlantic are quite different to those in the Mediterranean, and, as happened in the Second World War, when Italian submarines went into the Atlantic, they needed to be modified (for example, the positions of

VLS LAUNCHERS

These ships have VLS, in two sets of eight, at a very unusual position, at the side of the ship on either side of the funnel.

LOW SILHOUETTE

The Halifax is one of the ships that has most taken advantage of stealth technology. Radar, sonar and infrared methods find it hard to detect, the latter due to the filters on the funnel.

air inlets on the turrets had to be altered), because otherwise they would have had found it difficult to operate alongside their German counterparts. Every ship has to be adapted, as much as possible, to the climatic conditions of the country or region in which it is expected to operate.

Frigates can also be divided into groups according to their appearance; there are those frigates with multiple superstructures as opposed to vessels with a single superstructure.

The Halifax class

These frigates were originally designed for anti-submarine use, but as is normal for any kind of ship these days, they can be used for other purposes too.

Origins

In December 1977, the Canadian government announced that it would like to have a group of six ships that would be known collectively as the Canadian Patrol Frigate (CPF). Five different companies came forward with plans in 1978, which were eventually narrowed down to two.

The construction contract for the six ships was signed on 29th of June 1983, and another was signed on 18th of December 1987 for six more. The six ships that made up the first group were built by Saint John Shipbuilding Ltd, but three of them were subcontracted to Marine Industries Ltd. Saint John made all six of the second batch. The twelve ships were commissioned into the canadian navy between 1992 and 1996.

Modernization

These ships are being modernized with TIAPS (Towed Integrated Active/Passive Sonar) and four of the ships will be converted for aerial defence in 2002, when they will receive APAR radar and SAM Standard or ERSS (Extended Range Sea Sparrow) missiles.

STEALTH CONSTRUCTION
The inwardly sloping bulkheads of the Duke are one of the factors that contribute to the vessel's low radar signature, and the cooling filters over the gas exhaust make it harder for infrared to detect it either.

SUPERSTRUCTURE
The superstructure of the type 23 "Duke" class is also divided into three parts. Although the VLS launchers are the fore castle between the 114-mm gun and the bridge, in front of the SSM Harpoons.

General impression

These are some of the most interesting frigates that exist today; their hull is particularly high, with only a very slight sheer, with a drop at the end of the fore castle to allow the low firing of the Bofors 57/70 mm Mk 2 gun, a light calibre weapon if compared to the more usual 76/62 or 127/54 mm ones.

The superstructures are made up of three different blocks, one low down forward, housing the bridge and almost all the electronic sensors, another in the

COMPARISON OF CURRENT CHARACTERISTICS

CLASS/QUANT.	YR. INTROD	LTH/BTH/HGT	DISPLACE.	PROPULSION	ENGINES	HP	SPEED/AUTON.	ARMAMENT
Halifax (12)	1991/1996	135 x 16.4 x 7.1	4,770	CODOG	LM 2500 (2) SEMT-Pielstick 20 PA6 V280 (1)	47,494 8,800	29-3,930/18 NC-9,500/30	8 SSM Harpoon (2 x IV) 16 SAM Sea Sparrow VLS (2 x VIII) 1 57/70 mm gun 1 CIWS Vulcan Phalanx 8 12.7 mm machine guns 4 324 mm TL ASW (2 x II) 1 Helicopter
Duke/123 (16)	1990/2002	133 x 16.1 x 7.3	4,200	CODLAG	Spey SM1A/C (2) Paxman 12CM (4) GEC (2)	31,100 8,100 4,000	28 28 15-7,800/15	8 SSM Harpoon (2 x IV) 32 SAM/PDMS Seawolf VLS 1 114/55 mm gun 2 30/75 mm guns (2 x 1) 4 324 mm TL ASW (2 x II) 1 Helicopter

center that is made up the funnel and the two VLS, and the other at the stern made up of the hangar for the CH-124 Sea King helicopter. On the roof of the hangar are the Phalanx CIWS gun, the SATCOM antenna and the second Signaal SPG-503 (STIR 1.8) illuminator.

Type 23 Duke class

One of the priorities when it comes to modern ships is an acceptable balance between maximum capabilities and minimum cost.

Nevertheless, ships that are originally designed as cheap substitutes for models already in service often end up more expensive owing to the incorporation of new features. The British Duke class, or Type 23, were planned as replacements for the Leanders and the very expensive Type 22. However, following on from the hard lessons learned by the Royal Navy during the coastal battles of the Falklands Conflict, the new ship was updated, and not only was its completion heavily delayed, but it also turned out to be far more expensive than expected. Though the later ships of this class have been built for a very good price.

Propulsion

They are powered by the still rather unusual CODLAG (Combined Diesel, Electric and Gas) system, in which the three forms of power are used to drive the fixed pitch propellers. This system was

ASW WARFARE
The Maestrale are heavily equipped for ASW, of such strategic importance these days. They still use VDS rather than acoustics, and 533-mm A/S torpedoes. In the photo, one of the few ships that uses them can be seen.

necessary to permit compatibility with the Dowtry 2031Z rast, a long, complex passive search sensor that is nearly a mile long, operates on ULF (Ultra Low Frequency) and can detect submarines at long distances but needs to be used alongside a very quiet propulsion system.

Armaments

It has mixed weapons, another lesson learnt from the Falklands, with SSM Harpoon (2 x 4) missiles, a VLS with 32 SAM Seawolf missiles, a 114/55 mm Vickers Mk 8 gun, two (2 x 1) 30/75 mm Mk 1 Oerlikon/DES, four (2 x II) 324 mm ASW torpedo launch tubes and an ASW Sea King or EH-101 Merlin HAS 1 helicopter.

Platform

It looks similar to a Halifax, with a superstructure made up of three different blocks over a hull of considerable dead weight. The main armaments are on the fore castle (gun, VLS and Harpoon), most of the sensors are around the bridge, and the large, single funnel also has infrared filters. The stern superstructure houses the helicopter hangar, and also supports one of the Marconi Type 911 illuminators. The superstructure has an unusually arched roof, which is part of its anti-radar stealth system.

Italian frigates

The Marina Militare, one of the most important Mediterranean navies, has 18 frigates of four different types, Alpino (2), Artigliere (2), Lupo (2) and Maestrale (2).

Alpino, Lupo and Artigliere

The Alpino, introduced in 1968, is only used on secondary missions; the Artigliere, a modified version of the Lupo design, were built for sale to Iraq, but economic sanctions against Iraq as a consequence of the Gulf War prevented this. They were given to the Marina instead between 1994, 1995 and 1996. The original Lupos go back to 1977, 1978 and 1980 (2), being frigates with heavy anti-ship armaments (16 Teseo Mk 2/TG2 missiles in eight twin containers), and with the better SAM (1 octuple launcher with 8+8 Aspide missiles, currently being updated

CONVENTIONAL DESIGN

The Maestrale, designed in the late 1970s, did not make allowances for stealth radar, and its bulkheads were not slanted and the superstructure was relatively large.

to RIM-7M), conventional guns (one 127/54 mm OTO-Melara and four 40/70 mm Bofors/Breda) and ASW weapons (6 324 mm tubes with Mk 46 torpedoes). The electronic equipment has all the latest EW capabilities. The ships use CODOG at high speed, travelling at 35 knots with turbines and 21 knots with diesel.

The Venti (winds)

The Maestrale, introduced in 1982 and 1985, are similar to the Lupo, but are larger and of greater displacement, but fewer weapons. They have gas turbine engines, just like the Lupo, but 25% more displacement, with the maximum speed being reduced from 35 to 32 knots. On the other hand, they can still cruise at 21 knots, because the diesel engines generate 12,500 horsepower instead of 10,000. This offers better range, 6,000 miles instead of 4,350 at 16 knots.

Compared platform

The three frigates look relatively similar: a main deck running from the bow to the stern, with a very obvious sheer, a central area of the superstructure stretching from

SENSORS

At the top of the forward mast is the Plessey Type 996 3D aerial search radar, on E/F bands, under which are the ESM Racal UAF-1 Cutlass electronic warfare sensors.

side to side at the height of the bridge, with an open under the flight deck, where, in the case of the Maestrale, the VLS is located. One entire block of the superstructure houses the bridge, the armaments, the sensors, the funnel and the helicopter hangar.

Armament set-up

The armaments of the Maestrale consist of four SSM Teseo Mk 2 (TG2) missiles, 16 (8+8) Aspide SAM on octuple mounts, a 127/54 mm OTO-Melara gun, two 20 or 25 mm Oerlikon, six 324 mm tubes with Mk 46 torpedos and two of 533 (at the stern) with Whitehead A184 torpedos. The Lupos instead have sixteen SSM Teseo and do not have 533-mm tubes.

Electronics

The Maestrale's set of electronic sensors is made up of Selenia SPS-774 (RAN 10S) air/surface search radar on E/F bands; SMA SPS-702 surface search radar on band I; SMA SPN-703 navigation radar on band I; Selenia SPG-75 (RTN 30X) fire control for the SAMs and 127 mm gun, on I/J bands and two Selenia SPG-74 (RTN 20X) for the 40/70s, also on bands I/J: NA-30 weapons control for SAM and the 127 mm gun; IPN 20 (SADOC 2) combat system; data link 11 and SATCOM. It also

has two AB 212 ASW helicopters and Raytheon DE 1164 sonar and a VDS that can detect mines.

As countermeasures, it incorporates two 105-mm SCLAR Breda decoy launchers with 20 tubes, SLQ-25 anti-torpedo decoys and Prairie acoustic absorbers.

Other frigates

Whilst on the subject of these highly individual ships, it is worth mentioning the German 123/Brandenburg and 122/ Bremen and the Dutch Karel Doorman.

Nowadays, the development of a ship encompasses all kinds of technology. However, a new concept has arisen in recent years, that of cheaper 'modular' ships, designed with only one purpose in mind, as determined by the client.

From one unit to a long series

Although Henry Ford is usually credited as the inventor of the industrial production line, a similar system had actually been used many years earlier for the making of a muskette during the American War of Independence (1775-81).

Ships have always been built along more conventional lines, one after the other, although they do include parts that are made on production lines. This way, the keel is laid on the slipway, followed by the other parts that make up the hull until the ship can be launched. It is completed whilst afloat, moored to one of the outfitting piers of the shipyard. This later phase of construction while afloat can take far longer than the same process in a dry dock.

A warship, being far more complex to build, can take four, five or even more years to complete.

The Liberty and XXI submarines

During the First World War, trials for the mass production of ships were carried

FLOATING CONSTRUCTION
Once the ship has been launched, it is moored to the quay, where the final pieces are installed, mainly exterior ones like armaments and sensors.

out, such as those for Eagle class patrol boats (Ford were to build 100 ships, but only completed 60), the first attempts to produce ships on production lines. However, it was not until the Second World War, with the construction of the Liberty ship, that a fast mass construction process was used according to methods up until then only used in the motor on car industry. Henry J. Kaiser's Libertie ship which were based on a british design, were built at a rate of one a week. The period of construction while afloat only took two days, which would suggest that they were not launched until they were almost complete, with the engines and boilers already installed. Although these ships were built at almost legendary speeds, they proved highly resistant to attacks, and showed great survival power, thus demonstrating that the system did have potential.

Germany used a similar method for building its class XXI and XXIII submarines, which were built in sections at diffe-

NEW ZEALAND'S TE KAHA
Like the Australian ones, these ships are assembled by Transfield/Amecom in Melbourne/Williamstown, although some parts are made in Whangarei and are transported nearly 2000 miles over the sea.

rent shipyards, and which were finally pieced together with special protection against bombing (Valentin bunker), or at open air shipyards that were specially dedicated to assembly tasks.

Integrated construction

The boom of naval construction in the 1970s was made possible, more than anything else, by the application of production line techniques devised by the Japanese and Koreans. These methods could create economical ships of acceptable quality, although the system was more appropriate for building merchant ships and bulk carriers.

Modular construction

It is worth clarifying the difference between modular and integrated modular construction methods. Modular construction involves the use of a common platform whose armaments and systems are adapted to the individual needs of each client, with one module being substituted by another in an extremely flexible way. The base design is rarely changed, but any armament or another element can be replaced by a completely different device of a similar size.

Integrated modular construction

The process for integrated modular construction differs in that each module is almost entirely factory built, and arrives at the yard already painted and ready for

BUILDING DOCK

Different parts of the ship, called modules, are built separately and then assembled at a building dock. The seams are welded together on the inside and outside.

TURKISH YAVUZ

These are the oldest of all the MEKO 200, having a very attractive design. They use little known Swiss-Italian CIWS Contraves Sea Zenith guns.

use, with most of the interior elements incorporated at the factory (lighting, engines, services, accomadation, etc), and the final assembly process is both quick and simple. This means that the complete construction process takes less time, keeping costs down and improving its market competitiveness.

One important feature of this system is that the modules are built 'upside down', with the ceiling being the floor and the

deck being the ceiling, which saves on scaffolding, because the workers find it faster and more comfortable to walk on the ceiling. The main drawback of the method is in the design, computerised by necessity, that has to foresee every minor detail while at the same time taking into account that everything is completely back to front.

One of the best known examples of IMC is the Thai aircraft carrier Chakri Naruebet, built by E.N.Bazán at El Ferrol and it is considered as good a ship as any.

The MEKO

MEKO is an abbreviation of Mehr Kombitation (better combination), the name given by the first yards to use such a concept, Blohm & Voss in Hamburg and Howaldswerke in Kiel. The first ship of this type was the Nigerian frigate Aradu (formerly Republica), which was ordered in 1977 and entered service in 1982.

Serving in different navies

A total of 28 MEKO frigates are in current use (Argentina considers their four 360s as destroyers) in seven different navies, Argentina (four MEKO 360 and five MEKO 140), Australia (six MEKO 200 ANZ), Greece (four MEKO 200 HN), Nigeria (one MEKO 360), New Zealand (two MEKO 200 ANZ), Portugal (three MEKO 200) and Turkey (four MEKO 200

AUSTRALIAN ANZAC

These ships use stealth technology, as much to avoid radar as infrared and acoustic detection, which could be considered the Achilles' heel of the design.

SSM SEA SCUA MISSILES

Barbaros, like the Yavuz, use British Sea Skua anti-ship missiles that are deployed from helicopters. They, along with the Greek MEKOs, use CODOG propulsion, but have a one not advantage over the rest of the class.

and another four updated MEKO 200), as well as Argentina's MEKO 140, six Australian MEKO 200 and a modified Turkish 200 that will be introduced between 2000 and 2004.

A further six MEKO 100 OPV are expected to be added, and they will probably be built in Malaysia in 10 or 20 years time.

The MEKO 200

The most numerous subclass is the MEKO 200, of which there are 23 either in use or due to be completed very soon. These ships can be divided into four different versions (200, 200HN, 200 ANZ and modified 200), whose characteristics and features, though similar, are by no means identical.

Of all the members of the MEKO 200 group, the most recent units are the ANZ, or Australia and New Zealand models (six new units should be presented to the Australian navy between 2000 and 2004), and the oldest are the Turkish 200s that entered service in 1987.

The platform

These ships have high-sided hulls and large superstructures that run from the bridge to the hangar, including the masts and angled funnels. Propulsion systems vary from series to series, normally being CODAD or CODOG, and sometimes even COGOG.

Armaments

The armaments can vary enormously, which is logical really, considering that this level of flexibility is the very principle of modular construction. Generally, these ships only have one North American 127-mm gun (the Portuguese MEKOs have a French 100-mm gun and the Argentineans have a 127-mm OTO-Melara) and SSM and/or SAM missiles, the first being Harpoons and the latter Sea Sparrow on directable or VLS octuple launchers.

As for Point Defense Systems, the Greek and Portuguese ships use the multiple CIWS Vulcan Phalanx gun, whereas the Turks prefer an Oerlikon Contraves Sea Zenith and the ANZs don't use one at all.

The ASW armaments of all the ships consist of 324 mm tubes, on triple mounts, that use Mk 46 torpedos.

Detection

Due to their wide signature, ships of this type can be detected quite easily by radar, and also by infrared and acoustic systems, an inconvenience inherent of their design, for modular construction, due to cost cutting measures.

SSM MISSILES
Turkish MEKO usually carry a complete set of Harpoon missiles, something that would be unusual on the Greek, Portuguese, Australian and New Zealand models.

VLS LAUNCHERS

The Greek ships use a VLS launcher with 16 Sea Sparrow missiles, whereas two of the Turkish Barbaros use 24 Aspides, and the other two and the four Yavuz use an octuple Mk 29 mod. 1 launcher.

SSM MISSILES

MEKOs carry their SSM missiles between the two masts, usually in two quadruple or twin Harpoon containers, depending on the country and period.

SEA ZENITH

The eight Turkish ships are armed with two CIWS Sea Zenith mounts on either side of the hangar. The Greek versions only have one Vulcan Phalanx on top of the hangar.

FLIGHT DECK

All MEKOs have a flight deck at the stern, though few have such an advanced navigation system as Beartrap. The helicopters vary enormously, depending on each different country.

SEAGUARD RADAR

Over the helicopter hangar, the Turkish ships carry CIWS fire control radar, Contraves Seaguard on I/J bands. The Greek ships carry Vulcan Phalanx in the same place.

BRIDGE AND WAIST

The sensors on the bow mast of the Greek ships are Signaal/Magnavox DA-08 air and surface radar, fixed onto the maintop, and Signaal STIR for fire control.

BRIDGE

The bridge is extremely spacious, and has ailerons that improve maneuverability.

FORE CASTLE WEAPONS

On the Greek ships, the armaments at the fore castle are different, instead of the Swiss Sea Zenith they use the North American Vulcan Phalanx. The 127/54-mm gun, is of the same model and origin.

COMPARISON OF CURRENT CHARACTERISTICS

CLASS/QUANT.	YR. INTROD.	LTH/BTH/HGT	DISPLACE.	PROPULSION	ENGINES	HP	SPEED/RANGE	ARMAMENT
Anzac (8)	1996/2004	118 x 14.8 x 4.35	3,600	CODOG	LM 2500 (1) MTU 12V 1163 TB 83 (2)	30,172 8,840	27 NC-6,000/18	8 SAM/VLS Sea Sparrow RIM-7NP One 127/54 mm gun 2 (2x1) 12.7 mm machine guns 6 324 mm TL ASW (2 x III) 1 Helicopter
Hydra (4)	1992/1999	117 x 14.8 x 4.1	3,200	CODOG	LM 2500 (2) MTU 20V 956 TB 82 (2)	60,000 10,420	31 20-4,100/16	8 SSM Harpoon 16 SAM Sea Sparrow One 127/54 mm gun 2 CIWS Vulcan Phalanx 6 (2 x III) 324 mm TL ASW 1 Helicopter
Te Kaha (2)	1997/1999	118 x 14.8 x 4.4	3,600	CODOG	LM 2500 (1) MTU 12V 1163 TB 83 (2)	30,172 8,840	27 NC-6,000/18	8 SAM/VLS Sea Sparrow RIM-7NP One 127/54 mm gun 2 (2x1) 12.7 mm machine guns 6 (2 x III) 324 mm TL ASW 1 Helicopter

The concept of stealth is one of the most modern naval technologies, and ever since the Silver Shadow came into existence, all ship designers bare stealth technology in mind. The basic idea of stealth is to discover and develop ways in which ships can move about on the water without being detected by enemy sensors.

Stealth against detection

The chances of a ship being detected by one or several others depend on the number and quality of sensors systems that the ships use.

Nowadays, the most normal detection sensors are radar, sonar, infrared, hydrostatic and magnetic, not forgetting others that may still sound like they belong in science fiction, such as wave generators and laser. There are other much older methods, such as location using radio wave transmission, that are still used today in certain circumstances, but do not offer the same level of reliability and

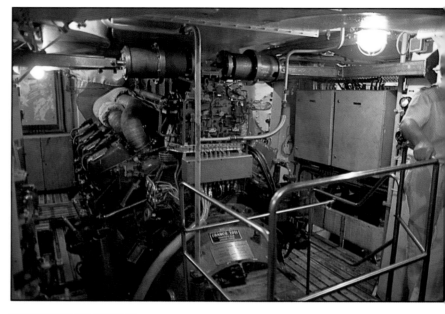

ELASTIC ASSEMBLIES

The engines of the Italian Gaeta class minesweepers were modified with the installation of elastic elements that reduced the quantity and volume of sound generated. This is important for a ship whose main purpose is anti-mine operation, in which it needs to detect mines with multiple influence fuses.

precision as newer methods.

Stealth technology aims, as much as possible, to avoid detection by enemy sensors, but not by eliminating or interfering with them, but by denying them the information they are seeking by decreasing or eliminating the echoes that our own ship generates.

SMYGE

The Swedish Karlskronavarvet also built this stealth prototype in 1991. It is a BES of GRP in sandwich formation with Kevlar reinforcements at certain points. It is 30 m long and has 140 t displacement. It incorporates diesel engines with water jets and can reach 45 knots, and has SSM missiles, a CIWS gun, mines and A/S and VDS torpedos that are launched from an interior moonpool.

Radar stealth

As radar is the most commonly used method of detection, most ships concentrate most of their stealth technology in this field. Quite spectacular conclusions have been reached.

Maximum radar reflection is produced when a wave falls perpendicularly onto a surface, and the reflection is even more powerful when it comes off a concave or rounded surface. Therefore, modern ships are designed with hulls and superstructures that are formed by flat plates that are at oblique angles to the waterline, of up to seven or more degrees, or of several plates that form a convex shape. Rounded masts are substituted with triangular or rhomboid ones, with one edge directed towards the most shielded part of the ship.

This means that the reflected waves are more dispersed, and therefore less return to their point of origin, if the echo can be picked up at all, it will be so weak that it could be erroneous.

In extreme cases, RAM (Radar Absorbent Material) is used; a spongy layer with special characteristics that is fixed over the surface that needs protection.

MONOCAREENING

Monocareening ships with buoyancy according to the Archimedes principle can also be used as minesweepers as long as their shape does not create too wide a hydrostatic field. In this photo, the Segura, the most recent Spanish minesweeper, built by E.N.Bazán/ Cartagena is shown. The fourth and last unit will be handed over in 2001.

SPECIAL PROFILES

North American Arleigh Burke destroyers, the first to make extensive use of stealth technology, changed their rounded profiles for a polyhedral form. This shows how, curiously, this kind of shape is harder for radar to detect.

Artificial military satellites are fitted with extremely accurate radar that can easily detect a ship because decks are highly efficient reflective surfaces. Therefore on Silver Shadows, Smyrge and any other ships constructed with this in mind, the typical deck surfaces are kept

to a minimum, and the plates are sloped as much as possible while the interiors of gunwales are, wherever possible, deflective, so as to minimize the chance of radar waves returning to their point of origin, be they radar situated on the horizon, radar situated on satellites, or carried by airplanes.

Using stealth radar technology, a ship is considerably harder to detect. For example, an American Arleigh Burke type des-

troyer, weighing more than 8,000 tons, generates a very small echo, comparable to that of a fishing trawler just a few hundred meters away.

Sonar stealth

Before sonar sensors, which can be used by submarines to detect surface vessels as well as other submarines, the most preferred method for reducing acoustic detection were the widely used isolators of generated sound (elastic assemblies, etc.) along with engines and special apparatus with unusual acoustic characteristics and the use of propellers with specially shaped blades to reduce sound and cavitation (the noise created by moving screws, etc.)

Prairie sound absorbers should also be mentioned at this point, based on bubbles of air that form a thin surface, and the widespread use by submarines of anecoic tiles.

Infrared stealth

The part of the electromagnetic spectrum between microwaves and visible light (i.e. approximately 1,000 to 500 thousand GHz) is known as infrared. IR, as it is commonly abbreviated, was discovered by the

cool the aforementioned gases, although some ships actually exploit these gases to generate heat and/or energy with steam boilers inserted at the outlets.

At the same time, ships can resort to panels and bulkheads in front of the gas exhausts, obliging them to travel longer distances and at the same time, lose temperature.

Hydrostatic stealth

When a ship sails, it produces a series of phenomena that cannot only be measured but must be used for its detection or so that it activates a fuse. One of the most notable is the so-called pressure wave.

The movement of the hull of a ship over waters of a certain depth, in a way that is directly related to its speed and angle of squat, generates a certain quantity of hydrostatic pressure on the sea bed, this is more noticeable the shallower the water. Hulls with bouyancy according to the Archimedes principle find this hard to avoid as a result of their own characteristics, and to do so in a more or less satisfactory manner, tend to use an alternative such as ANT (Advanced Naval Technologies), specially used on certain occasions and on certain kinds of ship.

Magnetic stealth

The ancient Greeks discovered magnetism. It is an inherent characteristic of iron and steel hulls, and led to the first important mine in history, the magnetic mine, used extensively by the Germans in the First and Second World Wars, and torpedo fuses.

The reduction of a ship's magnetic field is quite a complex technological process, beginning with a powerful source of electronic energy that is applied to the hull by large, powerful coils. Demagnetization is usually carried out at specially designed centers, and should be regularly repeated, although some ships have demagnetizers on board, and as long as the machines are in operation, magnetization is kept to a minimum.

German astronomer Freidrich Wilhelm Herschel around the year 1800.

Any object with a temperature above absolute zero (-273.15 °C) transmits infrared rays, of higher or lower intensity depending on its actual temperature. These rays can be detected by any adequate sensor.

Modern day armies use visors that are able to detect human body heat, but with respect to ships, the most normal and most easily detected sources of infrared transmission are the gases that come out of the engine or turbine exhausts.

To reduce the possibility of such infrared detection, different cooling systems are employed, such as special filters with or without the pulverization of products that

RADAR STEALTH

This feature, against radar beams, is obtained by giving a ship the adequate lines, which as a rule are angled. Here we see the bow of the Israeli Lahav corvette, on which such lines are clearly visible. The ship was built by the American Ingalls company.

Another way to reduce the magnetic field is to build the hull with as many non-magnetic materials as possible (GRP/PRFV, wood, etc.), and to use less magnetic metals (aluminium, titanium, etc.) or non-magnetic steels, or where there is no option but to use standard steel (in the engines, for example) to demagnetize them beforehand.

Non-magnetic steels can provoke unexpected problems; for example, seawater tends to have a corrosive effect on them, as happened a few years ago to a new series of submarines purchased by the German Bundesmarine.

Therefore, by trying to reduce the magnetic field, making them harder for MAD submarine detection systems to pick up, they were presented with new types of problems.

Futuristic sensors

It has often been said that some satellites have a special system that measures the height of the waves of the ocean, and can detect irregularities that suggest the presence of submarines.

Without going into too much detail, it seems clear that if this theory turns out to be correct, a new form of stealth technology would have to be investigated, because if the movement of water at the

SEA SHADOW
The Sea Shadow is a SWATH with a dead work at an angle of 45°. It displaces 560 tons and is 48.8 meters long. It is powered by diesel engines.

PROPULSION MODULES
What is known as active acoustic stealth refers to the reduction of noise generation. For such a purpose, assembling the propulsion equipment in modules enables them to use rubber supports.

surface is sufficient to give away the presence of a submarine, then an effective solution would need to be sought to prevent that from happening.

This is a clear example of the ongoing struggle between two technologies to outdo each other. As stealth technology find new ways of avoiding sensors, sensors find new ways of getting around the obstacles set by stealth, The struggle is unlikely to ever end.

Asian countries will have a lot to say as regards the future of naval technology, particularly with respect to escort ships such as frigates.

China

The western world is still largely unaware of the enormous industrial power of the People's Republic of China. This is a country with a population of over a thousand million people that, if managed adequately, will soon be able to compete with countries that are often considered well out of China's reach. This is at least true of specific areas, for what they may lack in technology, they are certainly not lacking when it comes to buying power, and it is worth remembering that an enormous quantity of products arrive on the western market from China.

Fleet

The current Chinese fleet has a good number of modern units with appropriate features. And although it is not possible to provide a detailed appraisal of them, it

> **PROPULSION**
> These ships use CODOG propulsion, using American Haribing gas turbines or Ukrainian Quingdao. The diesel engines are invariably German MTU.

> **ARMAMENTS**
> The guns are Chinese produced, as are the missiles, although they are really copies of foreign designs mainly of Russian SSM SS-N-4 Sardine or French SAM/CIWS Crotale, which the Chinese call YJ-1 and HQ-7 respectively.

would be foolish to underestimate their potential. Apart from a fleet of nuclear submarines (one strategic missile launcher and five attack submarines), a new type is currently being constructed based on Russian designs, and the fleet also possesses three Chinese made conventional submarines and four Kilos, as well as 60 conventional Romeos in reserve.

China also has seven modern frigates, which came into service in the 1990s. Many other large volume ships will come into service very soon, amongst which are two Russian Sovremenny destroyers, and more than 500 units of different types from auxiliary to amphibious or MCMV.

Luhu frigates

The Luhu class is made up of the two Haribing and Qingdao frigates. These intermediate displacement ships use CODOG propulsion with gas turbines, the former using LM 2500 and the latter using Ukraine, giving the ships the power to move at 31 knots on German MTU diesel engines. They were built at the Jiangnan shipyard.

Armament and sensors

The SSM weaponry is made up of YJ-1 (Eagle Strike) CSS-N-4 missiles or Chinese made subsonic CSS-8-Saccade, or other wise SAM CSA-4 on HQ-7 mounts (the Chinese version of Crotale). They also have a twin 100/56 mm mount and a further

ARMAMENT AND SENSORS
Jiangwei are built entirely in China, but there are obvious foreign influences, as are the mounts for the missiles and Sun Visor fire control radar, housed in a dome over the bridge, that have an unmistakably Russian feel to them.

four twin mounts of 37/63. The ASW weapons consist of two triple mounts of 324 mm Whitehead B515 torpedo launch tubes, with Mk 46 mod. I torpedos, mortar rocket launchers with 12 tubes and 120 rockets, and two Harbin Zhi-9A Haitun helicopters (a Chinese imitation of the French Dauphin 2).

BASIC DIFFERENCES
Korean Ulsan do not form a homogenous group of ships, some have twin 40/70 guns on their turrets, such as the Keong Buk in this photo, and others have four pairs of American 30 mm Emerson Electric guns. The first four units belong to the latter group.

The sensors, countermeasures and electronic warfare equipment are either Chinese or imported from the West, the former probably being copies of products that they had previously bought.

Jiangwei frigates

These four ships (Anoing, Huainan, Huaibei and Tgling) were completed between 1991 and 1994 by the Hudong shipbuilders. Like the previous class, there is a version used for export that has been quite successful in the Far East.

Features

Their displacement (2,250 t when fully loaded) is less than that of the Luhu, and they are also smaller. They are armed with six SSM YJ-1 (Eagle Strike) missiles and SAM RF-61 (CSA-N-2), more or less a copy of Sea Sparrow, currently being replaced with LY 60s. The artillery is exactly the same as that of the Luhu. For ASW, it only has two RBU 1200 rocket launchers and a Harbin Zhi-9A helicopter. Similarly, most of the electronics and decoy launchers are western (such as the American sextuple SBROC Mk 36).

Two units have been completed of an updated version, and a third should enter service within the next year.

Luda frigates

The Luda was the first entirely Chinese

design, although they were obviously influenced by the Russian Kotlins that China received in the 1960s. The complete series is made up of some 15 units that came into service between 1971 and 1991. There are two versions: one with a hangar and helicopter deck and another with guns at the stern.

Features and armaments

These ships displace 3,600 tons when fully loaded, and use SSM HY-2/CSS-C-3 A Seersucker missiles (six missiles on two triple ramps) and SAM CSA-4 on HQ-7 mounts. The gun armament is made up of two twin 130/58 mm in two turrets reduced to one on those ships that have helicopter decks, more than eight 37/63 or 57/70 on twin mounts and eight of 25 mm (copies of Russian guns of similar calibre), 324 mm ASW tubes and torpedos, FQF 2500 rocket launchers and antisubmarine mortar charges. The electronics are modelled on Russian systems but are made in China.

India

India has one of the biggest fleets in Asia, mainly passed on from Britain and Russia (one should not forget that India was once a British colony, or that it always enjoyed relatively good relations with the USSR), although over the last three decades it has been able to build its own

> **INDIGENOUS SHIPS**
>
> The five Nilgiri were the first significant ships to be constructed in India. At first, they were equipped with Sea Cat missiles, but they were later substituted by Russian AK-230 guns.

> **INCOMPLETE SERIES**
>
> The six Godavari, of which only four are in service, will include some variations. For example, the last two will have quadruple missile ramps for SSM SS-N-25 instead of the simpler SS-N-20.

ships based on those that it has received. At the moment, three highly updated Russian Krivak III frigates are pending (the number could be increased to six), and should be introduced in 2002. Like China, India maintains territorial disputes with its neighbors (a worrying fact considering the country's nuclear power), and in particular with another nuclear country, Pakistan, a circumstance that obliges the country to maintain and expand its powerful fleet.

Nilgiri frigates

These five ships are Indian made, but are almost identical to British Leander class. The ships are almost redundant nowadays, despite having been constantly updated. They are powered by conventional steam turbines, at 450°C with a pressure of 38.7 kg.cm^2.

The artillery and anti-submarine capabilities of this ship are conventional, with a helicopter that uses a telescopic hangar.

Godavari frigates

In the 1970s, India built, under British licence, half a dozen Leander frigates at Mazagon Dock Ltd in Bombay. All these ships were introduced between 1974 and 1981. They are little more than straight copies, adapted to use the sensors and armaments that India was capable of acquiring.

COSMOPOLITAN SHIPS
Despite being designed and built in China, Naresuan include a number of foreign features. For example, their 127-mm and SSM artillery are from the USA, and most of their electronics are either Dutch or American.

Original project

With that experience behind it, in the late 1970s, India set up Project 16 to build the Godovari, based on experiments with the Leander, but enlarged and adapted the diverse equipment that were going to be fitted to them. The complete class is made up of six ships, three from Project 16 and three more from 16A. They vary more in arms and sensors than in the physical characteristics of the hull and propulsion system, they are being fitted steam turbines at a time when gas turbines are the norm. Of the three 16 A ships, only one has been completed, the others will be ready between 1999 and 2003.

Armaments

Their armaments consist of SSM SS-N-2D Styx missiles (four in Project 16) or SS-N-25 (16 in the 16 A), as well as SAM SA-N-4, which on the 16 A can be replaced by Trishul or Barak.

DUTCH DESIGN
The three Indonesian Fatahillah class frigates were built in Holland, a country that it still maintains good relations with, although the armaments come from different places, particularly France and Sweden.

Thailand

This country operates on two different seas (the Anaman in the West and the Gulf of Siam and the East China Sea to the East), separated by the long Malay peninsula. The Thai fleet is currently undergoing an important phase of expansion, and has received important reinforcements (Chakri Naruebet aircraft carrier, Naresuan and Chao Phraya frigates) in the 1990s.

Naresuan frigates

These two ships (Naresuan and Taksin) were made in China, and were handed over to Thailand in 1994 and 1995. They can be considered highly modified but smaller versions of the Luhu.

Propulsion and armaments

Both the ship's armaments and electronics come from a wide variety of countries, in particular those of the West and China.

Their CODOG propulsion uses American LM 2,500 gas turbines and German MTU diesel engines, with Dutch Lips propellers. The armaments consist of SSM Harpoon missiles (in two quadruple containers) and SAM Sea Sparrow, with North American artillery (one 127/54-mm Mk45 mod.2 gun), with 324 mm ASW Mk 32 mod. 5 torpedo launch tubes and North American Honeywell Mk 46 torpedos, along with an SH-2G helicopter, soon to be replaced with an S-70B7.

CHINESE APPEARANCE

The Thai Chao Phraya bear an extraordinary resemblance to the Chinese Jianghu IV and V, and could even be considered part of that series. The standard of construction was somewhat questioned when they arrived in Thailand, and certain areas of the ship were in need of repair.

Electronics

The electronic sensors, countermeasures and EW set-up come from several countries. Thus, the Signaal LW 08 aerial search radar is Dutch, the Type 360 surface radar is Chinese and the two Raytheon SPS-64(V)5 are American. The ships also have SSM fire control radar, a 127 mm Signaal STIR gun, and two Chinese 37 mm 374G guns.

The countermeasures, four in total, are the Chinese 945 GPJ with 26 tubes, and the ESM/ECM Elettronica Newton Beta EW, which is Italian.

COMPARISON OF CURRENT CHARACTERISTICS

CLASS .	LUHU (2)	JIAGWEY I (4)	JIAGWEY II (3)	NILGIRI (5)	GODAVARI (6)	NARESUAN (II)	CHAO PHRAYA (4)	ULSAN (9)	FATAHILLAH (3)
YR. INTROD.	1994/1996	1991/1994	1998/1999	1974/1981	1983/2003	1994/1995	1991/1992	1981/1993	1979/1980
LTH/BTH/HGT	143 x 15.1 x 5.1	118 x 12.1 x 4.8	112 x 12.1 x 4.8	113 x 13 x 5.5	127 x 14.5 x 4.5	120 x 13 x 3.8	103 x 11.3 x 3.1	102 x 11.5 x 3.5	84 x 11.1 x 3.3
DISPLACE.	4,200	2,250	2,250	2,682	5,100	2,980	1,924	2,180	1,450
PROPULSION	CODOG	Diesel	Diesel	Vapor 850°/ 38kgcm²	Vapor 850°/ 38kgcm²	CODOG	Diesel	CODOG	CODOG
ENGINES	LM 2500 (2) o Ukraine (2) MTU 12V 1163	TB 83 (2)	12E 390 (2)	Jet engines (2)	Jet engines (2)	LM 2500 (2) MTU 20V 1163 TB83 (2)	MTU 20V 1163 TB83 (2)	LM 2500 (2) MTU 16V 538 TB82 (2)	Olympus TM3B MTU 20V 956 TB92 (2)
HP	55,000 or 48,600	8,840	14,400	30,000	30,000	44,250 or 11,780	29,440	53,640 or 5,940	25,440 or 11,070
SPEED/RANGE	31	NC-5,000/15	25-4,000/18	27-4,500/12	27-4,500/12	32-4,000/18	30-3,500/18	34 or 18-4,000/15	30-4,250/16
ARMAMENT	8 SSM YJ-1 Eagle Strike 8 SAM HQ-7 (Crotale) 2 guns of 100/56 mm (2 x II)	8 guns of 37/63 type 76A (4 x II) 6 TL ASW of 324 mm (3 x II) 2 ASW FQF 2500 mortars (2 x XII) 2 Helicopters Harbin Zhi-9A Haifun	6 SSM YJ-1 Eagle Strike 6 SAM RF-91 (CSA-N-2) 2 guns of 100/56 mm (1 x II) 8 guns of 37/63 Type 76A (4 x II) 2 ASW RUB 1200 mortars (2 x V) 1 Harbin Zhi-9A Helicopter	2 guns of 114/45 mm (1 x II) 4 guns of 30/65 mm (2 x II) AK 230 2 Oerlikon of 20/70 (2 x I) 6 TL ASW of 324 mm (2 x III) 1 ASW Bofors Mortar of 375 (1 x II) 1 Helicopter	4 SSM SS-N-2D Styx 20 SAM SA-N-4 Gecko 2 guns of 57/70 mm (1 x II) 8 guns of 30/65 mm (4 x II) AK 230 6 TL ASW of 324 mm (2 x III) 2 Helicopters	8 SSM Harpoon 8 SAM Sea Sparrow VLS 1 gun of 127/54 mm 4 guns of 37/76 mm 6 TL ASW of 324 mm (2 x III) 1 Helicopter	8 SSM YJ-1 Eagle Strike 2 o 4 guns of 100/56 mm 8 guns of 37/63 Type 76A (4 x II) 2 ASW RUB 1200 mortars (2 x V) 1 Helicopter (2/100)	8 SSM Harpoon 2 OTO Melara 76/62 mm (2 x I) 6 Breda 40/70 mm (3 x II) 6 TL ASW de 324 mm (2 x III) 12 Cargas A/S	4 SSM MM38 Exocet 1 Bofors gun 120/46 mm 2 guns of 40/70 mm (2 x I) 2 Rheinmetall of 20 mm (2 x I) 6 TL ASW of 324 mm (2 x III) 1 ASW Bofors mortar of 375 (1 x II) 1 Helicopter

The Marine Nationale uses the two most modern frigates in the world, La Fayette and Floréal, and in a few years will also possess the Horizon, a futuristic project shared with Italy and Great Britain.

A notable achievement

Now that stealth technology against enemy sensors is omnipresent all around the world, many countries have applied this technology to their ships. France was the first country to achieve successful results in this respect with its La Fayette class (La Fayette, Surcouf, Courbet and Aconit). Another ship, Guépratte, will be added in 2002.

The La Fayette is, without a shadow of a doubt, one of the most interesting ships of recent times, and has been exported very successfully. Its appearance is immediately striking, totally flat and without any protuberances, with panels slanted at 10°, and the fore castle and stern decks built into the superstructure. This means that the capstans, log reels and so on are completely protected and therefore immune to radar detection.

Export success
The news that France had authorized

SIMPLIFIED SILLHOUETTE

The La Fayette has taken stealth technology to limits unheard of before. As a result, its outline is so simple and lacking in features that it looks more like an enormous scale model than a 'real' warship.

AUTOMATIC TRACK

The automatic SAMAHE helicopter track includes a special feature, a hook that clips onto the undercarriage of the helicopter, and pulls it along grooves set into the flight deck.

the sale of 16 units to Taiwan in August 1991 caused quite an international stir. The ships were to be built in two batches, six in France, which have already been handed over, and the other 10 in Taiwan. However, it seems that they have been changed for 1,500 ton corvettes in order to cut costs.

Saudi Arabia has ordered three units, these however are quite different to the French originals, which are being built by DCN in Lorient, and will be completed in the years 2001, 2003 and 2005.

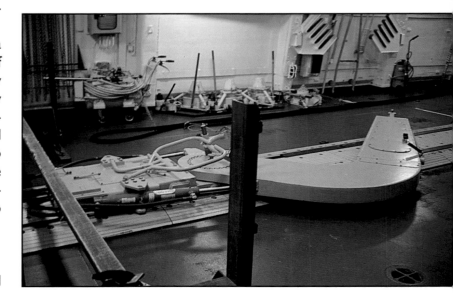

The La Fayette frigates

At first glance, these frigates do not look like they have been completed, because of the lack of any kind of exterior equipment. However, everything on these ships that could generate a radar echo has been shielded by bulkheads or curtains, and nothing is visible unless it is absolutely necessary. Even the spaces and decks for the lifeboats, situated near the middle of the ship, are shielded by a rolling metal curtain which has been designed to prevent radar detection. The fastening points for sea replenishment are treated in the same way, built into the funnel and covered by a mesh curtain.

All the mooring and anchoring equipment is located beneath the weather deck so that they do not up set the radar profile of the ship.

On arrival in port a set of panels are opened in the hull to allow the mooring ropes to be passed through.

A double hull

These ships are built with high-tension steel, and have a double hull from the waterline to the deck, designed to absorb the impact of missiles. Both 'hulls' are sepa-

ARRIVAL AT PORT
On arriving at port, when mooring maneuvers are essential, the La Fayette can open the port that guard the mooring gear from radar detection. Of course, when at base, there is no point observing stealth procedures.

rated by a passage that runs around the whole superstructure, and forms a kind of 'service gallery' from where all kinds of activities can be carried out. However, none of these activities are vital for the operation of the ship, so it is no immediate problem if the outer hull is struck by a missile.

Peculiarities

Every space is covered by a similar 10-mm steel shield, and there is a long, wide corridor in the main deck (known familiarly as Les Champs d'Elisées) which provides access to each adjacent area. One curious construction detail is that of the two funnels, and other high structures of the ship, that are built using a 'sandwich' of balsa and GRP, treated with fireproof elements, which keep the weight of the upper sections down to a minimum. This strange construction method has even been applied to the sides of the 100/55-mm mod. 68 CADAM turrets too.

Armaments

Strangely, considering the enormous efforts that have gone into the construction, these ships have relatively poor armaments, being little more than conventional ship. They have a 100/55-mm gun, another 20-mm Giat 20F2 gun on the bridge, wings and a pair of 12.7-mm machine guns.

As for missiles, they have a pair of quadruple mounts for SSM Exocet MM40 Block 2 missiles, as well as an octuple SAM Crotale Naval mount. Eventually they will

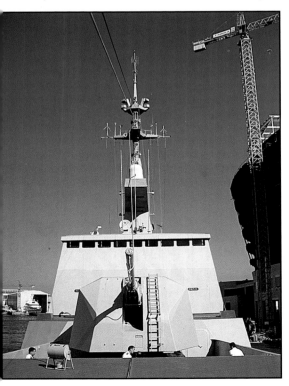

100 MM TURRET
The round shaped 100-mm Creusot-Loire turret, present on most ships in the Marine Nationale, has taken on a new, angled look, with balsa wood inside and GRP on the surface.

SLOPING BULKHEADS
Almost all bulkheads slope at about 10°, particularly those that cover the length of the ship and are more susceptible to radar beams.

modified to work with Arabel and SAAM (Système naval d'autodéfense moyen portée) radar. They do not have any anti-submarine weapons yet, unless the AS 565 MA Panther helicopter has such a provision. This helicopter could be replaced by a Super Frelon, since the hangar is big enough to house one. The flight deck has a SAMAHE system on an automatic track, as well as a Beartrap anchoring system.

Sensors

The electronic equipment is made up of Thompson Sea Tiger Mk2 air-surface radar on E/F bands for targets up to 2 m2; for navigation, two Racal-Decca 1229, one of which controls the helicopter on band I; for fire control, Thompson-CSF Castor 2J on band J, for targets up to 1 m2; for weapons control, Thompson-CSF CTM IR/radar; Sagem TDS 90 VIGY optronic system; Thompson-CSF TAVI-TAC 2000 combat data; two SATCOM Syracuse and OPSMER commando support.

As for countermeasures: two CSEE

ANCHOR DECK
The La Fayette is the only kind of ship in the world with a closed off anchor deck that can only be accessed by two large ports.

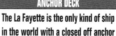

Dagaie Mk 2 decoy launchers; ESM Thomson-CSF ARBR-17.

The Floréal class

These ships are officially known as ocean patrollers or vigilance frigates. They entered service between 1992 and 1994, and are currently used in the French colonies (Antilles, Numea, Indian Ocean, Tahiti, etc.) as modern colonial ships.

Their funnels are specially designed to improve the warm air currents on the flight deck. They can operate independently for 50 days, with storage space for 100 tons at the stern. They are constructed in a standard way, with stabilizing fins and integrated air conditioning.

Weapons

Their armaments are made up of SSM Exocet, though this could soon be changed, as could the 100/55 mm gun and the two 20 mm Oelikon. The Dagaie decoy launchers will probably be replaced by SAM Mitra Simbad missiles.

The Horizon

These aerial defence ships are part of a trilateral project shared by France, Britain and Italy. The French have ordered two units, and will launch them in 2005 and 2007. A further two units will probably be ordered after, to be launched in 2010 and 2015. Britain is considering 12 ships, to be

presented in stages in 2005 and 2006, while the six Italian ships are planned for the year 2006.

Displacement and propulsion

These ships displace 6,500 tons when fully loaded, and their maximum length is 150 metres. They will probably be powered by CODLAG or CODLOG, with two propellers, and will reach speeds of 30 knots and will have a range of 7,000 miles at 18 knots. However, it is too early to reject the possibility of an alternative propulsion system.

Weapons

The weapons will vary according to each country, but will probably include SAM PAAMS (Principal Anti-Air Missile System) with 16 Aster 15 and 32 Aster 30 with common VLS. In addition, SSM missiles (ANNG on the French ships, Teseo Mk 3 on the Italian and Britain as yet undecided) will be included, eight 'per head' on two quadruple mounts.

FLORÉAL FRIGATES

These frigates have been named after the months of the 1789 Revolution. They were designed quickly to serve on colonial duties, and in many ways resemble civilian ships, with a bulbous bow with a bow truster.

INTERIOR COOIDOR

A long interior corridor runs along the whole length of these ships, facilitating access to each different area of the ship.

The artillery will probably consist of a 127 or 155 mm ASuM gun, and a pair of lesser calibre 20 or 30-mm guns.

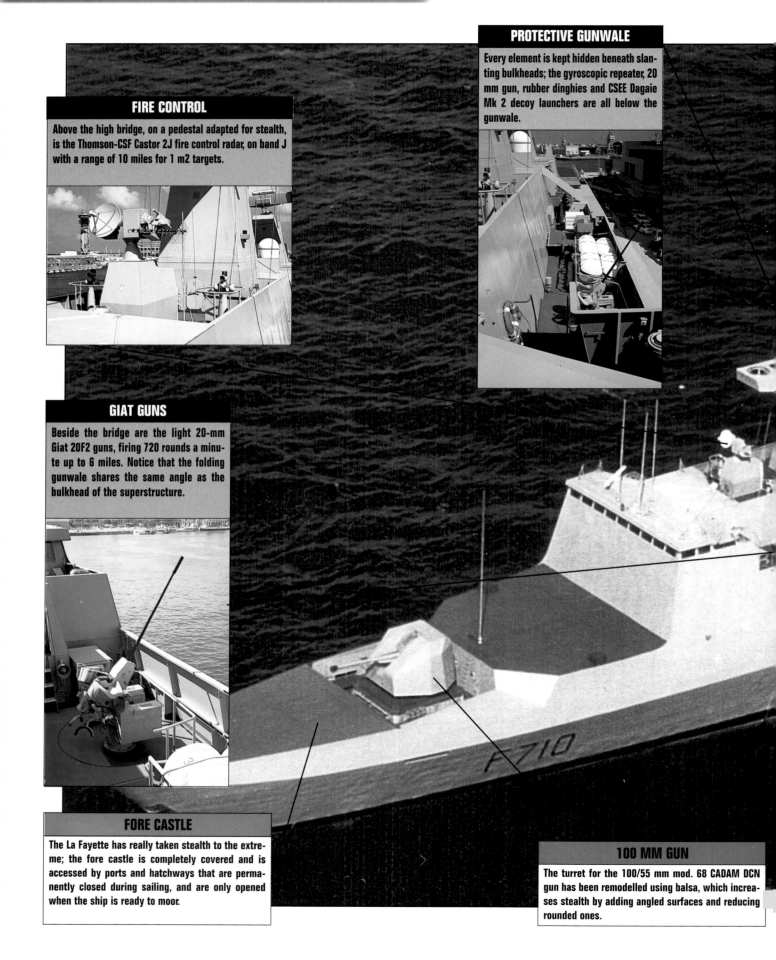

PROTECTIVE GUNWALE

Every element is kept hidden beneath slanting bulkheads; the gyroscopic repeater, 20 mm gun, rubber dinghies and CSEE Dagaie Mk 2 decoy launchers are all below the gunwale.

FIRE CONTROL

Above the high bridge, on a pedestal adapted for stealth, is the Thomson-CSF Castor 2J fire control radar, on band J with a range of 10 miles for 1 m2 targets.

GIAT GUNS

Beside the bridge are the light 20-mm Giat 20F2 guns, firing 720 rounds a minute up to 6 miles. Notice that the folding gunwale shares the same angle as the bulkhead of the superstructure.

FORE CASTLE

The La Fayette has really taken stealth to the extreme; the fore castle is completely covered and is accessed by ports and hatchways that are permanently closed during sailing, and are only opened when the ship is ready to moor.

100 MM GUN

The turret for the 100/55 mm mod. 68 CADAM DCN gun has been remodelled using balsa, which increases stealth by adding angled surfaces and reducing rounded ones.

MAST SENSORS

At the top of the bow mast there are ESM Thomson-CSF ARBR 17 countermeasures, and other sensors.

STERN FUNNEL

At the top of the aft funnel is the Thomson CFS Sea Tiger Mk 2 air and surface search radar. On the stern face, the engine exhausts are protected by a blow-drying panel and IR filters.

NAVAL CROTALE

This Close In Weapon System system is made up of eight missiles and several sensors. The missiles, unloaded in the photograph, are automatically loaded from hatchways in the deck.

FLIGHT DECK

The flight deck is big enough for large helicopters, such as the Super Frelon NH 90. It has a Beartrap emergency mooring system, and tracks and transport pulleys.

HIDDEN BOATS

A specially designed metal mesh protects the 'niche' where the boat is housed, because it, and its launching apparatus, are otherwise difficult to adapt for stealth.

35mm AHEAD round (152 spin
stabilized heavy metal
sub projectiles).

Payload ejection point from
witness plate 4 meters.

Point Defense, or Close In Weapon Systems (CIWS), are short-range self-defense systems that are exclusively used for taking out SSM or ASM missiles in the last phase of their flight.

Sea Skimmers

The Sea-Skimmer appeared at about the same time as the Exocet, Harpoon and other similar missiles. This kind of missile can be fired from the surface (SSM) or from the air (ASM), and travel less than 10 meters about the water, making them very hard for radar to detect because their echo is easily confused with that of the waves.

Early Warning, or EW, radar, on board helicopters and airplanes went part of the way to dealing with the danger, but just detecting the presence of a missile is not enough. Of course, the threat still exists, and somehow it must be destroyed.

This is where CIWS comes in, serving the single purpose of destroying missiles in the last phase of flight, the phase when the missile rises slightly before making its final dive, and the time when it is most vulnera-

---

DESTROYED MISSILE

The method of taking a missile out depends on whether a gun or another missile is being used. In the first case, destruction is caused by damage or serious breakdown, in the second, probably by the explosion on impact. Either way, the missile should be successfully eliminated. This photo shows a missile destroyed by the shots of a CIWS gun.

SEAWOLF

This small British anti-missile missile only weighs 82 kg, is not only capable of striking other missiles, but it is said that it is also capable of striking simple projectiles as small as 76 mm.

---

ble. This usually happens over the last 2,000 or 4,000 meters, or between seven and fifteen seconds.

PDGS and PDMS

PDGS (Point Defence Gun System) and/or PDMS (Point Defence Missile System) are specially designed to destroy missiles in such a short space of time; those few seconds that remain before a missile makes contact. Given the extremely short

missile are destroyed on impact, producing a high explosion between 10 and 40 kg, depending on the types of missile and warhead.

Point Defence Guns

These guns have a high rate of fire (up to 4/6.000 rounds a minute), always using many barrels, as the firing of so many shots would never be possible with a single barrel.

They are automatically directed and usually have some kind of in-built radar system, with another for adjudication, along with others for fire control, from infrared to laser and/or others, even optronic.

The system seeks to create a 'blanket effect'; it destroys missiles by creating such a thick 'wall' of bullets between the missile and the ship, that it is impossible for it to find a way through. The bullets are not explosive, although they may be filled with heavy metals that increase the effectiveness and force of impact.

An important consideration is the fact that a missile in flight is a delicately balanced object, and if it can be struck in the right place (a fin, for example) its aeronautic qualities can be radically altered. Therefore, if the missile can be struck in more than one place, its subsequent destruction is practically guaranteed.

These guns are automatically reloaded, and also have a reserve supply of ammuni-

period of time in which this operation must take place, it is has to be an automatic process, with little or no human intervention.

There are several phases to the interception of a missile that is approaching a ship: one from a distance in which attempts are made to discover it, and if necessary, destroy it; another at closer range, between 3 and 9 miles, in which missiles are used to attack it; and another that uses point defence systems, be they missiles or guns.

Depending on the launching distance and the speed and type of missile, a threat of this type materializes over a very short period of time, in practice never more than 60 seconds (a distance of about 10 miles if it is a missile that travels at 0.9 Mach, about 300 meters a second). Supersonic missiles take much less time.

Point defence missiles

These missiles operate in a conventional way (i.e. they aim to strike the attacker). They can be guided, depending on the model by active, passive and/or active/passive phases, by radar guidance systems, infrared, TV, etc. The most common models are the Italian Aspide, French Crotale Naval, Russian SA-N-4 Gekko and SA-N-9, American Sea Sparrow and RAM and British Sea Wolf.

Both the enemy missile and the defense

SA-N-4 GECKO

This Russian missile was first used on Grisha frigates in about 1969. Its mount can be complemented with a reserve of up to 20 missiles that are contained in four quintuple revolver loaders.

VULCAN PHALANX

The Vulcan Phalanx is the oldest CIWS mount in existence. It was first produced in 1977, though it was not used on any ship until 1980, on the Enterprise and America aircraft carriers. An estimated 500 Vulcan Phalanx are used on ships in twelve countries.

tion nearby, and often another too. Normally, they only have enough ammunition for a few seconds of fire, although, given the incredible speed at which they fire, those few seconds are usually enough to destroy one or more missiles.

The most commonly used point defense

guns are Russian AK 630, Dutch Goalkeeper, Spanish Meroka, Swiss Sea Zenith and American Vulcan Phalanx. There is another that mixes missiles and guns, the Russian CADS-N-I.

Aspide

The SAM Albatross missile system was developed between 1968 and 1971 out of a RIM-7H5/Sea Sparrow. Like the Sea Sparrow, it has a semi-active guidance system, with constant illumination from the launch ship.

It is fired from an octuple or quadruple launcher, depending on the capacity of the ship in question.

Crotale Naval 8S

Crotale Naval is based on the terrestrial SAM system. It is an anti-missile missile for destroying low and medium height or Sea Skimmer attacks.

MEROKA

This unique mount is made up of two lines of six guns, one on top of the other. Based on the CETME, it is produced at the Fábrica de Artllería de Bazán, in San Fernando, Spain. It is described as one of the CIWS with the most rapid firepower (right photograph).

RAM MISSILE

This is the most recent anti-missile missile. It is based on Sidewinder and Stinger, and has adopted many of their parts. It is the only rotating missile, thus its name, Rolling Airframe Missile. It is currently replacing Sea Sparrow on the ships of the US Navy (left photograph).

GOALKEEPER

This gun is the product of a Dutch-American joint venture, between Hollandse Signaalapparaten and General Electric. It is a naval variant of the GAU-8/A aerial gun, with seven tubes on a Gatling mount, a totally autonomous assembly with its own radar set-up (bottom photograph).

In case of emergency, they can also be used against ships. They are fired from an octuple mount with its own infrared and radar guidance system. The warhead is fitted with an infrared fuse with a time delay system that increases the effect of the explosion.

SA-N-4 Gekko

This is a single phase, solid propellant SAM missile that was first used in the early 1970s. It is fired from a retractable two-arm ramp, and can be reloaded with 18

missiles. It can be used against ships.

It uses semi-active guidance, and the target is lit by Top Dome radar. It is one of the most heavily exported Russian missiles, and is a regular part of the weaponry on Koni frigates and Nanuchka corvettes.

Sea Sparrow

This missile was developed at the beginning of the 1960s, based on the Sparrow, one of the most commonly used AAM missiles. For several years, it was a regular part of the set-up of almost all ships in the US Navy. Nowadays, RAM missiles tend to replace them.

CROTALE NAVAL
A small and light missile (2.89 meters long and weighing 85 kg) is the main anti-missile weapon on all ships in the Marine Nationale with a displacement greater than 500 tons. It has been exported to such countries as Saudi Arabia and China.

SEA ZENITH
The product of yet another joint venture, this time between Switzerland, Italy and the UK. It is said that it is the most effective CIWS in existence, although, as yet, only Turkey uses it on their ships. Each barrel is independently fed, adding to security, because if one gun gets jammed, the others will continue firing regardless.

SEA RAM
This mount, still incomplete, will substitute the Vulcan Phalanx gun mount with a container with 21 RAM missiles, The search and pursuit of the target will be carried out by monopulse Doppler radar on Band Q (left photograph).

RAM

The RIM-116A, Rolling Airframe Missile, or RAM, was based on the AAM Sidewinder, uses the same motor, fuselage and warhead, and operates with the same Stinger infrared search system. The initial phase of guidance is passive and totally radar controlled.

It fires from a multiple container with 21 tubes, ultralight octuple or in groups of five contained in an ASROC chamber. However, in most cases the container has 21 missiles. Apart from the USA, Germany and Denmark also use this missile, though it is quite likely that the number of users will increase.

AK 630

This sextuple 30-mm CIWS gun has

been found on all Russian ships since the 1970s. It has a vertical fire sector of +90 to −10, and can fire up to 3,000 rounds a minute, at an initial speed of 1,000 meters a second. Its fire is generally related to two Bass Tilt radar, or on smaller ships, the main fire control radar. It also has an optical ranger.

CADS-N-1
This is the name given by NATO to the latest Russian anti-missile system that is now used on Kirov class cruisers. It is made up of AK-630 guns and four or eight SA-N-19 missiles, which should prove highly effective. It probably works with Bass Tilt fire control radar, although it also has its own radar.

Goalkeeper

This was the product of a Dutch-American joint venture, and is used on British and Dutch ships, but not American ones. They use an independent mount, which is associated with radar on bands I/K. It may have explosive or incendiary projectiles for soft targets, and for hard targets they have a uranium nucleus with a tungsten alloy exterior.

AK 630
NATO calls this mount ADMG-630, and the first ship it appeared on was a Kresta II. It is fed by a continuous belt that reaches the mount from a store underneath the deck on which it is assembled.

Meroka

This Spanish CIWS is, undoubtedly, the most unusual mount, with its twelve 20-mm guns in two rows of six, rather than in the more common circular formation. It can fire up to 9,000 times a minute. It is a very complete system, with Doppler VPS2 radar on bands I/J and a thermal TV system.

It is produced by FABA (Fábrica de Artillería Bazán) at their factory in San Fernando (Cádiz). At the moment, only the Spanish Armada uses it on its own frigates, aircraft carriers and other military vessels.

Sea Zenith

This mount is made by a Swiss-Italian-British company, and stands out for its unusual rotation plane, which is slanted so as to allow angles of fire from −20 up to +127°. It is made up of four 25-mm guns that fire ballasted or incendiary projectiles. Their guidance/acquisition radar uses a band K radar system, FLIR (Forward Looking InfraRed) and laser.

C orvettes have always been considered a lower category of ship than frigates. In the Second World War, they were the most common escort ships on merchant convoys. They tend to be of less military importance, and are smaller than frigates, but serve an important role in anti-submarine warfare.

The role of the corvette

The modern day corvette is again not as large or as important as a frigate. They are not normally prepared for war, but rather to escort convoys and merchant ships. However, like frigates, over the years, they have grown in size and many features have been added to them. Corvettes can now have displacements of up to 1,500 tons, or more, and can be equipped with powerful anti-ship, anti-missile, anti-aircraft and/or anti-submarine weapons.

An undefined character

Therefore, it is now difficult to differentiate corvettes not only from frigates, but also patrol ships, as both of these ships can easily assume the roles of the others. The only distinctive feature of each type of ship seems to be their speeds. Corvettes tend to be the fastest, though even this is not necessarily so.

To complicate matters further, NATO does not recognize the corvette as a type of ship in its own right, and designates them either as 'F' for frigate, or 'P' for patrol ship. However, to further add to the confusion, different naval records do recognize the

SANCTIONED SHIPS
Iraq ordered four missile corvettes from the Italian company, Fincantieri, in 1981, but these were sanctioned after the Iraqi invasion of Kuwait in 1990-91. Eventually, Malaysia bought the ships, two in 1997 and another two in 1998.

GAS EXHAUSTS
The two large portals at the stern of the Tarantul are not, as may seem apparent, weapons of any kind. They are, in fact, the exhausts of the gas turbines.

corvette, coding it as FSG or FS, depending on whether or not it is armed with missiles.

Present and future

At present, there are some 40 separate classes of corvette operating in the different naval fleets of the world, from those purely designed for combat, to others prepared for patrol, surveillance and control. There are several others that are still in development, and it is hard to predict whether these will have any specific purpose to serve, or indeed, if they will ever even be built.

Amongst the classes of corvette that are being used today, the most outstanding, for a variety of reasons, are the Russian Tarantul and Nanuchka class, Israeli Eilat class, Indian Khukri class, Malaysian Laksamana class and Singaporean Victory class. Finally, the Swedish Visby class is a good example of a modern corvette that has been adapted to new trends.

Tarantul (Russia)

These powerful and agile ships were built between 1978 and 1997. As many as 60 units may have been constructed, including those that were exported (to Bulgaria, India, Poland,

Romania, Vietnam and Yemen) and those that are still being used by the Russian and Ukrainian fleets. It seems that the Russian have named them under two different categories, malvy raketny korabl (small missile ship) and raketny kater (missile cutter). Four different versions are known (Tarantul I, II, III and modified III).

Features

These ships weigh 455 tons when fully loaded and use COGAG propulsion (with Nikolaiev DR 76 or DR 77 gas turbines), or CODOG with two CM 504 diesel engines that substitute the group of cruise turbines that were used on the Tarantul III. They travel at high speeds, around 36 knots, which probably makes them the fastest corvettes in existence.

Armament

Their weapons depend upon each class. There are four SSM SS-N-2D Styx on the Tarantul I and II and SS-N-22 Sunburn on the III. All use SAM SA-N-5 for aerial defense, though their anti-missile options vary, on two AK 630 mounts, replaced by a

STERN MISSILES

Rattanakosin carry all their missiles at the stern, and the gun at the bow. This picture shows two twin supports for SSM Harpoon missiles, along with an octuple Aspide launcher. The radar is for air and surface surveillance, a Signaal DA 05 on bands E/F.

CADS-N-1 on the Tarantul II. All have a 76/60-mm gun in their fore castle.

Electronics

The electronics vary according to each class or group, but most of them use Plank Shave radar (air/surface search); Kivach III (for navigation) and Bass Tilt (fire control). For weapons control they have Hood Wink, Light Bulb, Band Stand and Bell Nest. They all use IFF High Pole, Sonar Soal Tail, ESM Foot Ball and/or Hald Hat, along with PK 16 or PK 10 countermeasures.

FAMOUS SSM

The SSM missiles used on the Tarantul (in the photo Tarantul III) are Styx SS-N-20, a later version of the one that sunk the Israeli destroyer, Eilat, in 1967, an event that caused world-wide commotion.

874

Nanuchka (Russia))

These appeared earlier than the Tarantul (built between 1968 and 1991) and are about 30% bigger (660 tons when fully loaded). Some units were exported to Algeria, India and Libya). They are also classified as MRK, and four different subclasses have been made, Nanuchka I, II, III and IV. The Russian navy currently has a total of 24 units in service (6 Nanuchka I/Burya, 17 III/Veter and one IV/Nakat) that are used in pairs or in threes along coastal waters.

Propulsion

They are powered by diesel engines, with six M 504 engines courled to three shafts, and are able to reach speeds of up to 33 knots.

Weapons

Their missile weaponry is made up of six SSM SS-N-9 Siren on two triple mounts (on the Nanuchka IV there are SS-N-25 missiles), with a SAM SA-N-4 Gecko twin launcher, and some have ASuW capabilities with a supply of 20 missiles. The artillery is made up of two 57/80-mm guns on the Nanuchka I or one 76/60-mm gun on the Nanuchka III and IV. The II and IV also have an AK 630 CIWS.

Eilat (Israel)

There are three Eilats, designed and built in the USA. The first two were handed over to Israel in 1992, and the third in 1997. They are

---

SAM MISSILES

As well as their artillery and anti-ship weapons, Nanuchka have a removable twin launcher for SA-N-4 Gecko missiles at the bow, on the castle and just in front of the bridge.

MODULAR DESIGN

The Eilat are ships that allow for the interchange of several weapons, and therefore they can serve on different kinds of missions. In front of the fore castle, the VLS with Barak missiles, it is possible to mount a 76/62-mm OTO Melara gun, a Vulcan Phalanx or a 57-mm Bofors.

---

designed for stealth, with flat, slanted sides to all of its superstructures, a funnel with a gas cooling system, plenty of RAM material, resilient thwarts for the machinery and water sprays for NBQ warfare. The hull is made of steel and the superstructure of aluminium.

Engines

Eilats use CODOG propulsion, with one LM 2500 turbine, two MTU diesel engines and two variable pitch Kamewa propellers.

Weapons and electronics

They have SSM weapons, eight Harpoon missiles; two SAM VLS with 32 cells and Barak missiles; one 76/62 mm Compatto OTO Melara gun that can be replaced by a 57 mm Bofors or a CIWS Vulcan Phalanx; two 25 mm CIWS Sea Vulcan; and six 324 mm ASW torpedo launch tubes, with Honeywell Mk 46 torpedoes. Most of the electronics are Israeli.

Khukri (India)

There are eight of these ships, designed and built in India. Five entered service in 1989, 1990, 1991 (2) and 1998. The other three are expected in 2001 (2) and 2003. The last three have been delayed by difficulties in obtaining certain pieces of equipment from Russia. About 65% of the material used was Indian, even the diesel engines (French SEMT-Pielstick) were built under licence in India by Kirloskar. They have horizontal stabilizers and a general air conditioning system.

The first four units were planned for

use as ASW ships, and the other four for anti-aircraft and multi-purpose tasks, although they do not have either ASW weapons or sonar. They will probably operate with Advanced Light Helicopters (ALH) armed with ASM Sea Eagle missiles, ASW torpedos and VDS.

Weapons

The first four ships have four SSM SS-N-2D Styx missiles, and the other four should have eight SS-N-25, as well as SAM SA-N-5 Grail. They are also armed with a 76/60 mm

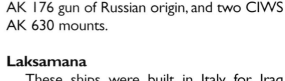

NEW PROJECT

As well as the Victory, Singapore is working on the NGPV project in collaboration with Kockum. These eight ships should have a revolutionary look, displacing 1000 tons with a trimaran hull built entirely with GRP and Kevlar in places. they will be built with stealth in mind, and will probably come into service in ten years' time.

AK 176 gun of Russian origin, and two CIWS AK 630 mounts.

Laksamana

These ships were built in Italy for Iraq (ordered in February 1981). They were going to make up the Assad class, but the sanctions imposed against Iraq as a consequence of the invasion of Kuwait meant that a new buyer had to found. This turned out to be Malaysia, who received two ships in 1997 and another two in 1998. They were sold at a cheaper price to compensate for the fact that the weapons and systems are not the ones that the Malaysian navy is used to having, which could lead to maintenance problems.

Weapons

They have six SSM OTO Melara/Matra Otomat Teseo Mk 2 (TG2) and eight SAM Aspide. As for artillery, there is one 76/62 mm OTO Melara Compatto and two 40/70 mm Breda/Bofors with two triple mounts of 324 mm TL ASW. The electronics are almost exclusively Italian, except for the Kelvin Hughes 1007 radar and Atlas sonar.

Victory (Singapore)

These six ships were designed in Germany as MGB 62 at Lürssen Werft. The prototypes were built in Germany, and were finished off in Singapore. They are similar to the Bahraini Al Manama and the Muray Jib of the United Arab Emirates. They were launched in two groups of three, in August 1990 and May 1991.

Features

These ships run on integrated diesel propulsion, with four engines and four propellers, at a maximum speed of 35 knots. They have stabilizing fins that are only fitted after delivery to improve performance.

Weapons

They are armed with eight SSM Harpoon and sixteen SAM Barak, one 76/62 mm OTO Melara gun and four 12.7 mm machine guns, six 324 mm ASW tubes with Whitehead A-244 S torpedos.

Rattanakosin (Thailand)

These two ships were designed and built at Tacoma in the United States. They are vaguely similar to the Saudi Arabian Bad, which were built at the same shipyard.

These ships weigh 960 tons and are 76.8 meters long. They are driven by two German MTU diesel engines. They are heavily armed considering their small size with eight SSM Harpoon missiles, 24 SAM Aspide on a multiple launcher, a 76/62 mm OTO Melara, two 40/70 mm Bredas, two 20 mm Oerlikon and 324 mm A/S torpedo launchers.

Visby (Sweden)

These four ships should be ready for the years 2000 and 2001, and a direct progression from the Smyge, an experimental ship that uses advanced technology. They are planned as ASW/MCM units, and other further four or expected that will be designed more for ASuW. They will include the latest stealth technology.

RELATIVE ASW CAPABILITIES

Although these ships are officially corvettes for anti-submarine use, this is little more than theoretical. In fact, the first four do not have sonar equipment or anti-submarine torpedos.

Propulsion

They will use CODOG propulsion with four Allied Signal gas turbines and two diesel engines. Instead of propellers, they will use Kamewa water jets.

Apart from corvettes that are used in combat, there are other types that are used for the patrol of costal waters seas, for customs control or observing fishing-grounds, although they are also equipped for their most natural purpose, combat.

The all purpose corvette

These ships have larger displacements are more comfortable than those used strictly for combat, because they are expected to stay at sea for longer periods and have bigger crews. Therefore, they must be larger to maintain themselves so long on a sea that, in the space of a few days, can change drastically, and this should not be too difficult a situation for the crew.

Sanction missions

Although these ships were not designed for this purpose, the reinforcement of international embargos is a mission to which they are perfectly suited. An example of these missions are the important operations carried out by Spanish F-31 Descubierta corvettes in monitoring embargos against Iraq.

Other ships that have shown how capable they are of adapting themselves to all kinds of mission are the eight of the Italian Minerva class, who, like the Descubierta, are also used as training ships.

SUCCESSFUL LINES

The lines of the hull of the Descubierta class corvettes are highly effective, the result of extensive studies, that allow the ship to remain stable even when the sea gets rough.

The Descubierta

Very few ships have ever been so well designed and perfectly prepared for their particular mission as the six Spanish corvettes of this class (Descubierta, Diana, Infanta Elena, Infanta Cristina, Cazadora and Vencedora).

Spanish design

These ships are one of the greatest successes of Spanish naval technology, which is centred on the Empresa Nacional Bazán and their shipyard at Cartagena. The Spanish Armada requested a high-speed all-purpose escort ship, with defensive and offensive weaponry, and at a relatively low price, without too much expensive and sophisticated equipment. The hull had to be a strong and sea worthy with ample opportunity for maintenance at sea. Basically, a ship that within a certain size limit, would be enough to

STABILISING FINS

Although these ships are extremely stable, they have stabilizing fins that make stability even better.

atisfy any medium strength navy. The end result was a ship that has gone on to enjoy export success, with two sales to Egypt and one to Morocco.

A national product

85% of the material was produced in Spain. There are two subclasses, the first is formed by the four that were built at Bazán-Cartagena (Descubierta, Diana and the two Infantas) and the other four from Bazán-Ferrol. Spain only held on to two of these (Cazadora and Vencedora), with the others being sold to Egypt (Serviola became Abu Qir, and Centinela became El Suez), and in return the Armada received its fourth Santa María class frigate, the Reina Sofia, F-84.

Export and voyages

A ninth unit was built on order from the Kingdom of Morocco, the Lieutenant Colonel Errhamani, which was commisioned on the 28th of March 1983. The two Egyptian acquisitions were commissioned in 1984 and six Spanish ones between 1978 and 1983.

Early in 1980 the Descubierta and Diana sailed 20,000 miles to South America without having any problems, which says a

SSM MISSILES
The SSM Harpoon missiles are on the waist of these ships, although when sailing on home seas they do not usually carry less than the minimum of four missiles, as opposed to the complete set of eight which are carried on active service.

lot in favor of these excellent and reliable ships. Similarly, the Infanta Elena travelled to Kiel to appear in the famous Naval Week in 1980.

Light or heavy?

Some might say that these ships are related to the Portuguese Joao Coutinho, a corvette designed by the Germans Blohm & Voss in the 1970s, of which three were built in Germany and another three at Bazán in

SPACE FOR EXPANSION
The Minerva have set aside space and displacement that can be used for expansion, which is why the ships may seem to either be lacking in armaments or to have an awful lot of redundant space.

Catagena. Another four modified units were produced later on, and were used in the Portuguese colonial wars in Angola and Mozambique.

Given the enormous differences between a Joao Coutinho and a Descubierta, it is hard to accept that the two projects were related in any way, although there is no doubt that they shared a common origin. There is no doubt that both ships are truly Spanish.

Effective propulsion

All nine ships use the same propulsion system, German patented MTU 16V 956 TB91 diesel engines, made by Bazán at their yard in Cartagena, using CODAD, two by two, and with propellers that can be reversed using watertight reducers. Both propellers can release air at high pressure to reduce cavitation. The maximum continuous power that each engine can provide is 4,000 horsepower at 1,515 rpm, and working for 30 minutes every six hours they can produce 4,500 hp at 1,575 rpm. In trials, they were able to reach speeds over 26 knots, and in service they operate at 24.5 knots. They have an autonomous range of 4,000 miles at 18 knots.

Weapons and sensors

A Descubierta is armed with eight SSM Harpoon missiles positioned on the waist, between the bridge and the angled funnels, and 24 SAM Sea Sparrow or Aspide (on an octuple launcher with two recharges), as well as a 76/62 mm OTO Melara gun on the fore castle and two 40/70 mm Bofors/Bazán, one over the other on the superstructure of the stern. For ASW there are two triple mounts of 324-mm tubes with Honeywell/Alliant Mk 46 torpedoes and a 375-mm Bofors twin mortar.

The sensors consist of Signaal DA 15/2 surface and air surveillance radar on bands E/F, that can reach up to 75 miles for $2m^2$ targets; another is Signaal ZW 06 for surface search on band I; for navigation there is radar on band I and for fire control there is Signaal WM22/41 (or WM25), reaching up to 25 miles.

SATCOM
Although at first there were no plans for any SATCOM satellite communication systems on these ships, the UN operations to isolate Iraq demanded their presence. They were mounted on the waist deck, just behind the bridge.

INFRARED
Although these ships were designed with stealth in mind, it was not until later that the funnels were remodelled, both to reduce the infrared signature and the turbulence that the gases produced.

The combat data system is a Titan IV, with data-link II. It has a SATCOM satellite communication system. It also has Raytheon 1160B hull sonar, for active and passive search, but it does not have VDS. As for countermeasures, it launches Loral Hycor SBROC Mk 36 decoys from six tubes, and it also has a Prairie sound absorber. For ESM/ECM there is an Elsag Mk 100 (Deneb) or Mk 1600 interceptor and a Ceselsa Canopus or Mk 1900 disturber.

The exported Descubierta

Although the platform is the same, the Descubiertas that have been sold to the aforementioned countries do contain some differences in relation to their weapons and electronic systems. The two major diferences are

that the Moroccan Errhamani uses SSM Exocet missiles instead of Harpoon, and the two Egyptian models are equipped with a Raytheon 1167 VDS.

The Minerva

These eight ships were built in two series of four, the first batch in 1987 and 1988, and the second in 1990 and 1991. A further series had originally been expected, but it all came to nothing when the Italian Marina had to take charge of the four Lupo/Artigliere frigates that had been built to comply with the now defunct Iraqi order. These ships were specially designed as administrative corvettes, in other words, to work in the control of the ZEE, to protect fishing-grounds, for escort and protection of commercial traffic, advanced training and other tasks.

Good size and features

Their size is misleading, because although they may appear small at first glance, when they are studied close-up, one realizes that this is a false impression, for they are in fact a lot larger than they may seem. Even more space is achieved by housing almost all the important features inside the hull. Only the officers quarters and the bridge are located on the bow block of the superstructure. They are extremely comfortable to live and

ITALIAN MINERVA

Although there were plans to build twelve of these ships, only eight were eventually built when the Marina Italiana had to take charge of four frigates that had been ordered by Iraq.

MOROCCAN CORVETTE

The kingdom of Morocco bought one unit, the Lieutenant Colonel Errhamani, in 1983. The protective covering for the two 40/70-mm guns lends an individualistic appearance to this vessel.

work on, and can operate independently for 30 days without causing any suffering to the crew.

The ships are very smooth to handle, fitted with a complete set of stabilizing fins and excellent bouyoncy. Although there were no original plans for the funnel to be fitted with cooling filters, the ship's infrared signature was such that later one was installed to reduce it. The Minerva has been modified with stealth in mind, although the shape and structure of the ship never had a particularly large infrared signature.

Propulsion

The ship only uses two Fincantieri GMT BM 230.20 DVM diesel engines with 6,300 hp each, with two variable pitch propellers.

BOFORS ASW MORTAR

Immediately behind the 76-mm gun, these ships have a 375-mm twin anti-submarine mortar. It fires 250-kg projectiles at distances up to 3,625 meters.

FIRE CONTROL

At the top of the bow mast is the radome that contains the Signaal WM22/41 or WM25 fire control radar on bands I/J, reaching 46 km and using self-stabilizing systems.

76 MM GUN

Descubierta class corvettes' main artillery weapon is an all-purpose 76/62-mm OTO Melara gun, manufactured in San Fernando by FABA/Bazán.

EW ELEMENTS

The electronic warfare sensors are housed on the sides of the bow mast. Depending on the ship, they are Elsag Mk 100, Mk 1600, K 1900, Canopus and/or Deneb.

COMPARISON OF CURRENT CHARACTERISTICS

CLASS/QUANT.	YR.INTROD.	LTH/BTH/HGT	DISPLACE.	PROPULSION	ENGINES	HP	SPEED/AUTON.	ARMAMENT
Descubierta (6+3)	1978/1984	89 x 10.4 x 3.8	1,666	Diesel	MTU-Bazán 16V 956 TB 91 (4)	15,000	25-7,500/12	8 SSM Harpoon 24 SAM Sea Sparrow/Aspide 1 OTO Melara 76/62 mm gun 2 40/70 mm guns (2 x I) 6 324 mm TL ASW (2 x III) 1 375 mm Bofors ASW mortar (1 x II)
Minerva (8)	1987/1991	87 x 10.5 x 3.2	1,285	Diesel	GMT BM 230.20 DVM (2)	12,600	24-3,500/18	8 SAM Aspide 1 OTO Melara 76/62 mm gun 6 324 mm TL ASW (2 x III)

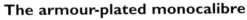

Naval battles were once fought by 'boarding', but ships have used guns since the 16th Century, the time of the Great Spanish Armada (often called the Invincible Armada, although Spanish historians insist that this name was invented by foreigners).

Multicalibre ships

When it comes to arming a ship, the criteria are always difficult to predict. As technology developed, a wide range of different models and calibres appeared, and ships have tended to employ such an extensive variety of weapons that the stocking of ammunition and the operation of all the different kinds of armament became an extremely complex operation.

OTO MELARA 76/62
This medium all-purpose gun is the commonly used one in all navies these days. The two most important versions are the Compatto and the Super Rapid.

127/54 MK 42 GUN
The 127/54 Mk 42 is never used by the US Navy. It fires twenty 31.8-kg projectiles up to 14.2 miles (naval fire) and 10 miles (anti-aircraft). Its initial speed is 810 meters/second and its angle of elevation is –5 to +80.

The armour-plated monocalibre

The armour-plated single calibre main armament gets over this problem, based on theories that go back to the start of the 20th Century. The first example was the Dreadnought, and all later models that have used the same basic design have been referred to by the same name.

The main characteristic of the Dreadnought was that it only had one main calibre, complemented by the so-called anti-torpedo guns or low-calibre rapid-fire (a complete round, with projectile and propellant in shell case). The main guns on these ships were reserved for action with other ships, and the secondary weapons were used against torpedos or light units that were considered a threat.

Ships soon faced danger from the air,

too, and needed to be armed with anti-air-craft guns, and at the same time, the introduction of aircraft carriers brought about the disappearance of large gun actions and the subsequent removal of high calibre guns and the battleship in all navies other than the United States Navy.

The Washington ships

Not long after the end of the First World War, at the time of hot debate over the benefits of the battleship in comparison to aircraft carriers, the influential Washington Conference was held with the aim to standardize ships and calibres, making the different fleets of the world more compatible with one another.

As for guns, the maximum calibre was set at 12 inches, although the arms race of the 1930s ruined the plan. For heavy cruisers, the limit was set at 8 inches, and for light cruisers, it was 6 inches. The lowest calibres were reserved for destroyers and other minor units.

The Washington limitations became obsolete with the aforementioned arms

BOFORS 40/70

Shown here is one of the most successful guns in anti-aircraft history, the Bofors 40/70 and its blast shield. It fires 300 rounds a minute, with 1-kg projectiles and its naval fire can reach 7.5 miles.

race and the outbreak of the Second World War, and ended during the immediate post-war period, the cold war, the armed peace and the peaceful co-existence that followed.

Guns versus missiles

As soon as ships started making use of missiles, a new trend started disposing of all guns and only using missile weapons.

RUSSIAN GUNS

Russia has also been known for its guns, to the extent that in the Second World War, the Germans captured several that were being transported on tanks. The 130/70 AK 130 fires 45 33.5-kg projectiles a minute, at distances up to 15 miles.

Later, guns did come back into favor, albeit only those of calibres below 130 mm, although now they were totally automatic, all-purpose and had much higher firepower. Sea Skimmers appeared along with CIWS (point defense) mounts, specially designed to throw large quantities of projectiles at in-coming missiles, thus increasing the chances of making a hit.

Along with the appearance of peace-making wars and fundamentalism came a new threat, that of the 'pasdaran' and its launches, from which it carried out surprise attacks against any ship within its reach. To defend themselves against this danger, ships needed rapid and effective light weapons.

New artillery designs

The guns used on modern military ships are invariably rapid-fire, all-purpose and automatic. They can be sub-divided into 'heavy' (from 76 to 130 mm) and 'medium/light' (less than 76 mm), and there are also grenade launchers and special purpose guns, such as the multiple anti-missile gun.

A gun is nowhere near capable of matching a missile for distance (a few miles at the most, compared to hundreds), but the cost per shot is substantially cheaper. For

WINGS

The bodies with wings on the projectiles (shown in the picture French made 55 mm RAP munition) greatly increase the range, and also accuracy by illuminating the target with infrared or any other suitable form of radiation.

this reason, more traditional artillery has come back into fashion, and new, advanced projectiles have been developed, now able to reach distances that until not long ago would have seemed like pure fantasy. Neither can a shell be decoyed away from its target.

The RAP projectile

RAP, Rocket Assisted Projectiles, are charged by a rocket and use a homing device that can detect certain reflections. They also have foldable fins that open when the projectile begins its flight. They are fired by a normal gun, at least as normal as a gun can be that is capable of firing such ammunition, but follow a modified flight path that can be extended thanks to the rocket. The fins do likewise, controlled by the homing device that detects the reflection of the target by previously illuminating it with infrared technology. The projectile is directed, within certain limitations, towards its objective. Logically, the higher the calibre, the more accurate these projectiles are, and therefore the most recent projects have shown a tendency to employ higher calibre projectiles.

127 mm, 155 mm and higher

Western armies use a higher calibre than marines do, of 155 mm, by no means

enormous, but enough to greatly increase the capabilities of their projectiles. This can also benefit from RAPs, also known as 'intelligent munition', although in the US Navy the name ERGM (Extended Range Guided Munition) is preferred.

The truth is that the US Navy experimented with a new 203 mm gun several years ago, the MCLWG Mk 71 (Major Calibre Light Weight Gun), and planned to equipped their new, at the time, Spruance class destroyers with them. However, things did not work out as planned, and the project was scrapped.

Therefore, and for some time now, several countries have turned to the terrestrial 155, and the last edition of Euronaval presents a detailed Giat Industries project that analyzes the viability of adapting a terrestrial 155/52 to a naval turret.

This gun would be completely all-purpose (naval, anti-aircraft, anti-missile, support fire for landings, etc.), and the possibility of its appearance on the market has caused a stir in naval gossip shops all over the world.

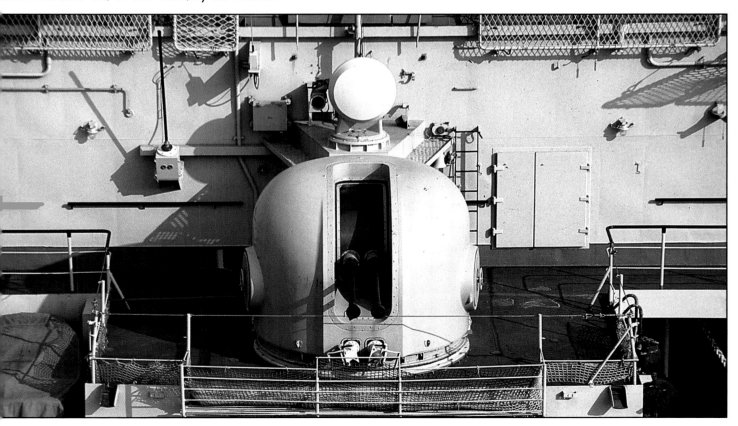

127 mm Mk 45

The United States has spent a long period of time working on the adaptation of their 127/62 mm Mk 45 naval guns to the use of ERGM munition, which would extend their range to about 60 miles. However, if there is to be a form of artillery fire that can reach such distances,

RUSSIAN TURRET

Each one of the 57/80 guns of this Russian turret fires projectiles of at least 2.8 kg over 3.5 miles. They are used on lesser or intermediate ships, such as corvettes, patrol ships and frigates.

there must also be a method of controlling the direction. Such distance would magnify the already inherent problem of such fire, for if the average flight time of a 127 mm projectile is around 30 seconds (for a 15 mile shot), with an ERGM this would become two minutes, making it very difficult to achieve much accuracy.

Grenade launchers and similar weapons

A grenade launcher is something of a machine gun that has been developed to fire higher calibre projectiles. However, it is by no means a regular gun, because its projectiles, though explosive on contact, are much more sophisticated than those of a gun, and do not use a conventional fuse. A grenade launcher has far greater firepower (200-250 rounds a minute) than a gun, but has a shorter range (about one mile).

Nevertheless, this is one more option that has been used on board the most modern ships. They are generally only used for very specific tasks, such as the fight against terrorism, so it is reassuring to know that they exist.

RAPID FIRE

This revolver gun was designed by the Swiss company Oerlikon-Contraves, a 35 mm with exceptionally rapid fire for operation with a single tube CIWS. It is not yet in active use.

CHINESE GUNS
Several ships use guns of Russian or Chinese origin. Here is a Chinese 100/56-mm twin mount, with firepower of 25 rounds a minute (per barrel), firing 15.9-kg projectiles up to 13 miles.

Lesser calibres

40 mm or lesser anti-aircraft guns, so highly praised in the Second World War, are still used on ships, though in very much modified forms due to the fact that, apart from their normal uses, they are now used for several other less common ones too.

It was the appearance of a new potential threat, mainly that posed by commando attacks, such as the famous Iranian 'pasdaran', that brought about the need for light calibre rapid-fire artillery that could comfortably and reliably eliminate large quantities of projectiles of every kind, from incendiary to explosive or shrapnel. Such weapons include 30 and 25 mm calibre guns, sometimes even less, such as the American 25/87 mm Bushmaster Mk 38 (M242 gun, with 0.5 kg projectiles and an initial speed of 1,200 meter/second firing sudden blasts of up to 200 rounds a minute). It is said that this gun is so effective and has such impressive systems that it can destroy an objective in a matter of seconds.

EXPORTABLE WEAPON
Without exception, every industrialized country strives to produce weaponry that cannot only be used on their own ships, but that can also be exported. Here is a South African 35-mm anti-aircraft gun, the Denel LIW Vektor.

Another weapon that is omnipresent on every ship, and is used as a possible deterrent, is the 12.7-mm machine gun. Its worth as a naval weapon has come to be rather disregarded. It is not considered particularly effective in modern naval combat, and it seems like in the not too distant future this weapon will have become a thing of the past.

INDEX

US Navy destroyers 4

European destroyers. 10

Other destroyers 15

Russian destroyers 20

Electronic sensors. 26

Russian frigates. 31

The Oliver Hardy Perry and similar ships 36

Frigates of the future 42

Modern day frigates 47

Meko frigates 52

Stealth technology 58

Asian frigates 63

French frigates of the past and future 68

Point defence 74

Combat corvettes 79

All purpose corvettes 84

Naval artillery. 90

£5.99

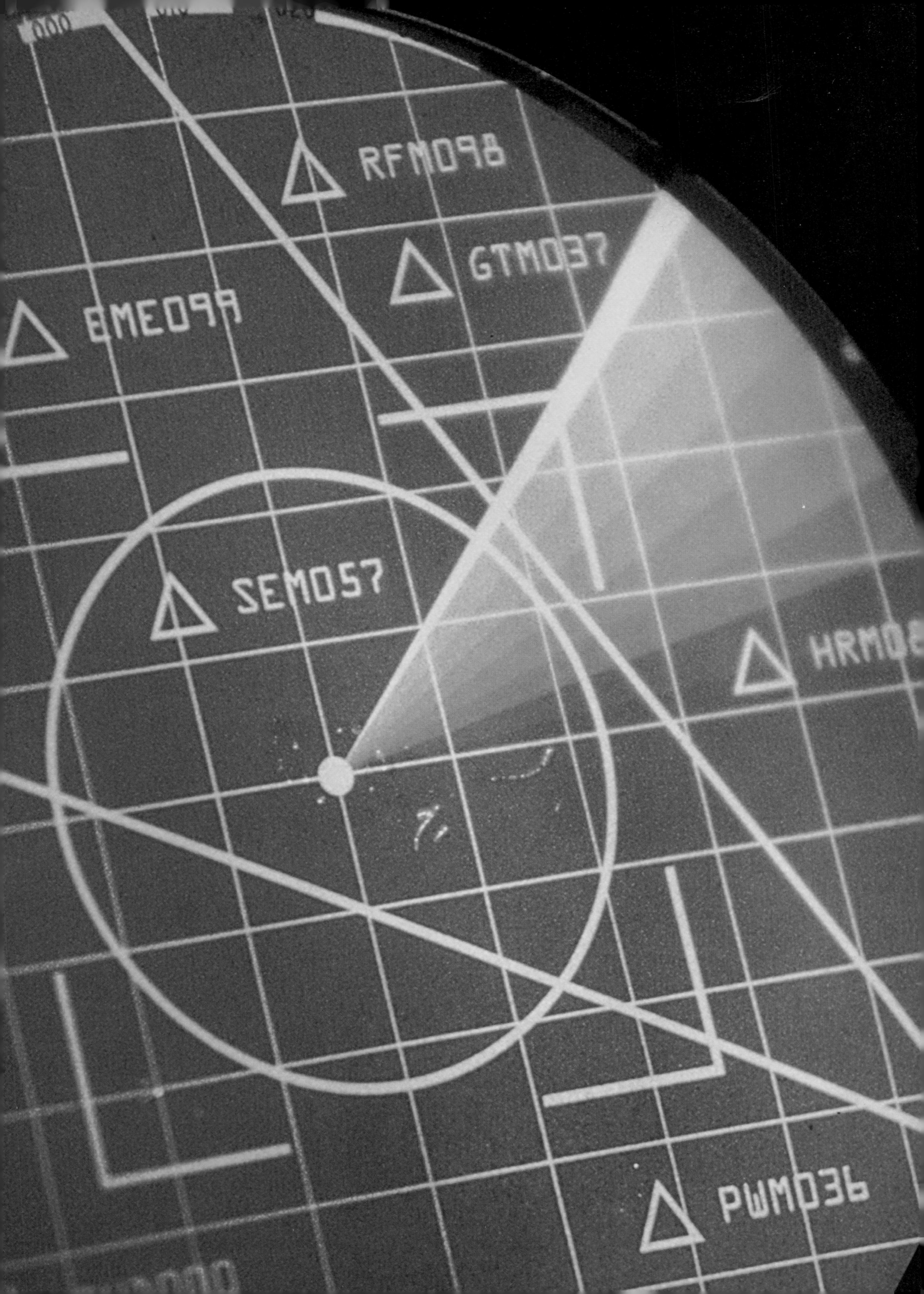
RFM098
GTM037
EME099
SEM057
PWM036

Ten years ago, all it took was one man
– and one car – to get the job done.

Now, the Foundation for Law and
Government has assembled five highly
skilled operatives and paired them with
the most advanced vehicles to take on
a new breed of outlaw. They are...

This Official Annual from Grandreams
profiles each member of the TKR team
and their incredible vehicles...takes a
look inside Sky One...and presents an
exciting TEAM KNIGHT RIDER story...

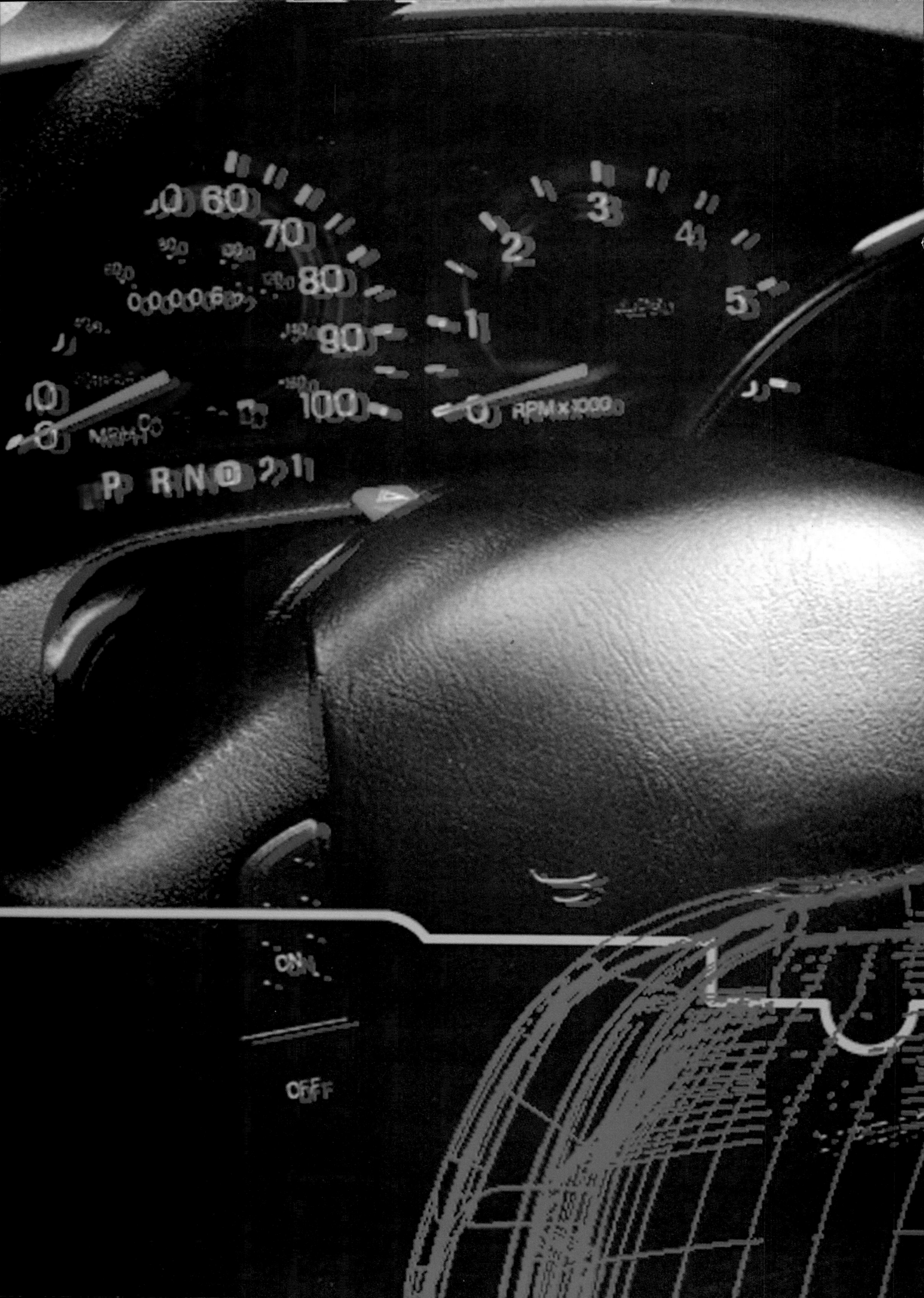
60
70
80
90
100
MPH
1
2
3
4
5
RPM x 1000
P R N D 2 1
ON
OFF

CONTENTS

Meet Team Knight Rider   8

Kyle Stewart   12

Jenny Andrews   14

Duke DePalma   16

Erica West   18

Trek Sanders   20

Fallen Nation – Part One   22

Sky One   40

Fallen Nation – Part Two   42

TKR = Action, Adventure & Acceleration!   58

Edited by Tony Lynch
Designed by Jason Bazini

Published by
Grandreams Ltd
435-437 Edgware Road
Little Venice
London W2 1TH

Printed in Belgium

MEET TEAM KNIGHT RIDER

Ten years ago the sleek black car code-named Kitt, and its driver, Michael Knight, were backed by the Foundation for Law and Government (FLAG). Together they had taken on the world's injustices, from common street thugs to the most sophisticated criminals and their underworld organisations.

Technology that had previously only appeared in science fiction novels and movies supported Knight's tireless crusade. More often than not it gave him the critical edge over those who had believed themselves invincible. Those who believed themselves above and beyond the law.

But that technology, incredible as it was, was little more than just one of Knight's most effective hunting tools. He would probably have succeeded without it anyway, one way or another. It would have been a little harder, perhaps, and taken a little longer, but the odds would have been in his favour.

Michael Knight never claimed to be a god or a saint. Nor was he immortal. But the commitment to what he believed in, what he and Kitt stood for, was as powerful as any futuristic weapon he had at his disposal.

That commitment gave him a true edge. It served him well.

Ten years ago.

Then, as suddenly as it began, the crusade ended. Without warning Michael Knight was gone, and so was the remarkable Kitt.

A decade passed before FLAG stepped back into the vacuum left by Knight's departure, bringing

MEET TEAM KNIGHT RIDER

with it resources that the original Rider could only have dreamed of. Resources of such profound sophistication and imagination that few outside the Foundation's walls even know they exist.

There were other changes too. Instead of Knight's lumbering eighteen-wheeler laden with repair equipment and electronic devices, now there is the Skybase — code named Sky One — an immense flying fortress that serves the same purpose, but with far more manoeuvrability and speed.

Now there are high-tech wrist-worn telecommunication devices...powerful weapons that cover the entire laser spectrum...and sources of information the original Rider never had.

But the biggest change of all is the team itself. Now there are five instead of one.

Five because the enemy and the complexity of contemporary crime had multiplied. With no area of the world completely isolated, with global communications virtually instantaneous, the enemy has ready access to resources only dreamed of a mere decade ago.

Five. Three men and two women. Five fighters, five members of the new TEAM KNIGHT RIDER.

MEET TEAM KNIGHT RIDER... KYLE STEWART

BRIXTON KARNES stars as TKR leader **KYLE STEWART.** Kyle is a former undercover spy whose field experience and know-how make him the ideal team leader. Kyle is fair and honest, but ruthless when necessary.

PROFILE

Full Name:

Kyle Stewart

Speciality:

Leader of TKR

Background:

Former Deep Cover

CIA Operative

Persona:

Fair, honest,

relentless

VEHICLE
DNT·1 – DANTE
Fast, versatile,
rugged – Kyle's
persona to the
extreme! A modified
Sport Utility Vehicle
large enough to hold
the TKR Team and
an arsenal of high-
tech equipment.
Dante is the TKR
travelling command
post, and speaks
in a very proper,
very smooth
English accent.

MEET TEAM KNIGHT RIDER... JENNY ANDREWS

CHRISTINE STEEL plays **JENNY ANDREWS,** a disciplined gymnast and martial arts expert. Jenny is a gorgeous brunette who you'd never guess to be a tough ex-soldier.

PROFILE

Full Name:
Jenny Andrews
Speciality:
Disciplined gymnast,
martial arts expert
Background:
An ex-marine
with killer appeal
Persona:
Shy, petite – deadly!
Thrives on speed,
and is self-conscious
of her incredible
beauty

VEHICLE

DMO1 – DOMINO
A modified Mustang
with seductive
power and an exotic
voice of experience.
Fast, sleek and sexy,
Domino is Jenny's
alter-ego who
tempts her into
taking risks.

MEET TEAM KNIGHT RIDER... DUKE DePALMA

DUANE DAVIS portrays **DUKE DePALMA**, an articulate ex-cop and former boxer. Now he is a no-nonsense heavy metal warrior with an unmatched expertise in weapons and surveillance. Duke is unstoppable, but what surprises people is how incredibly sensitive he can be.

ATTACK BEAST

PROFILE

Full Name:

Duke DePalma

Speciality:

Weapons and surveillance expert

Background:

Former small-time boxer with mob connections

Persona:

Tough, street smart, stoic – a total heavy metal warrior

VEHICLE

ATTACK BEAST

Part all-terrain vehicle, part tank. Attack Beast is the full mobile control centre for TKR, with a succession of winches, cranes and high-tech weaponry. The Beast is loyal to Duke, but has a crush on Jenny Andrews.

MEET TEAM KNIGHT RIDER... ERICA WEST

KATHY TRAGESER plays **ERICA WEST**, the beautiful, deceptive con-woman with a mysterious past. She's a sexy smooth talker whose chief talent is manipulating people into giving her exactly what she wants. Erica knows how her incredible looks affect others, and when she wants to she will use those looks as a devastating weapon!

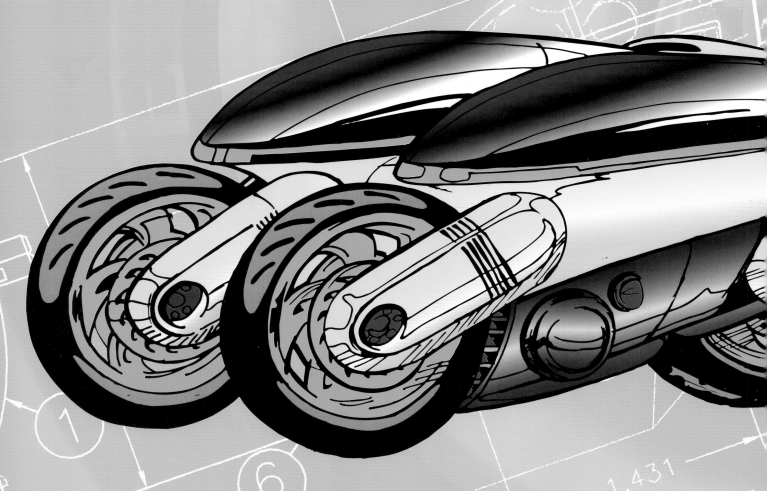

KAT

PROFILE

Full Name:

Erica West

Speciality:

Technical expert, security specialist

Background:

Deceptive con-artist with a mysterious past

Persona:

Highly imaginative with the ability to think around corners

VEHICLE

KAT

Kat is a hybrid motorcycle and sidecar that joins with Trek's vehicle, Plato, to form a high-pursuit vehicle. Kat is 'Miss Manners', by-the-book, and definitely does not approve of Erica's ways!

MEET TEAM KNIGHT RIDER... TREK SANDERS

NICK WECHSLER plays **TREK SANDERS**, a scientific genius. He's not far into his twenties and is sometimes known as 'The kid'. Trek is the gadget guy and the one who can make a bomb out of a couple of coins and a box of paper clips.

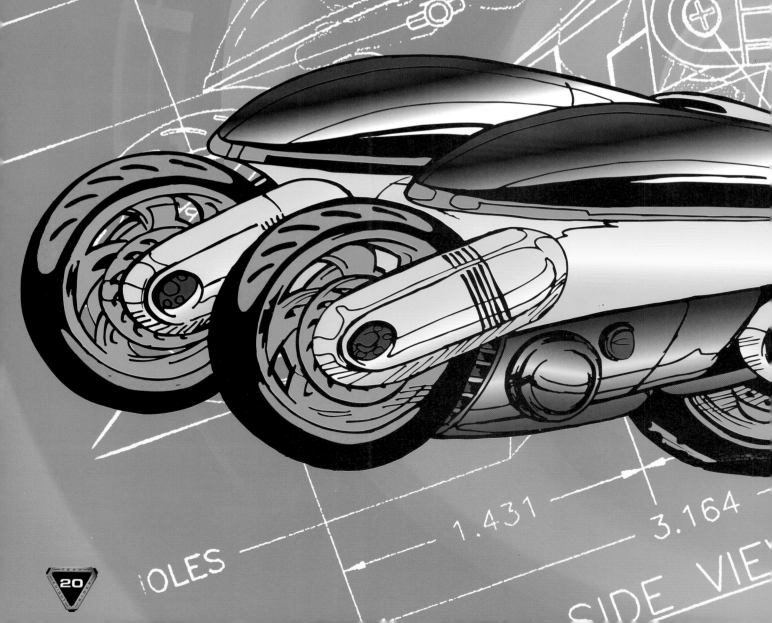

PROFILE

Full Name:
Trek Sanders
Speciality:
Technical expert,
wonder-kid
Background:
Former boy-genius
turned hacker
Persona:
A linear thinker
and an avid realist;
an inventive mind
with dangerous
enthusiasm; 'twin'
of Erica West

VEHICLE

PLATO

Trek's half of the

high-pursuit vehicle

he shares with Erica.

Plato has the voice

of a science nerd, a

'brainiac' who is

totally consumed

with facts, figures

and data.

FALLEN NATION
PART ONE

One warm Virginia afternoon, a team of gardeners were working on the shrubs outside General Stephen Butler's office window. A pool man scooped leaves from the calm surface of the swimming pool, while a uniformed maid cleaned the French door panes.

The only sign that the General was no ordinary citizen, or ordinary General, were the security guards walking the perimeter of the backyard. They wore suits that were obviously too warm for the day, and they glared disapprovingly whenever one of the gardeners shared a joke with his friends.

The General's office was large and comfortable, yet it reflected his military requirements for neatness and precision. Right now, his highly polished desk was clear of work.

The General, comfortably dressed in civilian clothes, was reading at a marble-topped table near the patio doors. He barely looked up from his book when James, the butler, entered the room and placed a tray on the table.

'What's this?' asked the General, unhappily.

'Dessert,' replied James, glancing down at the fruit, salad and vegetables attractively arranged on the tray.

Butler sighed and closed his book, keeping his place with a finger. 'I asked you to bring me a piece of pecan pie...and don't tell me we're out, I saw half a pan in the fridge this morning.'

James raised a disapproving eyebrow. 'I gave that to the new gardeners. You don't need it.'

'Then bring me that bag of Fig Newtons you have stashed in the pantry,' said the General. 'That's an order, James.'

James retrieved the tray and delivered a parting shot. 'You're the General,' he said, curtly. 'You keep this up and you'll end up as fat as Schwarzkopf.'

The General didn't bother to reply. Once James had closed the door behind him, he began to read again.

Outside, the security guards continued their patrol, watching the General through the French doors, and wondering why it was taking that maid so long to clean the windows.

As one guard passed a large shrub, a gardener suddenly straightened, flipped the large hedge clippers over in his hand and clubbed the man across the chest, sending him reeling off-balance.

It was the signal.

The pool man instantly swung his net over the head of the nearest guard, yanked it tight around the man's neck, and whipped him around until he flew into the pool and out of commission.

The second gardener aimed the handle of his clippers at a third guard, pressed a small trigger at the base and fired a tiny dart into the man's leg. The guard took one step and collapsed, unconscious.

A third gardener promptly opened the cuttings bag at the back of his mower and pulled out several handguns and machine pistols, tossing one to a nearby colleague before heading for the house.

The last security guard, seeing the others so swiftly put out of commission, raced for the French doors, gun in hand. The maid spun around and sprayed the ammonia mixture into his eyes. Before he could cry out, he was grabbed and dealt with by one of the attackers.

The maid checked to see that the General

hadn't noticed the commotion, then helped the others drag the guards out of sight. She said nothing to them, but the expression on her face told them she was pleased.

The entire operation had been conducted without a sound.

The intruders were out of sight when the General heard running footsteps outside the door. Then the door burst open.

'James?' he said.

There was no answer.

From behind, a gun barrel was pressed against his temple. Instinct made him turn to fight, but a second man strode across the room and clubbed him with a pistol. The General collapsed, blood smeared across his brow just above his left eye.

When James returned with the Fig Newtons, the room was empty.

The General was gone.

Across his chair lay a white towel, with the words 'Fallen Nation' spray-painted on it — in red.

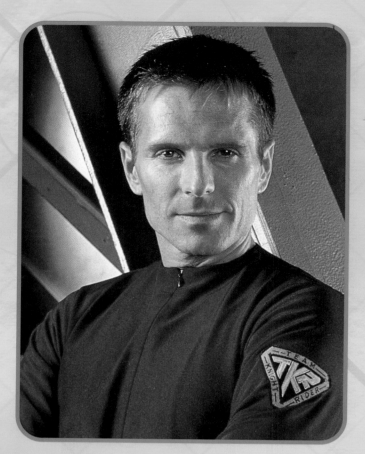

Sky One soared over the mountains of the New Mexico Desert, south of Albuquerque. The craft's four powerful engines roared as it banked sharply and began to lose altitude. Several hundred feet above the barren ground, the engine mounts swivelled downwards and the plane hovered, then settled slowly into its landing with a cloud of dust and grit swirling around it. Nearby a lizard hissed from its rock and slipped away.

Suddenly, out of the shimmering heat haze, five shadows raced towards the rear of Sky One. Leading the chase was a burnished silver van, followed by a vivid red Mustang with two broad white stripes down its hood and trunk. Then came an equally sleek black truck with an extended cab and a large bed covered with a tarp. Just behind were two motorcycles, their chassis wrapped in a

gleaming shell of mercury-hued metal.

As they approached, dust surrounded them like a storm cloud, Sky One opened its rear cargo bay and extended a long ramp to the ground.

The five vehicles lined-up and took the ramp at speed. Before the last cycle was completely aboard, the ramp began to retract and the engines began to whine. By the time the door had closed, Sky One was airborne again.

Only the lizard knew it had ever been there.

Duke DePalma sat alone in the TKR Situation Room on Sky One's second level. He had been hoping for some quiet time, time to figure out how to make the Attack Beast behave. He seemed to spend more time arguing with the truck than getting any work done, and he hated the Beast's taste in music!

As his fingers attacked the inlaid keyboard in front of him, he wondered if Michael Knight had ever had such misery as this.

The computer screen blinked at him. He knew the technology that allowed Beast to be the vehicle it was, had been carefully designed to prevent tampering. In other words, he was stuck with it.

Raised voices in the hall outside made him look up. From the sound of it, Jenny and Kyle were at it again.

'Look, Jenny,' said Kyle as they entered, 'every law enforcement agency is involved with this, which is why FLAG's placing us on stand-by status.'

'Stand-by status?' said Jenny Andrews, incredulously. 'You're kidding me...Kyle, we can't let them kill General Butler just to prove some fanatical point.'

Kyle didn't look up. 'Jenny, we all know your history with the General.'

Jenny stiffened at the implied criticism of her impartiality, and it took her a few seconds to regain control. 'I think we should have Sky One change course for Virginia immediately.'

Kyle straightened, then pointed. 'Jenny, you see this chair? This is the chair where the boss sits. Do you see your name on it? No. This is my chair.'

Duke shifted uncomfortably as they glared at each other, then he broke the silence. 'Is it me, or is it getting a little warm in here?'

Jenny took her seat to the right of Kyle's and stared blindly at the monitor.

Kyle leaned over the desk and said, 'Erica, we need that tape.'

Erica West strode in, cassette in hand. 'I can only run so fast, Kyle. I'm wearing heels,' she said, brightly, handing the tape over.

Seemingly oblivious to the tension in the room, Erica took her seat beside Jenny.

Kyle slipped the tape into a slot on the desk. 'Where's Trek?' he asked.

No one answered. They didn't have to. Trek Sanders professed an airy disdain for

low-rent thugs...'

The tape ended abruptly in a shower of static.

The room was silent.

Duke, who had been watching Jenny's pained reactions, looked at Kyle. 'So, what do we have on Fallen Nation?'

'Nothing,' said Kyle. 'But given our stand-by status—'

'We're stuck on the sidelines,' said Jenny in utter disgust.

Kyle continued. 'I was going to say, FLAG's allowing us to pursue our own investigation. Duke, see

meetings of any kind. Duke and the others knew it was only a front, but no one ever called him in on it.

They directed their attention to one of the wall screens, where a haggard General Butler sat at a table reading from a sheet of paper in his trembling hands. 'I'm General Stephen Butler. I've been told to read this: "We are a group called Fallen Nation. We want no ransom. We have no demands for your weak and helpless government. We simply want to use the General to announce to the world our intention to bring America to her knees...What better way to illustrate our resolve than to capture one of your great military heroes and use him as our puppet?"'

Butler inhaled slowly, and suddenly flung the paper away. 'I'm not gonna do this,' he yelled, leaning towards the camera. 'Don't listen to these fanatics. They're nothing but a bunch of

what the other agencies are up to. Erica, check with the garage, see if the vehicles are primed and ready if we need 'em...and, uh, somebody find Trek.'

Moments later Kyle was left alone with Jenny. Her expression left no doubt of her anger and disappointment at not being given an assignment.

'Jenny,' he said softly. 'I think you might be a little too close to this.'

'So, what are you saying? You want me to sit this one out?'

He shrugged. 'Well...some time off might not be a bad idea.'

Jenny stood, shook her head. 'I'll take a vacation when that General's home safe.'

Before Kyle could answer, she marched from the room.

Great, he thought; just...great.

Sky One's garage area bustled with activity, as mechanics checked the team's vehicles under Erica's supervision.

Kyle spotted Trek seated on Plato. As he approached, he heard a TV newsreader's voice note with mild astonishment an inexplicable swing in the stock market's numbers, '...it's almost as if someone's playing ping pong with the Dow Jones average.'

Kyle tapped the younger man on the shoulder. 'Trek, we missed you at the staff meeting.'

'Oh,' Trek swallowed. 'Well, Kyle, you know I'm not a morning person.'

'Well, I'll give you a chance to make it up to me,' said Kyle pulling the video cassette from his pocket. 'Got any idea where you think this tape was made?'

Trek inserted the tape into a slot below the computer, and froze the screen when the General's face appeared. 'It's either an industrial bunker or a basement...It's probably a basement, since the electrical outlet there in the corner is a commercial one...basement of a residential home

narrows it down a bit.'

Kyle nodded for him to go on.

'Okay, now, Plato's gonna run a three-dimensional scan of the room to get the measurements. Hopefully, then he'll be able to narrow down a possible architectural design for the rest of the house.'

Three hours later Kyle ordered the rest

of the team to the Situation Room where the air began to crackle with the subtle excitement of a mission about to launch.

After reviewing his own monitor, Kyle briefed the others on the latest information. It was interesting, but he wasn't pleased. 'There's got to be something missing.'

Duke said, 'Some neighbours saw a van heading north from General Butler's house. We 'should be zeroing in on that area.'

'The police closed off the roads within minutes,' said Jenny. 'They couldn't have gotten far.'

'Just got off the phone with the FBI,' said Erica. 'They're doing house-to-house in Alexandria, but so far...nada.'

'What if they didn't go north?' Jenny asked Duke.

'Five different witnesses say they did.'

'Which,' said Kyle, 'makes it all the more likely they went south.'

Duke frowned. 'How do you figure?'

'1978. The Red Brigade snatched former Prime Minister Aldo Moro in Rome. They used two vans. One took the visible route. The other had the hostage.'

'Should I be taking notes?' asked Erica with a slow-spreading smile. 'I mean, are we going to be tested on this?'

'Don't listen to her, Kyle,' said Kat from the screen. 'I think you're brilliant.'

'That's my motorcycle up there,' complained Erica. 'Who programmed her to talk back to me?'

Kyle had learned long ago to ignore Kat's flattery. He slapped a button on the desk and said, 'Trek, how you comin'?'

Trek's face immediately replaced Kat's image on the screen. To one side of him they could see a rotating 3-D image of a typical Virginia farmhouse.

'Well,' said Trek. 'Among the architectural styles in the area. This kind of house is the only one that would have the right size basement. The good news is, though, there are less of them to the south.'

'Plato, can you find a match?' asked Kyle.

The image flattened over a map of the countryside south of Alexandria. Within seconds it blinked rapidly and shrank to cover the silhouette of a building isolated amid fields and pastures.

'Tell her what she's won, Johnny,' said Plato gleefully.

'Hey,' said Trek. 'You'd be lost without us, wouldn't you?'

Kyle examined the screen. 'Of course, this is assuming the tape was made in a basement. Otherwise, we've got nothing.'

'You know,' said Trek, 'you really know how to suck the joy out of even the smallest victory.'

Kyle almost smiled. 'But since it's nothing concrete, we'll follow this lead ourselves. I don't want to alert the authorities prematurely.'

He looked at Jenny and nodded. Then he turned to Duke. 'It's time to let the Beast out of his cage.'

Sky One swooped over the low hills just south of the target and set down in a deserted meadow. Within minutes the ramp was extended, and the Beast growled out of the aircraft's belly. Duke drove, with Kyle beside him and Jenny in the back.

No one spoke until Kyle asked them to check their wristwatches for communication and video links with Sky One. Then he watched as Duke expertly manoeuvred the huge truck through the trees until they reached a narrow paved road.

'Beast,' said Duke. 'What's our ETA?'

'We'll get there when we get there,' replied the Beast. Then the rough male voice softened. 'How are you doing, Jenny? Are you comfortable?'

'I'm fine, thank you, Beast,' said Jenny, smiling at Duke's displeasure.

'You just let me know what I can do to make your ride more enjoyable,' continued the Beast. 'If you're chilly, I'd be happy to turn up the heat.'

'I can't even get him to turn on the radio,' said Duke.

Kyle chuckled. 'Maybe if you talked to him like a friend instead of a car.'

'It is a car,' said Duke.

'It is a truck,' insisted the Beast.

Duke decided not to press the point and concentrated on getting them to their destination. It wasn't long before he took them back off the road and across a small, weed-choked field. The Beast stopped at the edge of a band of trees.

The house stood directly ahead. Its low peaked roof showed gaps where the tiles had blown away, the long porch and its roof sagged in several places and paint peeled in curled strips from the walls. No one had lived here in years.

The trio went swiftly and silently to the side of the house, ducking behind some trees. There was no sign of intruders, but at this stage Kyle did not want to take any chances. 'Beast,' he said into his wrist-com, 'scan the area. Let us know what you've got.'

After a short pause the truck answered.

'No infra-red readings in the barn or the upper floor of the house. The basement is shielded. I can't tell you what's down there.'

'That must be where they're hiding him,' said Jenny. 'Let's move.'

Kyle put a restraining hand on her shoulder. 'Since we don't know what's waiting for us down there, we'll go slow. Stay behind me.'

From the condition of the porch it was clear that no one had used it recently, but when Kyle rounded the far corner, there was no question that they had found the right place. The cellar doors were made of steel, and set with a thick electronic lock. Duke passed a small scanner over the doors. 'We've got a magnetic lock with a ten-digit combination. And the doors are four inches thick. We won't be kicking 'em in.'

'Booby traps?'

'None that I can detect,' said Duke. 'But I may have something in the back of the Beast to cut through that lock.' He activated his wrist-com. 'Beast, are you carrying the diamond blade mini-saw?'

'I don't know, look for yourself,' replied the Beast. 'But Jenny, if you're in a hurry, I could just burn through that lock with my microwave laser beam.'

Jenny shrugged. 'Uh...sure, Beast. That would be great.'

Duke just managed to step safely aside when a dense beam blasted out of the wood and burned quickly through the lock, snapping it open. Duke turned to Kyle. 'I've got to talk to you about switching cars.'

Jenny patted his arm sympathetically and followed Kyle down the steps and into a cellar that ran half the length of the building.

'No one's here,' said Kyle, squinting in the dim light. 'They must have moved.'

Then he spotted a chair covered by a cloth in the middle of the floor. Someone, or something, was under the cloth.

Jenny inhaled sharply and moved towards the chair. Kyle tried to stop her but she brushed his hand away.

'Kyle, I can handle this.'

He watched as she moved towards the chair. Then he saw it, a thin red beam stretching across the floor. Before he could warn her, Jenny had stepped through it.

The cellar filled with a loud warning signal.

'It's coming from under there,' said Kyle, indicating the chair.

Jenny pulled the cloth away and revealed a three-foot-tall silver canister with a series of LED indicators all blinking wildly.

Duke checked it out. 'C-four,' he said, 'with a timed fuse.'

Kyle shook his head. 'How much time?'

'About a minute. When the whistle stops...boom!'

Kyle threw himself against the door until he thought his shoulder would break.

Duke spoke into his wrist-com. 'Beast, come in! Beast!'

'Nah,' said Kyle, 'he said the basement was shielded. Whatever they're using is blocking transmission.'

'Think, think,' said Jenny. 'There's gotta be a way out.'

Duke yanked the scanner from his pocket and turned in a slow circle. 'All the conventional exits have been sealed. But we have an air shaft in the upper corner of the east wall. It's welded shut.'

Kyle passed a hand over his face. 'Any way we can somehow blow it open?'

'Nope,' said Duke, pointing at the bomb. 'But in about forty seconds that thing will do it for us.'

Jenny threw herself up the steps at the door. She pounded on it, then stepped back. 'Wait. I hear something.'

Kyle stepped up to the door, and he could hear it too. The deep rumble of a powerful engine.

Duke heard it and quickly realised it was the Beast. 'Clear out! Move!'

A split second later, Beast smashed through the cellar doors, bellowing, 'All aboard! Hurry!'

Unfortunately, Beast's dramatic entrance caused the bomb to sway on the chair. Duke lunged for it before it hit the floor and detonated too soon. 'Beast, get 'em out of here!'

Kyle reacted instantly. He shoved Jenny into Beast's cab as it backed out of the wreckage, picking up speed, tyres squealing and smoking. Then, sitting up, he realised the signal had stopped.

Time stretched and in what seemed like tortuous slow-motion, he watched Duke explode from the cellar and race towards them, followed soon after by an immense fireball that blew apart the wall.

Suddenly Duke was in the air, and the shock waves hit Beast, rocking it as the farmhouse disintegrated into flaming wooden shrapnel. He landed on the hood and lay spread-eagled across the windshield. With bits of farmhouse falling out

of the sky, he scrambled for the door, yanked it open and scrambled into the back seat.

'Nice going, Beast,' he said. 'Finally came through for me.'

Without missing a beat the truck answered, 'Are you okay, Jenny?'

They moved out in case the terrorists had another surprise in store.

'They must have moved the General,' said Jenny. 'But why? How could they know we were on to them?'

Before they could consider the question, a voice came through Kyle's wrist-com. 'Kyle? It's Erica.'

'What's up?'

'You guys better get back here. You're not gonna believe this.'

A TV news report was showing on a monitor in the Situation Room. A reporter was speaking amid a mass of others all jockeying for position outside General Butler's Alexandria home. 'Just over an hour ago, General Stephen Butler made a heroic escape from his captors, who call themselves Fallen Nation. General, how did you escape?'

The General, looking rumpled and worn, held up his hands in an attempt to establish some order. 'Uh...they actually...uh...were trying to move me to a new location. And...uh...I was in a truck with one guard...and I was just lucky enough to get the drop on him.'

Another reporter asked, 'General Butler, just who is Fallen Nation?'

Butler shrugged. 'I really don't know. Uh...I didn't understand most of what they were saying, but it was hard to miss the contempt they held for us, or the intention to do us harm.'

Trek picked up a pen and tapped it lightly against his lips. 'How do they plan on doing that, General?'

'And how did they plan on doing that?' asked the reporter.

Butler shrugged again. 'I wish I knew, but they're not going to stop with a failed kidnapping. Next time these guys will raise the stakes.'

'But what can you do about it?' said Trek, staring intently at the screen.

Kyle gave him a tolerant glare as the reporter asked the same question.

Butler hesitated dramatically before answering. 'Well, I talked it over with some of my colleagues, and we're going to meet with the President and see what we can do to help.'

There was a faint smattering of applause as the General backed away, indicating that he was tired and the press conference was over.

Trek grinned and looked at the others. 'I can also watch "Family Matters" and tell you the punch line to every joke before Urkel can.'

Duke shook his head. 'And that's how you graduated MIT when you were eleven?'

'Ten,' said Trek, cocking an eyebrow.

Erica sighed loudly as she massaged the back of her neck. 'We better not invoice an expense account for our rescue of the General, being as he wound up saving himself.'

Jenny did not appreciate the humour. 'I just thank God he got out alive.'

Kyle agreed and the others settled down. He was still annoyed at their walking straight into a trap and now, General or not, this mission had become personal. 'Well,' he said, 'whoever these

Fallen Nation guys are, they're sophisticated and well organised, and we don't have a clue as to what they're planning.' He paused for a moment. 'Jenny, you need to talk to Butler.'

Jenny shook her head in disbelief. 'After what he's been through, you want me to go there and help him relive it? I don't think so.'

'He's the one lead we've got,' Kyle insisted.

'I don't care, okay,' said Jenny. 'I'm still not going.'

Oblivious to the others, Kyle leaned closer to her. 'You're not thinking this through, Jenny. Butler's the only person who can identify these guys. If I were a terrorist, I'd consider that a loose end.'

Domino took the highway straight and fast. At the wheel, Jenny used the wind that blasted over the windshield to clear her mind.

She really hated it when Kyle was right – especially when he was right and she was wrong. But when he cut through her personal involvement like that, in front of everyone else, well...

Still, his point had been well made. General Butler was in danger, and whatever information she could uncover would only serve to protect him.

Jenny did not slow down until she reached the driveway to the General's home.

TV vans were blocking the end of the road, and reporters were milling about on the front lawn. A handful of Marine guards prevented them from actually getting too close.

A Lieutenant stepped into the road and flagged her down. She recognised him as Mark Davis from her days on the General's staff.

'Mmm,' said Domino, as the Lieutenant

As Davis backed away, Domino purred, 'Ah Lieutenant...you single?'

A guard directed Jenny to a parking area beyond the news van. Then another guard hustled her away quickly from the reporters before they

stepped up to the car. 'I love a man in uniform.'

Davis made a disgusted face as Jenny smiled up at him. 'We're very busy,' he said. 'The General doesn't have time to talk to you right now.'

'Look, Davis,' replied Jenny. 'I was one of his soldiers too. I care for him as much as you do.'

'I didn't desert him for some fancy car club,' said Davis.

Just then Butler's voice came over the walkie-talkie. 'Lieutenant, let her through.'

realised what had happened.

She met General Butler outside his office. He greeted her warmly and they walked away from the house.

'Lee Majors called me this morning,' he said. 'Wants to play me in the TV movie based on my experience.'

'Hold out for James Garner,' said Jenny, smiling.

The General looked around the garden, then turned back to her. 'I fought in three wars, and nobody took notice. I get kidnapped by a bunch of crackpots, and I'm on the cover of Newsweek.'

'You seem to be taking it in your stride.'

'I have to tell you something,' he said, seriously. 'This time, I was pretty scared.'

'I never heard you say that before,' said Jenny in some surprise.

The General looked at her. 'I've never faced anything like this. I'm just grateful that Georgia was away visiting the grandkids.'

They walked on through the garden. Jenny paused to touch a rose petal and breathe in its fragrance. 'What did the President have to say?' she asked.

'Oh...he wants me to lend a hand. I can't blame him. I mean we were all caught flat-footed by this bunch.'

Jenny stopped. 'Are you sure you want to take this on, after all you've been through?'

The General stopped too. 'Oh, I won't be doing it alone. I have an outstanding team backing me up. Of course, there's always room for one more...'

'General, I—' said Jenny.

'I really could use you,' continued the General.

'Gen—'

'Oh, I know,' he interrupted again, 'you're with the Foundation now, working for Kyle Stewart. I heard he's not doing too well after his accident.

That he's...uh...not quite back up to speed.'

Jenny frowned, wondering where he got that kind of information. 'That's not true. Kyle's as good as he ever was when he was with the CIA. He holds the whole team together. He's a natural leader. I really admire him.'

He looked wistfully at her. 'You used to say that about me.'

'I still do,' she smiled. 'And believe me, I'm going to do everything I can to help.

'Good,' said Butler with a sharp nod. 'Because the one thing I know for sure — we're going to hear from these guys again.'

Turbines thrummed in an isolated power station surrounded by a high chain-link fence and topped with concertina wire. As the night crew worked inside, a guard lay sprawled at the entrance. Blood slowly seeped from a wound on the back of his head.

On the main floor two men in hard hats worked at a large console, noting where more electricity was needed, where electricity usage was at its greatest in the state of Virginia.

The crewmen were used to the noise of the place and did not see the black-clad men sneak up behind them. They did not stand a chance as they were knocked unconscious.

In less than a minute one of the attackers had shut the power down, while his partner

clubbed the console beyond repair.

Within five minutes Virginia began to go dark.

Kyle could not suppress a yawn. He and Duke had been in the Situation Room for so long, it was beginning to seem as if they lived there. They were monitoring computer checks run by Sky One, Dante and Kat.

When Dante came up empty, Kyle rubbed the back of his neck and said, 'Did you try cross-referencing Interpol's terrorism data base with the CIA's?'

Dante replied, 'Not one match with Fallen Nation. Shouldn't you be out looking for them?'

'No,' said Kyle. 'I want a new lead before we make a move. Besides, we'd just be tripping all over the other law enforcement agencies who are doing the same thing.'

Duke studied the monitors for a moment. 'I've got an idea. How about checking alternate spellings under the FBI's Domestic Radicals Index?'

'I've checked everybody,' said Dante, in his very proper English accent. 'Interpol, CIA, FBI, IRS...'

'What about the NFL?' quipped Duke.

'Don't be cute,' said Dante. 'I'm telling you, I've got no record of them anywhere.'

Kat joined in. 'That's because he's got a really small memory. I can store a lot more information than he can.'

'Do you have anything on them?' said Kyle.

'No,' admitted Kat. 'But if I did, I'd have more than him.'

Dante snapped, 'This whole TKR program went to hell the day they started making female cars.'

Kyle stabbed a button on the console. 'Uh...Trek, how you comin'?'

Trek replied from Sky One's lab. 'We've gone over the forensic evidence from the crime scene. I agree with the FBI — there's nothing.'

Then he added, jokingly, 'And our lab is much better.'

'Does anyone have anything useful to say to me?' asked Kyle.

As if on cue, Erica came in, beaming. 'Kyle, Communications just got word — there's a state-wide blackout in Virginia.'

'You got here fast with that,' said Kyle.

She winked at him. 'I lost the heels.'

Kat joined in. 'I can show you a grid of all the affected power stations, since Dante isn't programmed to provide such a service.'

'Kiss up,' muttered Dante.

After giving the grinning Erica a sharp look, Kyle studied Kat's map.

'I've traced the source to one relay station,' continued Kat, smugly. 'It's definitely not a mechanical failure.'

'You think it's related?' asked Duke, frowning.

Kyle checked the location of the relay station. 'We're close,' he shrugged. 'Check it out.'

Twenty minutes later Beast pulled up in front of the relay station. They spotted the fallen guard.

'He's still breathing,' said Trek.

'All right,' said Duke. 'Get in.'

'I'll call the paramedics,' said Trek, priming his wrist-com.

The heavy metal entrance door was slightly ajar. Trek went in and quickly located the central console. Dismay crossed his face when he saw all the damage.

Trek shook his head as Duke came in. 'The whole computer system's been tampered with, as well as all the backup programs. It's gonna take days to restore this power, man.'

Duke let his gaze wander until he fixed on a security camera near the console. It didn't look right, and when he went closer, he nodded to himself and yanked it down.

'Well,' said Trek. 'We won't get anything from that.'

Duke smiled slowly. 'Don't be too sure,' and he pointed to a small grille beneath the lens. A quick twist, and he drew out a tiny microphone. Another twist, and an equally tiny audio cassette fell into his palm.

'Oh,' said Trek.

They didn't wait for the paramedics. Beast got them back to base in record time, and within minutes they were in the Situation Room, watching a sonic graph peak and ebb as the computers analysed the muffled voice pattern discovered on the tape.

Jenny, still on the road in Domino, was also present at the meeting — in the form of a holographic image projected above the desk.

Dante spoke. 'Of the five million voice prints I've tried, not one matches with the recording from the camera.'

'Same here,' said Kat. 'Sorry, Kyle.'

Kyle turned to Plato. 'Let me guess...you came up empty.'

'You are correct, sir,' replied Plato.

Kyle rubbed his eyes. 'Which leaves us right back where we started. Fallen Nation can strike at any time, and we can't do a thing about it.'

Jenny's holographic image joined in. 'Kyle, we just received a transmission of that voice print from Dante... Domino's running a check.'

'Tell her to forget it,' said Duke, miserably. 'We're never going to find a match.'

Kyle hated to admit it, but he agreed, and couldn't believe it when, not ten seconds later, Domino said, 'I know who it is.'

'But how?' said Kyle. 'None of the other cars...'

'Because I've just added that voice to my file,' said Domino.

Although the others couldn't see the image that flashed on Domino's dashboard screen, they could hear Jenny's soft, shocked voice.

'Davis...it's Mark Davis.'

TKR FALLEN NATION

continues on page 42

39

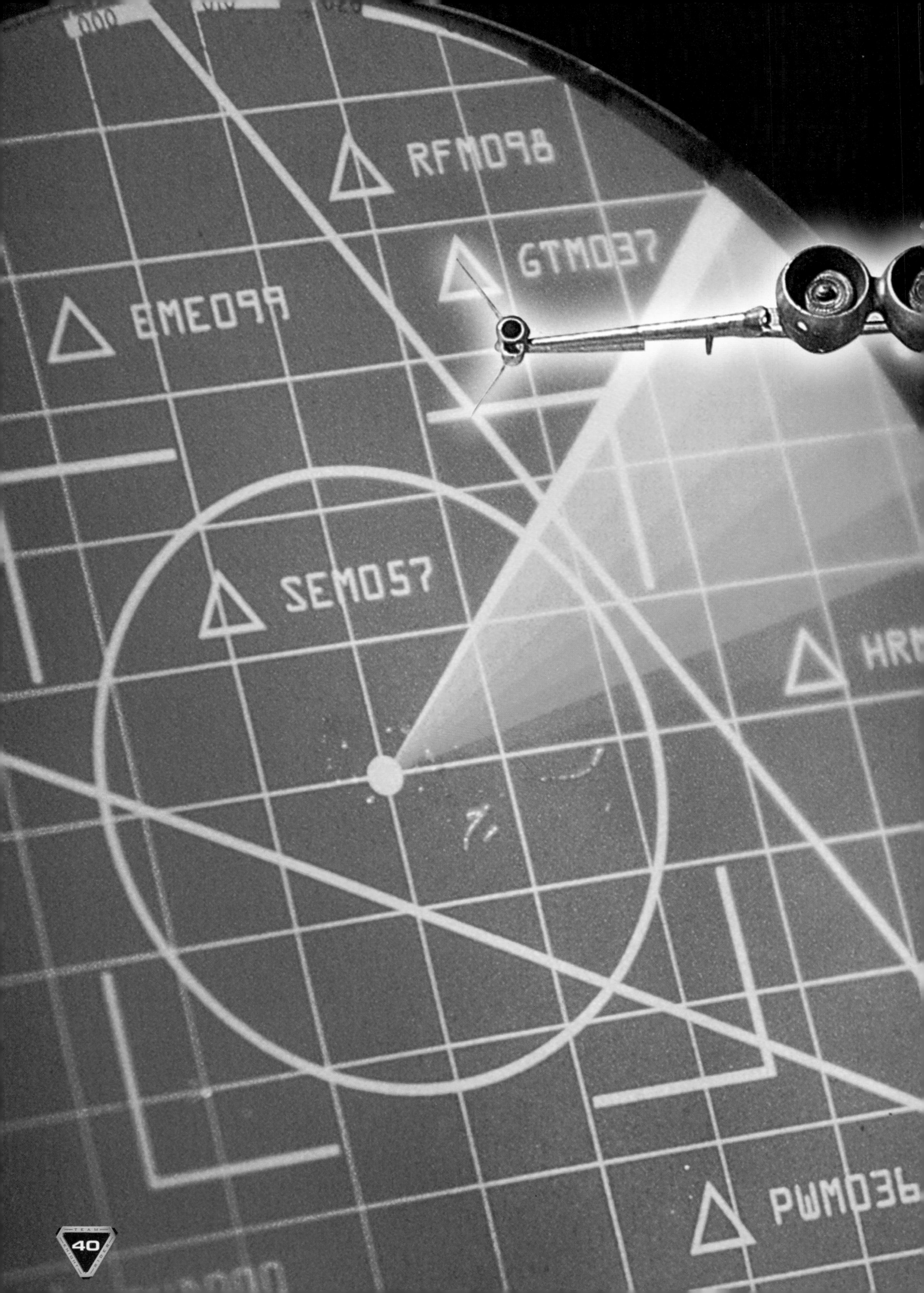
RFM098
GTM037
EME099
SEM057
PWM036

SKY ONE

Sky One is the enormous CSA military transport plane which serves as the headquarters for the TKR team. This remarkable craft is outfitted

with garages, sleeping quarters, target ranges and even a gym. Sky One is a fully operational base which allows TKR to mobilise and deploy anywhere in the world.

FALLEN NATION PART TWO

Tension spread through the room as every available computer checked through every on-line telephone book to search for Mark Davis and his address.

It didn't help that one of the monitors was constantly tuned to the TV news. Its screen showed massive traffic jams, helpless police, and areas so dark that the camera lights were unable to penetrate them.

The newsreader sounded calm. 'As emergency generators continue to fall, Virginia plunges deeper into chaos tonight. Fallen Nation, the terrorist group responsible for capturing General Butler, have openly claimed responsibility for the state-wide blackout.'

Erica slumped back in her seat. 'We're never gonna find him this way. There's gotta be hundreds of listings for "Mark Davis".'

Jenny's holographic image still hovered above the desk. 'I'm heading back to the General's house to warn him,' she said.

Kyle shook his head. 'Not yet. Give us a chance to grab Davis first.'

Jenny's face darkened with concern and defiance. 'Butler has to know that Davis is a traitor.'

Kyle leaned close to the holographic image, lowering his voice, ignoring the others. 'He might not be the only one. If there are other people close to the General who are working with Davis, he could get tipped-off before we get to him.'

Jenny's voice was just as intense. 'And if Davis finds out we're on to him, it could cost Butler his life.'

They glared at each other, until Duke finally cleared his throat. 'Uh...Should we leave?'

Kyle shot him a glance. Duke shrugged. Erica raised a knowing eyebrow.

'Jenny,' said Kyle, 'I'm giving you an order. Don't tell Butler anything...'

Jenny's glare deepened, and a second later her image wavered and then vanished.

'...Jenny?'

There was no answer.

'Jenny!'

No answer.

Trek coughed lightly. 'I think she hung up.'

'Yeah, I know,' said Kyle. 'Look, we gotta

find Davis...fast.'

Kyle turned angrily from the desk and stared intently at the monitors. Then, a decision taken, he stepped close to Dante's image and whispered something that no one else could hear.

In the Communications Room at the Annapolis Naval Air Station, a lone sergeant was doing her best to keep up with events outside. She was juggling orders from her superiors with frantic calls from people wanting to know if Maryland was next on Fallen Nation's list. So, it came as a relief when the next voice she heard had a cultured British accent.

'Hello,' it said, smoothly. 'Can you tell me how I can find a Lieutenant Mark Davis?'

'I'm sorry, sir,' she replied. 'I'm not authorised to release that information.'

'Oh, are you sure? Not even for me?'

She couldn't hide a fleeting smile. 'I'm afraid so.'

'You know,' said the voice, now smoother, more intimate, 'I never usually say things like this, but has anyone ever told you what a lovely voice you have?'

The sergeant glanced nervously around the room, feeling guilty because she knew she had begun to blush.

She giggled slightly.

'He's in Baltimore,' Dante told Kyle, 'assembling troops for the crisis in Virginia. She even gave me her home address. Said she wants to meet me. I didn't have the heart to tell her I was a car.'

Jenny slapped Domino's steering wheel in increasing frustration. She had been making good time, but the traffic had thickened considerably to slow her down.

On Domino's dashboard monitor, the calm TV newsreader kept viewers updated on the blackout situation. 'As the number of highway accidents and reports of looting continue to rise, efforts to restore power to Virginia have been unsuccessful. Army and National Guard units have been reassigned and posted across the state in order to calm fearful, anxious residents...'

Jenny slapped the wheel again, as the newsreader continued. '...The Governor has declared a state of emergency, and the President plans on making a statement tonight. We caught up with General Butler at his home in Alexandria. He had this to say...'

Jenny glanced at the screen as Butler's face appeared and he began to speak. 'An attack like this is meant to cause panic. Now, the best thing we can do is to remain calm...'

A reporter asked, 'General, do you know what the President is going to say tonight?'

'No,' replied Butler. 'But the divisions under my command are on full alert. I'm sure the President is going to demand a swift and immediate action.'

'General,' said another reporter. 'A recent Gallup Poll puts your approval rating twenty points ahead of the President...'

'We're in good hands, with the President,' said Butler, reassuringly. 'I back him one hundred per cent.'

Jenny gave a weak smile. Her old boss had not lost his touch.

Outside an apartment complex in Baltimore, Trek and Erica waited in the PlatoKat combination. It looked like a very expensive, very futuristic sports car.

'He's on his way in,' said Trek. 'Now, remember, Kyle said stick to the plan. That means no improvising.'

Erica opened her side of the vehicle and climbed out, leaving her helmet behind.

'Hey, it's not like I've never done this before,' she said.

Trek blinked, but experience had taught him not to ask any questions. Then he saw a car drive up behind him and park at the kerb in front of the apartments.

Lieutenant Mark Davis slid out of the car, wearing a well-cut, very smart civilian suit. He stretched, yawned, then told his driver to stick around. He'd be back in a few minutes.

Trek crossed his fingers.

Things were moving fast, and Mark Davis didn't have much time. He hurried up the steps, coded himself in, and hurried to his apartment. Once he stepped inside, he froze.

He could hear water splashing off the tiles in the shower. Pulling a service revolver from his jacket he edged cautiously down the hall.

With one hand he pushed open the bathroom door and was surprised to see an officer's uniform on the floor.

He charged in and yanked the shower curtain aside just as the water was shut off.

He gaped in astonishment — at Erica.

'Oh!' she gasped, looking at him over her shoulder. 'I didn't expect you home so soon.'

He continued to gape.

She smiled. 'As you can see, I'm a Captain — so you have to be nice to me.'

'Yes, ma'am,' said Davis, as Erica wrapped herself in a thick, fluffy towel.

'Actually,' she said, 'I was hoping you could introduce me to General Butler...I just have to meet him.'

Davis preened.

'Well, I...I am the General's most trusted aide. If anyone can get you to see him, I can.'

'Oh!' purred Erica. 'How lucky for both of us, But, you know, it never occurred to me that his Lieutenant would be far more attractive than the General himself.'

Trek, listening in from outside the apartment complex, was dismayed. 'Why can't she ever stick to the script?'

He heard Erica gasp in pain as Davis grabbed a handful of her hair and pressed a revolver to her temple.

Then he heard the Lieutenant say, 'I don't know who you are, but I'm not buying it!'

'I'm telling the truth, I swear,' said Erica.

Davis explained. 'You almost had me convinced, right up till you said I was more attractive than Butler. They always prefer him.'

He shoved her away, but she spun and came right back, flattening him against the wall. Then he felt a tiny jab in his neck. As his legs buckled under him, he was sure he saw a needle sticking out of her forefinger.

He was right.

Erica breathed a huge sigh of relief as she retracted the needle into her false nail. Then she lifted Davis in a fireman's carry and quickly hauled him out of the apartment and down the stairs. It wasn't until she reached the entrance hall that she realised she was still wrapped in the towel.

Thankfully, Trek had pulled PlatoKat closer to the entrance. Together they bundled the unconscious Lieutenant into the back half of her part of the vehicle.

Erica jumped in, grinning at Trek's startled look. She heard Davis's limousine driver call out a warning. Then he tried to start his engine, but it sputtered and died on him.

Erica looked at Trek. 'How'd you disable the limo?'

'Beverly Hills Cop,' replied Plato. 'Paramount Pictures, 1984...'

Erica was puzzled.

'...Eddie Murphy stuffed a banana in Judge Reinhold's exhaust pipe,' explained Plato.

'You guys scare me,' said Erica.

Kat spoke up. 'You two just better be quiet and listen to the police band.'

Accepting the advice, Erica switched on the radio, and they heard a police officer's voice reporting their position, 'Suspects are up ahead, approaching Northside Freeway...'

A crackle of static and another police voice, 'Right on the Ten.'

The police band crackled again, 'We're seconds away.'

That was answered by another voice. 'We see you. All units stand by.'

Trek frowned. 'You know, I think we should've spent a little more time planning our escape route.'

Erica giggled, enjoying herself. 'Live a little on the edge, will ya?'

Trek yelled in surprise when a squad car passed them at high speed. He didn't bother to look back when he heard tyres squealing as the cop car did a U-turn up ahead.

They took a corner on two wheels and turned into a wide boulevard only to find the way ahead blocked by three police cruisers. A reflex turn took them into another side street.

Another turn, and another pair of speeding cruisers, with screaming sirens and spinning lights, piled into the street behind them.

Now they were heading at top speed for one of the bridges over the river. Right across the middle of it sat half a dozen squad cars. The barricade was solid, and backed by almost a dozen uniformed cops leaning on the hoods and roofs, their shotguns and pistols aimed at the oncoming PlatoKat.

No more side streets. No chance of turning around.

Their only hope was a manoeuvre they had practised only a couple of times before...and that had been in the middle of the desert.

Trek looked at Erica. She just smiled and shrugged. It was his call.

With the barricade less than fifty yards ahead, he took a deep breath and flicked a switch under the right handlebar. After a moment's hesitation, the lights flickered once, and suddenly the midsection of the combo-bike folded away.

Plato yelled deliriously, 'It's two...two...two mints in one!' as Trek veered sharply to the left, heading straight for the narrow pedestrian walkway, then running along the low, concrete bridge wall.

The police just gaped in astonishment as he jumped the kerb, forcing several of them to leap for their lives, and sped away.

Erica wasn't so lucky. With no room on her right, she reared Kat onto its back wheel. The front wheel caught the closest cruiser on the hood, and Kat roared up and over the car, taking to the air with sparks trailing. She landed safely a good twenty yards away, and before any of the cops thought to turn and fire, she was gone too.

Kyle paced the narrow confines of the interrogation room, staring down every so often at the weary and dishevelled Mark Davis.

Davis's eyes followed him with a look of contempt. 'Like I said, I never even heard of Fallen Nation till they kidnapped the General.'

'You know,' said Kyle, reasonably. 'If you're not gonna be honest, how are we gonna be friends?'

Davis sneered. 'I got enough friends.'

Kyle shrugged, left the room and joined Duke behind the one-way mirror that looked into the interrogation room.

'Eighteen hours,' said Duke, 'and we've still got nothing.'

'He's not gonna talk,' said Kyle.

'Too bad,' said Duke. 'He just ran out of options.'

Kyle followed Duke back into the interrogation room, and watched as he grabbed Davis by the shirtfront, hauled him to his feet and dragged him roughly into the corridor.

'Hey, pal,' said Davis. 'Don't mess with me! I'm a Lieutenant in the United States Marine Corps!'

Duke's expression didn't change. 'I'd love for you to show off your fancy combat training.'

'We're not allowed to use it on civilians,' said Davis as Duke shoved him along.

A computer voice announced, 'Sky One has reached cruising altitude of twenty-eight thousand feet.'

'Hey, look, I told you everything I know!' said Davis.

'I believe you,' said Duke.

They reached the door, and Davis's relieved smile turned to consternation as Duke punched a code into a keypad.

'Well, then, what more do you want from me?' demanded Davis as the door began to hiss open.

'Nothing,' said Duke, shoving him into the airlock. 'You're free to go.'

'Hey!' said Davis, as Duke stepped back, slammed the door and tapped in the locking code.

Kyle joined him and they watched through a small window as realisation and panic began to twist Davis's features.

A red light in the airlock flared and a computer voice said, 'Warning. Opening of outer doors will cause explosive decompression in the airlock...Warning. Opening of outer doors...'

'Wait, please! Wait! Please!' screamed Davis.

'...will cause explosive decompression in the airlock...'

'Hey! Hey!' yelled the terrified Lieutenant, as the outer doors slowly began to swing open.

He clawed at the inner door. 'I...I'll tell you everything I know! There is no Fallen Nation! It's just a bunch of guys working for Butler! It's all part of his plan!'

'Butler?' whispered Kyle.

Now the escaping air began to pull Davis away from the inner door. 'They're gonna destroy Washington and take over the country! Please help me!'

The outer door swung fully open and Davis was sucked out of the lock, screaming, his arms and legs flailing – until he hit the ground. About six feet below.

Dazed, he rolled onto his back and blinked rapidly. He moaned when Duke appeared in the opening, his arms folded across his chest and a smile on his face.

After ordering Duke to throw Davis into the worst cell on the aircraft, Kyle ran to the Situation Room and made contact with Jenny and Domino.

Jenny watched as Kyle spoke on Domino's monitor. 'The blackout was a diversion, to keep the armed forces busy. And if it all goes according to plan, Butler's men, pretending to be part of Fallen Nation, will launch a nuclear missile against Washington.'

Jenny's holographic image flickered. 'That's the most ridiculous thing I've ever heard,' she said.

'Davis is clearly trying to throw us off track.'

'That was my first reaction,' said Kyle. 'But think about it, Jenny. We wake up tomorrow and there's a big hole between Maryland and Virginia, who do you think the country's gonna turn to?'

Jenny looked away. She knew the answer, but she didn't want to say it aloud.

Her image flickered again.

'Jenny,' pleaded Kyle, 'for God's sake, don't hang up on me again.'

But the image flickered again and then vanished.

As Domino raced on through the night, Jenny's anger rose and by the time she arrived at the General's house her temper was at full-bore. Davis was going to pay for this bit of nonsense, and as soon as she warned Butler of the treachery within his ranks, she was going back to Sky One to deal with Davis personally.

No one stopped her this time. As soon as the new aide recognised her he led her straight to Butler's office.

The General was reading at his desk when she came in. He stood immediately, a look of concern on his face. 'Jenny? Anything the matter?'

'No,' Jenny hesitated. 'Well, yes. It's about Lieutenant Davis.'

'Is he okay?' asked Butler.

'Yes...but...'

'Oh, that's a relief. I don't know what I'd do without him. He's a good man, a good soldier.'

'I don't think you know him as well as you thought,' said Jenny.

Butler smiled. 'There isn't anything you can say to me that's going to shake my confidence in him.'

The door opened, and two uniformed guards slipped into the office. Something about the atmosphere had changed. She wasn't sure what it was, but with a surreptitious move she switched on her wrist-com; just in case.

'He's involved in something...' she said.

The General cut her off with a wave. 'I don't think you're following me. Anything Mark Davis has done, he's done on my orders.'

The realisation hit her in a sickening wave, as Butler continued, 'Jenny, take a hard look around you. America is falling apart at the seams. Now, there's a lot of important work to do in the days ahead.'

'You made it all up,' she said, stepping back.

'You said it yourself, Jenny. The country needs me.'

She took another step back. 'So, now what? You're going to wipe out the government of the United States?'

'I have no intention,' replied Butler. 'Fallen Nation will do that for me.'

Suddenly the two guards were at her side. If she made a move towards Butler they would grab her.

'So,' she said with contempt, 'your Fallen Nation is going to wipe out Washington?'

Butler shrugged. 'It's no big loss.'

The TKR team sat in the Situation Room, listening with growing anger at Butler's smugness.

Then they heard Jenny say, 'Stephen, stop this now.'

'Tell me the truth,' replied Butler. 'You really gonna miss it?'

Kyle turned to the team. 'How easy is it gonna be to launch a nuclear missile?'

Trek leaned back, stared at the ceiling for a moment. 'A General with his kind of clout could probably get his hands on the necessary access codes, give 'em to a few of his psycho Marines. Some of whom have been stationed at the missile silo at one point, might know it pretty well...'

Trek frowned, then shook his head in reluctant admiration. 'Boy, you know, it's so easy. I'm surprised someone hasn't done it before.'

'Great,' said Kyle, closing his eyes.

Trek suddenly realised what he had said, but it was too late to take it back.

Duke grumbled, 'The country will be so desperate for leadership, he won't have to run for President...they'll crown him King.'

Kyle paced up and down the room, thinking as fast and hard as he could. 'Davis says Butler is going to launch at nine o'clock.'

Erica said, 'I thought people did this kind of thing at midnight.'

Kyle clasped his hands under his chin. 'There's no time to alert anyone. We're on our own. Let's move it.'

'What about Jenny?' asked Erica.

Jenny felt sick as she watched Butler, her mentor and oldest friend, calmly discussing the nuclear annihilation of the capital. She spoke up. 'The blood of a million people will be on your hands. Is that how you want history to remember you?'

Butler shook his head in disappointment. 'Jenny, you don't remember anything I taught you. It's a battlefield decision. To win, to save, you must always be prepared to sacrifice a few.'

She thought for a moment that she could get to him, but a shift in his eyes brought the guards closer to her sides. They grabbed her hands, pinning her.

'I'm sorry you won't be going with me,' said Butler.

He nodded, and the guards took her away. She knew that the others would be searching for a way to stop the launch. Her only hope was herself. And, with a little luck, Domino.

Just after sunset, a pair of Jeeps and a canvas-top truck pulled up to the gate of the Shenandoah Missile Installation. The guard stepped out of his gatehouse, saw the Jeeps' occupants and saluted smartly. A high steel-rod barrier slid aside and the convoy rumbled through.

The truck veered into the shadows with the second Jeep. The first Jeep moved on, stopping in front of a massive steel gate set in the hillside. The lone guard, puzzled but alert, widened his eyes as a stocky Colonel and a well-muscled Major stepped out of the vehicle.

The Colonel smiled.

The Major pulled a slender dart gun from his holster and shot the guard in the neck. He dropped immediately, and the Colonel wasted no time hurrying to the palm-print lock and slamming his open hand on it.

The doors opened.

The two officers entered the Control Room, where two Marines snapped immediately to attention.

The Colonel smiled.

The Major darted both guards and dragged their unconscious bodies to one side.

Not a word had been spoken. None had been needed.

The officers knew what had to be done. The Colonel opened a wall safe and pulled out the Code Book. The Major sat at the computer and began to punch in the numbers read out to him by the Colonel.

A steel blind opened in the north wall, allowing them to see the waiting missile in its silo.

Another six numbers, and the missile rose into launch position as the overhead silo doors began to slide open.

The time on the arming clock was exactly 8:35.

After being held in the pool house for several hours, Jenny was brought out by two guards in full battle gear. But she wasn't worried. As they hauled her towards the parking area, she heard a brief hissing and guessed that Domino had used her laser to pop a tyre on the guards' Jeep.

'Listen to me,' she said. 'You two are betraying your country.'

'Shut up!' said one of the guards, kicking at the flat tyre.

The other one pointed at Domino. 'Let's just take her car.'

Jenny didn't argue.

They shoved her into the back seat and demanded the keys.

Jenny sat back to enjoy the ride.

The first twenty yards were easy. After that Domino took over the steering, swinging wildly back and forth while the guards argued with each other as they tried to figure out what was going on!

Jenny grinned. It would have been a lot more fun if the situation wasn't so desperate.

In the Missile Control Room the renegade Colonel, Major and Sergeant checked the nuclear missile's co-ordinates, as they aimed it towards Washington.

'At zero per cent deviation,' said the Sergeant.

The Major leaned over the keyboard. 'Right sixteen, left twenty-six, right four.'

'Alpha. Delta. Two-eight-nine,' confirmed the Colonel.

Kyle and Dante were leading the way, Duke and Beast right behind, the motorcycles trailing.

Trek said, 'Plato and I can probably take out their back-up generator, so we can get up close without them seeing us.'

Kyle asked, 'How long's it gonna take?'

'Six, maybe seven minutes,' said Trek.

Kyle checked the dashboard clock – 8:40 – and grimaced. 'No. We don't have time for subtlety.'

'How about loosening them up with some heavy artillery?' suggested Beast.

'No,' said Kyle. 'We'd give 'em too much warning.' He glanced at the clock again, shook his head, changed his mind. 'Drat, I hate making a mess.'

Duke grinned broadly. 'Okay, let's take it to 'em, Beast.'

The Beast pulled around and in front of Dante and roared down the narrow country road, swinging easily around the long curve at the base of the hill. A hundred yards ahead Duke could see the lights of the installation compound.

The Beast bellowed and picked up speed. Kat pulled in behind him, weaving back and forth as Erica prayed the huge truck would do its job.

'Whooo!' said Duke, as the Beast struck the gate. It fell in an explosion of sparks and smoke.

The Beast swung close to the nearest building, scattering a handful of unprepared soldiers.

Erica went left, huddling as close to Kat as possible when rifles began to fire, ricocheting harmlessly off the cycle's sides and tinted windscreen. Despite the danger, Erica couldn't help a delighted laugh when Kat complained, 'This is completely against regulations. We are not to engage in battle if we have no protective covering. I'm not the Beast, you know.'

The two guards were still arguing as Domino sped erratically along.

'What the hell you doing?! Quit fooling around.'

'It's steering itself, man! It could flip! This is dangerous!'

'I knew I shouldn't have let you drive. Turn around. Try something!'

'Oh, this...this thing's outta control.'

'Hit the brakes or something! Come on!'

Suddenly Domino stopped and the guards sighed with relief. She said, 'Goodbye boys,' and activated an ejection device that sent the men yelling into the air.

'Where to now?' Domino asked Jenny. 'As if I couldn't guess.'

Duke aimed the Beast towards the silo. Bullets sparked off the doors and hood, soldiers scattered out of the way.

You wanted a diversion, thought Duke, gleefully, as the Beast slewed around to charge

The two men ran in, pausing only when they discovered the officers in the Control Room – each standing with a launch key in his hand while a computer-voice announced, 'Missile launch sequence activated. One minute to lift off.'

Kyle leapt over the console and felled the Major with a drop-kick, then turned to take on the Colonel.

again, okay, you got one!

As the firing escalated, Dante braked in a cloud of dust and stones in front of the Missile Control Room door. 'Get it,' Kyle ordered as soon as he realised how thick it was, and Dante slid a compartment open in its roof, raised a small rocket launcher, and fired.

The door buckled, then toppled off its hinges just as Trek pulled up alongside him.

Trek ran to the panel and groaned.

The clock was set at 8:47.

'Oh, great,' he said. 'You know, you idiots were supposed to wait until nine!'

He jumped into the operator's seat and took the fastest familiarisation course in his life before attacking the keys.

The computer voice said, 'Fifty seconds to lift off.'

Kyle dodged a punch, threw a flurry of his own, and was dragged backwards when the Major regained his feet and slammed an arm around his throat.

Trek wiped perspiration from his eyes, tried another sequence, and moaned when nothing happened.

'Forty seconds...'

The Colonel fell over the console, with Kyle's arm wrapped around his chest.

'Hey, Trek,' said Kyle. 'Can you give me a little more time?'

'Yeah. But could you get him off the thing, please?'

Kyle braced himself and pulled, and the two of them rolled onto the floor.

'Thirty seconds...'

Outside, the Beast took out a half-track with a laser shot at the front wheel. 'Kyle,' said Duke. 'You guys better hurry up. We can't hold these guys off forever.'

Erica ploughed through a hastily formed wall of riflemen, skidded into a one-eighty turn and ploughed through them again. Kat still complained, but Erica just grinned.

'Twenty seconds...Lift off in ten...nine... eight...seven...six...five...four...three...two...one. Missile launched.'

Outside, everything stopped.

Erica, Duke, the installation troops — they all watched the missile lift on its fiery tail above the mountain and climb into the night sky.

'We're too late,' said Duke.

Erica wanted to cry.

The click of the keyboard was the only sound in the Control Room until Trek said, 'Oh, boy,' and let his hands fall into his lap.

Kyle leaned over his shoulder. 'Can...you

alter its trajectory?'

Trek held up one finger, then nodded. 'I think so, yeah...All right, the missile still has a little ways to go before it...uh...turns back and...you know...boom!'

'Beginning initiation of re-entry sequence,' said the computer voice, as numbers on the screen scrolled up rapidly.

'Oh...' said Trek.

'What did you do?' said Kyle.

Trek gave him a quick painful smile. 'Well, I, uh...I seem to have sped up its re-entry. It's gonna be hitting the ground about...uh...five minutes sooner now.'

Kyle made a sound as if he'd just received a punch. He straightened and activated his wrist-com. 'Dante.'

Dante replied. 'Secret Service reports Air Force One is off the ground. The President is safe.'

'Great,' said Kyle. 'Now all we gotta do is worry about the nine hundred thousand other people in the DC area.'

'No,' said Trek. 'Look-look-look-look, as long as I can...uh...I can disarm the nuclear warhead, the damage should be minimal, and we should...'

'Warhead armed,' said the computer voice.

'Great,' said Trek.

'What's that?' said Kyle as alarms began to sound.

'Well, now,' said Trek. 'I just armed the warhead.'

Kyle's mouth dropped open as he leaned against the console. 'Come on, Trek.'

Growing more frantic, Trek didn't bother to look up. 'No pressure, all right? No pressure.'

Kyle rubbed an exasperated hand over his

chin. 'If it blows up in the atmosphere, it'll spread radiation across three continents.'

'I know how a nuclear missile works,' snapped Trek.

'All right,' said Kyle, his face drenched in sweat. 'All right.'

Taking a deep breath, licking his lips nervously, Trek entered the last series he knew. Then he reached out and held his finger over the red self-destruct button.

Kyle nodded.

Trek pressed the button...and nothing happened.

None of the indicators changed; the missile was still on its way.

Outside Duke and Erica stared at the sky. Waiting.

Domino pulled into Butler's driveway. This time the guard tried to stop Jenny from entering, but a simple side-kick to his chest dropped him into the bushes.

Trek stared intently at the monitor, urging it to do something...before it was too late.

It did.

The warning siren cut off abruptly, the numbers stopped scrolling, and the 'Self-destruct Accomplished' code flashed across the screen.

The missile had been destroyed. Safely.

'Nice going,' said Kyle.

'Ah...I wasn't worried,' said Trek, panting.

'No,' said Kyle, slapping him heartily on the back.

The guard outside General Butler's door went for his revolver when Jenny came around the corner. When he saw her dragging his buddy with one hand, and saw a gun in the other, he backed away. She cautioned him with a gesture to keep silent, then tied him up with his own belt and gagged him with a balled-up handkerchief.

She kicked open the door and tossed in the unconscious Marine ahead of her. Butler was at his desk, reading.

'It's finished,' she said.

He realised she wasn't bluffing. 'Now that it's over, I only have one regret.'

'What's that?' she asked.

'That I lost your respect.' He stood up and put down the book. 'Well, at least you'll get one thing out of this...' He gave her a long pity-filled look. '...You'll be a hero.'

She didn't take the bait. After giving him a look of such contempt that he turned away, she said, 'I don't know what that is anymore.'

Back on Sky One, mechanics swarmed over the vehicles as they returned one-by-one...Equipment was checked...Ammunition replaced...The pilot ran down his checklist as the engines warmed-up...Onboard computers processed all the new information gathered by the vehicles.

Erica pulled in and parked Kat gratefully. She pulled off her helmet, shook her hair loose, took a deep breath.

Kat was unhappy. 'Erica, I am going to have to report you for your flagrant disregard for regulations. One stray bullet could have irreparably damaged my program.'

'What's your point?' asked Erica, heading for the nearest shower.

'Nice job blowing up that missile,' Duke said to Trek. 'How'd you figure it out?'

Trek looked everywhere, except at Kyle. 'I didn't. I just typed in my mother's birthday and hoped for the best.'

'Ah,' said Duke, walking away.

Trek shrugged sheepishly at Kyle and followed.

For a moment the garage was quiet, nothing but the muffled thrum of the engines.

Then Domino rolled in, parked, and Jenny climbed out, very slowly.

Kyle, relieved that she was all right and sorry he couldn't have sent her support, waited. 'Welcome back,' he said.

Jenny bit her lower lip. 'Kyle...I don't know what to say.'

'This was a hard one,' he said. 'It's over.'

'I was totally insubordinate.'

'Yeh,' he said. 'You'd be in real trouble if this was the Marines.' He touched her shoulder. 'You did what you thought was right. That's worth more to me than someone who just follows orders.'

At last she smiled, accepting the forgiveness.

It had been a long, long day.

TKR = ACTION, ADVENTURE

Take a look at these great shots from selected

from 'Return of Mecaman'

& ACCELERATION

episodes of Team Knight Rider...

from 'K.R.O.'

from 'The A List'

TKR = ACTION, ADVENTURE & ACCELERATION

from 'Iron Maiden'

from 'Inside Traitor'

from 'Choctaw'